A-Level Year 2

Chemistry

The Complete Course for AQA

Let's face it, Chemistry is a tough subject. You'll need to get to grips with a lot of difficult concepts, and have plenty of practical skills up your lab-coat sleeve.

But don't worry — this brilliant CGP book covers everything you'll need for the new AQA course. It's packed with clear explanations, exam practice, advice on maths skills and practical investigations... and much more!

It even includes a free Online Edition to read on your PC, Mac or tablet.

How to get your free Online Edition

Go to **cgpbooks.co.uk/extras** and enter this code...

2213 0817 8952 5187

This code will only work once. If someone has used this book before you, they may have already claimed the Online Edition.

Contents

Unit 3

Section 5: Isomerism and Carbonyl Compounds

Section 6: Aromatic Compounds and Amines

Section 7: Polymers

Section 8: Amino Acids, Proteins and DNA

Section 9: Further Synthesis and Analysis

Maths Skills

Exam Help

Reference

How to use this book

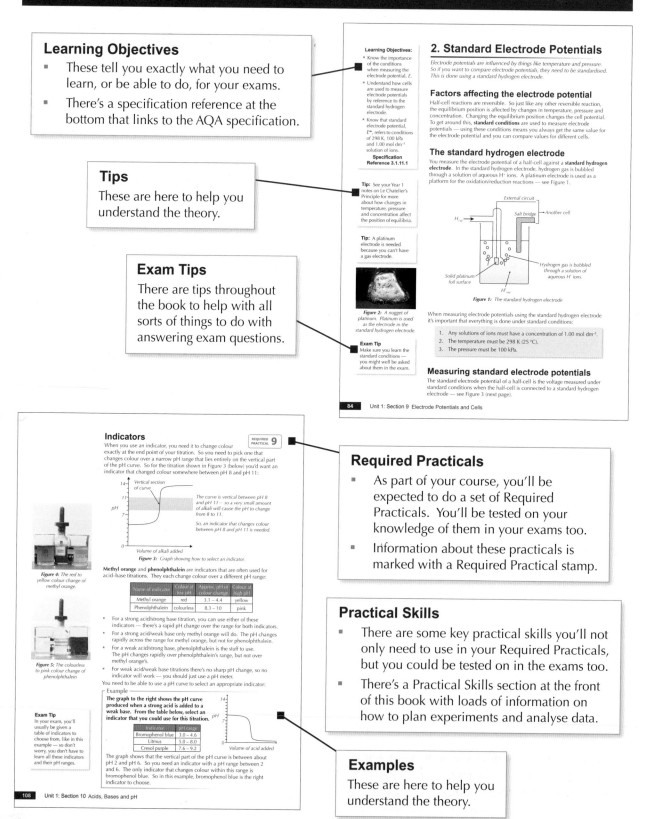

Learning Objectives

- These tell you exactly what you need to learn, or be able to do, for your exams.
- There's a specification reference at the bottom that links to the AQA specification.

Tips

These are here to help you understand the theory.

Exam Tips

There are tips throughout the book to help with all sorts of things to do with answering exam questions.

Learning Objectives:
- Know the importance of the conditions when measuring the electrode potential, E.
- Understand how cells are used to measure electrode potentials by reference to the standard hydrogen electrode.
- Know that standard electrode potential, E°, refers to conditions of 298 K, 100 kPa and 1.00 mol dm⁻³ solution of ions.
  Specification Reference 3.1.11.1

Tip: See your Year 1 notes on Le Chatelier's Principle for more about how changes in temperature, pressure and concentration affect the position of equilibria.

Tip: A platinum electrode is needed because you can't have a gas electrode.

Figure 2: A nugget of platinum. Platinum is used as the electrode in the standard hydrogen electrode.

Exam Tip
Make sure you learn the standard conditions — you might well be asked about them in the exam.

2. Standard Electrode Potentials

Electrode potentials are influenced by things like temperature and pressure. So if you want to compare electrode potentials, they need to be standardised. This is done using a standard hydrogen electrode.

Factors affecting the electrode potential

Half-cell reactions are reversible. So just like any other reversible reaction, the equilibrium position is affected by changes in temperature, pressure and concentration. Changing the equilibrium position changes the cell potential. To get around this, **standard conditions** are used to measure electrode potentials — using these conditions means you always get the same value for the electrode potential and you can compare values for different cells.

The standard hydrogen electrode

You measure the electrode potential of a half-cell against a **standard hydrogen electrode**. In the standard hydrogen electrode, hydrogen gas is bubbled through a solution of aqueous H^+ ions. A platinum electrode is used as a platform for the oxidation/reduction reactions — see Figure 1.

Figure 1: The standard hydrogen electrode

When measuring electrode potentials using the standard hydrogen electrode it's important that everything is done under standard conditions:

1. Any solutions of ions must have a concentration of 1.00 mol dm⁻³.
2. The temperature must be 298 K (25 °C).
3. The pressure must be 100 kPa.

Measuring standard electrode potentials

The standard electrode potential of a half-cell is the voltage measured under standard conditions when the half-cell is connected to a standard hydrogen electrode — see Figure 3 (next page).

84   Unit 1: Section 9 Electrode Potentials and Cells

Indicators   **REQUIRED PRACTICAL 9**

When you use an indicator, you need it to change colour exactly at the end point of your titration. So you need to pick one that changes colour over a narrow pH range that lies entirely on the vertical part of the pH curve. So for the titration shown in Figure 3 (below) you'd want an indicator that changed colour somewhere between pH 8 and pH 11:

The curve is vertical between pH 8 and pH 11 — so a very small amount of alkali will cause the pH to change from 8 to 11.

So, an indicator that changes colour between pH 8 and pH 11 is needed.

Figure 3: Graph showing how to select an indicator.

Methyl orange and **phenolphthalein** are indicators that are often used for acid–base titrations. They each change colour over a different pH range:

Name of indicator	Colour at low pH	Approx. pH of colour change	Colour at high pH
Methyl orange	red	3.1 – 4.4	yellow
Phenolphthalein	colourless	8.3 – 10	pink

- For a strong acid/strong base titration, you can use either of these indicators — there's a rapid pH change over the range for both indicators.
- For a strong acid/weak base only methyl orange will do. The pH changes rapidly across the range for methyl orange, but not for phenolphthalein.
- For a weak acid/strong base, phenolphthalein is the stuff to use. The pH changes rapidly over phenolphthalein's range, but not over methyl orange's.
- For weak acid/weak base titrations there's no sharp pH change, so no indicator will work — you should just use a pH meter.

You need to be able to use a pH curve to select an appropriate indicator:

Figure 4: The red to yellow colour change of methyl orange.

Figure 5: The colourless to pink colour change of phenolphthalein

Exam Tip
In your exam, you'll usually be given a table of indicators to choose from, like in this example — so don't worry, you don't have to learn all these indicators and their pH ranges.

— Example —

The graph to the right shows the pH curve produced when a strong acid is added to a weak base. From the table below, select an indicator that you could use for this titration.

Indicator	pH range
Bromophenol blue	3.0 – 4.6
Litmus	5.0 – 8.0
Cresol purple	7.6 – 9.2

The graph shows that the vertical part of the pH curve is between about pH 2 and pH 6. So you need an indicator with a pH range between 2 and 6. The only indicator that changes colour within this range is bromophenol blue. So in this example, bromophenol blue is the right indicator to choose.

108   Unit 1: Section 10 Acids, Bases and pH

Required Practicals

- As part of your course, you'll be expected to do a set of Required Practicals. You'll be tested on your knowledge of them in your exams too.
- Information about these practicals is marked with a Required Practical stamp.

Practical Skills

- There are some key practical skills you'll not only need to use in your Required Practicals, but you could be tested on in the exams too.
- There's a Practical Skills section at the front of this book with loads of information on how to plan experiments and analyse data.

Examples

These are here to help you understand the theory.

i

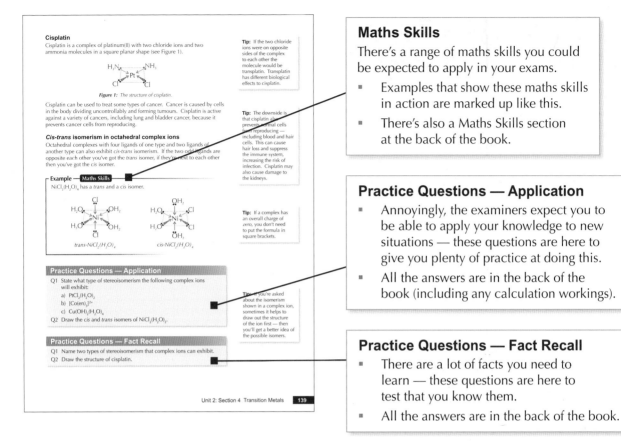

Cisplatin

Cisplatin is a complex of platinum(II) with two chloride ions and two ammonia molecules in a square planar shape (see Figure 1).

Figure 1: The structure of cisplatin.

Cisplatin can be used to treat some types of cancer. Cancer is caused by cells in the body dividing uncontrollably and forming tumours. Cisplatin is active against a variety of cancers, including lung and bladder cancer, because it prevents cancer cells from reproducing.

Cis-trans isomerism in octahedral complex ions

Octahedral complexes with four ligands of one type and two ligands of another type can also exhibit *cis-trans* isomerism. If the two odd ligands are opposite each other you've got the *trans* isomer, if they're next to each other then you've got the *cis* isomer.

Example — Maths Skills

$NiCl_2(H_2O)_4$ has a *trans* and a *cis* isomer.

trans-NiCl₂(H₂O)₄ — *cis-NiCl₂(H₂O)₄*

Practice Questions — Application

Q1 State what type of stereoisomerism the following complex ions will exhibit:
a) $PtCl_2(H_2O)_2$
b) $[Co(en)_3]^{2+}$
c) $Cu(OH)_2(H_2O)_4$
Q2 Draw the *cis* and *trans* isomers of $NiCl_2(H_2O)_2$.

Practice Questions — Fact Recall

Q1 Name two types of stereoisomerism that complex ions can exhibit.
Q2 Draw the structure of cisplatin.

Tip: If the two chloride ions were on opposite sides of the complex to each other the molecule would be transplatin. Transplatin has different biological effects to cisplatin.

Tip: The downside is that cisplatin also prevents normal cells from reproducing — including blood and hair cells. This can cause hair loss and suppress the immune system, increasing the risk of infection. Cisplatin may also cause damage to the kidneys.

Tip: If a complex has an overall charge of zero, you don't need to put the formula in square brackets.

Tip: If you're asked about the isomerism shown in a complex ion, sometimes it helps to draw out the structure of the ion first — then you'll get a better idea of the possible isomers.

Unit 2: Section 4 Transition Metals 139

Maths Skills

There's a range of maths skills you could be expected to apply in your exams.

- Examples that show these maths skills in action are marked up like this.
- There's also a Maths Skills section at the back of the book.

Practice Questions — Application

- Annoyingly, the examiners expect you to be able to apply your knowledge to new situations — these questions are here to give you plenty of practice at doing this.
- All the answers are in the back of the book (including any calculation workings).

Practice Questions — Fact Recall

- There are a lot of facts you need to learn — these questions are here to test that you know them.
- All the answers are in the back of the book.

Exam-style Questions

- Practising exam-style questions is really important — you'll find some at the end of each section.
- They're the same style as the ones you'll get in the real exams — some will test your knowledge and understanding and some will test that you can apply your knowledge.
- All the answers are in the back of the book, along with a mark scheme to show you how you get the marks.

Exam Help

There's a section at the back of the book stuffed full of things to help with your exams.

Glossary

There's a glossary at the back of the book full of all the definitions you need to know for your exams, plus loads of other useful words.

Exam-style Questions

1 Which of the options below shows the correct monomers that are formed when the general polymer shown below is hydrolysed by water?

	Monomer 1	Monomer 2
A	HO–R'–OH	HOOC–R–COOH
B	HO–R–OH	HOOC–R'–COOH
C	HO–R'–COOH	HOOC–R–OH
D	HO–R'–CONH₂	H₂NOC–R–OH

(1 mark)

2 The diagram below shows the repeating unit formed when two amino acids polymerise to form a peptide:

2.1 Draw the two amino acids which have joined together to make this repeating unit.
(2 marks)
2.2 What type of polymerisation occurs between the amino acids to form this polymer?
(1 mark)
2.3 What is the name of the link that forms between two amino acids?
(1 mark)

3 Nylon 6,6 is made from hexanedioic acid and 1,6-diaminohexane.

3.1 What type of condensation polymer is nylon 6,6?
(1 mark)
3.2 Draw the repeating unit of nylon 6,6.
(1 mark)
3.3 Is nylon 6,6 biodegradable or non-biodegradable? Explain your answer.
(4 marks)
3.4 Discuss the advantages and disadvantages of recycling objects made from nylon 6,6.
(4 marks)

Unit 3: Section 7 Polymers 231

ii

Published by CGP

Editors:
Katie Braid, Mary Falkner, Katherine Faudemer, Gordon Henderson, Emily Howe, Paul Jordin,
Rachel Kordan, Sophie Scott, Ben Train.

Contributors:
Mike Bossart, Robert Clarke, Ian H. Davis, John Duffy, Lucy Muncaster, Paul Warren.

ISBN: 978 1 78294 326 6

With thanks to Jamie Sinclair and Karen Wells for the proofreading.
With thanks to Jan Greenway for the copyright research.
AQA Specification material is reproduced by permission of AQA.

Printed by Elanders Ltd, Newcastle upon Tyne.
Clipart from Corel®

1. Planning Experiments

You'll get to do loads of practicals in class during this course, which is great.
Unfortunately, you can also get tested on how to carry out experiments in
your exams. The first thing you need is a good plan...

Initial Planning

Scientists solve problems by suggesting answers and then doing experiments
that test their ideas to see if the evidence supports them. Being able to plan
experiments that will give you valid and accurate results (see page 15) is a
very important part of this process. Here's how you go about it:

First, you have to identify what question you are trying to answer.
This is the **aim** of your experiment. It could be something like 'the aim of this
experiment is to determine how temperature affects the rate of this reaction'.
You can then make a **prediction** — a specific, testable statement about
what will happen in the experiment, based on observation, experience or a
hypothesis (a suggested explanation for a fact or observation).

The next step is to identify what the independent and dependent
variables (see below) are for your experiment. You can then decide what data
you need to collect and how to collect it. This includes working out what
equipment would be appropriate to use (see pages 2 and 3) — it needs to be
the right size and have the right level of sensitivity.

Next you write out a detailed **method** for your experiment. As part
of this, you'll need to do a **risk assessment** and plan any safety precautions.
This ensures that you minimise the risk of any dangers there might be in your
experiment, such as harmful chemicals you might be using. Your method will
also need to include details of what steps you are going to take to control any
other variables which may affect your results.

Finally, it's time to carry out the experiment — by following your
method you can gather evidence to address the aim of your experiment.

> **Tip:** Science
> experiments are all
> about identifying
> problems and using the
> knowledge you already
> have to solve them.

Variables

You probably know this all off by heart, but it's easy to get mixed up
sometimes. So here's a quick recap. A **variable** is a quantity that has the
potential to change, e.g. temperature, mass or volume. There are two types of
variable commonly referred to in experiments:

> **Independent variable** — the thing that you change in an experiment.

> **Dependent variable** — the thing that you measure in an experiment.

As well as the independent and dependent variables, you
need to think of all the other variables that could affect the result of the
experiment and plan ways to keep each of them the same. These other
variables are called **control variables**.

> **Tip:** When drawing
> graphs, the dependent
> variable should go
> on the y-axis, the
> independent variable on
> the x-axis.

You could investigate the effect of changing the Cu^{2+} ion concentration in a $Cu^{2+}_{(aq)}/Cu_{(s)}$ half-cell on the EMF of the cell using the apparatus in Figure 1, below:

Tip: There's lots more about what electrochemical cells are and how you set them up on pages 79-80.

Figure 1: *Apparatus for measuring the EMF of an electrochemical cell.*

- The independent variable is the concentration of Cu^{2+} ions in the electrolyte of the $Cu^{2+}_{(aq)}/Cu_{(s)}$ half-cell.

- The dependent variable is the voltage (EMF) of the cell.

- For this experiment to be a fair test, all other variables must be kept the same each time. This includes the concentration of Zn^{2+} ions in the $Zn^{2+}_{(aq)}/Zn_{(s)}$ half cell, the volume of both electrolyte solutions, the pressure and the temperature. It also means using the same equipment (such as the wires and voltmeter) each time.

Tip: In a fair test, you only change one variable between experiments. This means you can directly compare the results from each experiment to see how they depend on the variable you've been changing.

Risks, hazards and ethical considerations

When you plan an experiment, you need to think about how you're going to make sure that you work safely. This involves carrying out a risk assessment, where you identify all the hazards that might be involved in your experiment and come up with ways to reduce the risks that these hazards pose. There's more detail about risk assessments on pages 4 and 5.

You need to make sure you work ethically, too. This is most important if there are other people or animals involved. You have to put their welfare first.

Figure 2: *Hazard symbols on bottles of chemicals can tell you if a chemical is dangerous, for example if it is flammable or toxic.*

Choosing equipment

When you're planning an experiment, you should always plan to use equipment that is appropriate for the experiment you're doing.

Example

If you want to measure the amount of gas produced in a reaction, you need to make sure you use apparatus which will collect the gas, without letting any escape.

The equipment that you use needs to be the right size for your experiment too.

Example

If you're using a gas syringe to measure the volume of a gas produced by a reaction, it needs to be big enough to collect all the gas, or the plunger will be pushed out of the end. You might need to do some rough calculations to work out what size of equipment to use.

The equipment also needs to have the right level of sensitivity.

Example

If you want to measure out 3.8 g of a substance, you need a balance that measures to the nearest tenth of a gram, not the nearest gram.

If you want to measure out 6 cm³ of a solution, you need to use a measuring cylinder that has a scale marked off in steps of 1 cm³, not one that only has markings every 10 cm³.

If you want to measure very small changes in pH, then you need to use a pH meter, which can measure pH to several decimal places, rather than using indicator paper.

Tip: If you want to measure out a solution really accurately (e.g. 20.0 cm³ of solution) you'll need to use a burette or a pipette.

Tip: There's more about using pH meters and other methods to measure the pH of a solution on page 6.

Methods

When you come to write out your method, you need to keep all of the things on the preceding pages in mind.

The method must be clear and detailed enough for anyone to follow — it's important that other people can recreate your experiment and get the same results. Make sure your method includes:

- All the substances needed and what quantity of each to use.
- How to control variables.
- The exact apparatus needed (a diagram is often helpful to show the set-up).
- Any safety precautions that should be taken.
- What data to collect and how to collect it.

Evaluating experiment plans

If you ever need to evaluate the plan for someone else's experiment, you need to think about the same sorts of things that you would if you were designing the experiment yourself:

- Does the experiment actually test what it sets out to test?
- Is the method clear enough for someone else to follow?
- Apart from the independent and dependent variables, is everything else going to be properly controlled?
- Are the apparatus and techniques appropriate for what's being measured? Will they be used correctly?
- Are enough repeated measurements going to be taken?
- Is the experiment going to be conducted safely?

Exam Tip
This is the sort of thing you could be asked to do in an exam as a written test of your practical skills — either to evaluate an experiment plan, or to spot any issues with a small bit of it, e.g. the safety precautions.

2. Working Safely

When you do an experiment, you need to carry out a risk assessment and work safely at all times. This reduces the risk of anyone being hurt.

Risks and hazards

Many chemistry experiments have risks associated with them. These can include risks associated with the equipment you're using (such as the risk of burning from an electric heater) as well as risks associated with chemicals.

    When you're planning an experiment, you need to identify all the hazards and what the risk is from each hazard. This includes working out how likely it is that something could go wrong, and how serious it would be if it did. You then need to think of ways to reduce these risks. This procedure is called **a risk assessment**.

    Any hazardous chemicals you use should come with a list of dangers associated with them — this can be often be found on the bottle they come in, or you can look the information up on a Material Safety Data Sheet.

Tip: The CLEAPSS® website has a database with details of the potential harm lots of the hazardous chemicals you're likely to come across could cause. It also has student safety sheets, and your school or college may have CLEAPSS® Hazcards® you can use. These are all good sources of information if you're writing a risk assessment.

Tip: This isn't a comprehensive list of all the types of hazard you may encounter — just some of the more common ones.

Hazard word	Potential harm	Examples of how to reduce the risk
Corrosive	May cause chemical burns to tissues such as skin and eyes.	Use as little of the substance as possible. If the chemical is a solution, use it in low concentrations. If the chemical is a gas, carry out the experiment in a fume cupboard. Wear a lab coat, goggles and gloves when handling the chemical.
Irritant	May cause inflammation and discomfort.	Use as little of the substance as possible. If the chemical is a solution, use it in low concentrations. If the chemical is a gas, carry out the experiment in a fume cupboard. Wear a lab coat, goggles and gloves when handling the chemical.
Flammable	May catch fire.	Keep the chemical away from any naked flames. If you have to heat it, use a water bath, an electric heater or a sand bath instead of a Bunsen burner.
Toxic	May cause illness or even death.	Use as little of the substance as possible. If the chemical is a solution, use it in low concentrations. If the chemical is a gas, carry out the experiment in a fume cupboard. Wear a lab coat, goggles and gloves when handling the chemical.
Oxidising	Reacts to form oxygen, so other substances may burn more easily in its presence.	Use as little of the substance as possible. Use it in solution rather than as a solid powder. Use in clean, well-ventilated areas. Keep away from combustible materials, such as wood or paper.

Figure 2: Some common types of hazard and how to reduce the risks they present.

Figure 1: The hazard symbols for flammable (top left), oxidising (top middle), toxic (top right), corrosive (bottom left) and irritant (bottom right).

Imagine that you have been asked to synthesise a small amount of the ester propyl ethanoate using the following procedure:

- Add some propan-1-ol and concentrated ethanoic acid to a test tube containing concentrated sulfuric acid.
- Gently heat the mixture for 1 minute.
- Cool the mixture.
- Pour the mixture into a solution of sodium carbonate and mix to neutralise any remaining acid.

Before carrying out the experiment, you would need to do a risk assessment to identify any steps you should take to ensure that you were working safely.

The experiment involves hazards in both the procedure and the chemicals used. The hazards associated with the chemicals in the experiment are summarised in the table below.

Hazard	Type of hazard	Ways to reduce the risk
Propan-1-ol	Flammable	Keep away from naked flames — carry out the experiment using a water bath to heat the reaction mixture.
	Irritant	Use as little propan-1-ol as possible. Wear a lab coat, goggles and gloves when handling it.
Concentrated ethanoic acid	Corrosive	Use as little concentrated ethanoic acid as possible. Wear a lab coat, goggles and gloves when handling it.
Concentrated sulfuric acid	Corrosive	Use as little concentrated sulfuric acid as possible. Wear a lab coat, goggles and gloves when handling it.
Sodium carbonate solution	Irritant	Use as little sodium carbonate solution as possible, in a low concentration. Wear a lab coat, goggles and gloves when handling it.

Figure 3: Chemical hazards in an experiment to synthesise propyl ethanoate.

The main hazard in the procedure comes from the need to heat the reaction mixture. To reduce the risk of being burnt by any equipment, you shouldn't touch the apparatus during or soon after the heating step. You should use tongs to remove the test tube from the heating apparatus and allow it to cool completely before continuing with the experiment.

You could now rewrite the procedure, taking into account the steps that you should take in order to reduce the risks in this experiment:

- Wear a lab coat, goggles and gloves throughout the procedure.
- Add 1 cm^3 propan-1-ol and 1 cm^3 concentrated ethanoic acid to a test-tube containing 0.5 cm^3 concentrated sulfuric acid.
- Gently heat the mixture in a water bath for 1 minute.
- Remove the test tube from the water bath using tongs, and leave it in a test tube rack on a heatproof mat to cool.
- Pour the mixture into 5 cm^3 of sodium carbonate solution and mix.

Tip: Esters are organic compounds made by reacting carboxylic acids with alcohols. There's more about how to synthesise them and how they react on pages 182-184.

Tip: The hazard symbols in Figure 1 are quite new, so you may come across the old-style ones on bottles in your laboratory. The symbols are very similar, but they're in orange squares instead of red and white diamonds (see Figure 4).

Figure 4: A bottle of ethanoic acid with a 'corrosive' hazard symbol.

Tip: The risk associated with a solution might change depending on how concentrated it is. For example, whilst concentrated sulfuric acid is corrosive, dilute sulfuric acid is an irritant.

3. Practical Techniques

This section is an introduction to some of the techniques you'll be expected to know for A-level Chemistry. You'll have met many of them before, and others will be covered in more detail as they crop up throughout the book.

Measuring pH

The pH of a solution is a measure of how acidic or basic it is. There's more than one way of measuring this — you can use pH charts, pH meters or pH probes.

pH charts

Universal indicator is a substance that changes colour according to the pH of the solution that it is added to. A **pH chart** tells you what colour an indicator will be at different pHs.

The pH chart for universal indicator is shown in Figure 1. So, if you add a few drops of Universal indicator to a solution, you can compare the resulting colour to a pH chart and determine the pH of the solution.

Colour:

pH: 1 2 3 4 5 6 7 8 9 10 11 12 13 14

Figure 1: *The pH chart of Universal indicator.*

pH charts are good for giving a rough value of the pH of the solution, but since the colour of a solution is a qualitative observation (it's based on opinion), the data won't be precise.

pH meters

A **pH meter** is an electronic gadget that can be used to give a precise value for the pH of a solution. A pH meter is made up of a probe attached to a digital display. The probe is placed in the solution, and the pH reading is shown on the display.

Figure 2: *A pH meter.*

pH probe on a data logger

A pH probe can be attached to something called a **data logger**. A data logger is a device that will record the readings from the pH probe at set intervals and store them so you can look back at them later. This makes them useful for experiments where you're measuring how pH changes, as the data logger will record the results, meaning you don't have to write them down separately. You might have to connect the data logger to a computer or tablet to collect the results from it. You may also need to print the results off once the experiment is complete, so you can keep a record of them in your lab book.

Heating substances

Many chemical substances are flammable, so are at risk of catching fire if they're heated with a naked flame, e.g. with a Bunsen burner. Luckily, there are a number of other techniques you can use to heat a reaction mixture.

Electric heaters

Electric heaters are often made up of a metal plate that can be heated to a specified temperature. The reaction vessel is placed on top of the hot plate (see Figure 2). The mixture is only heated from below, so you'll usually have to stir the reaction mixture to make sure it's heated evenly.

Water baths

A **water bath** is a container filled with water that can be heated to a specific temperature (see Figure 3). You place the reaction vessel in the water bath. The level of the water outside the vessel should be just above the level of the reaction mixture inside the vessel. The mixture will then be warmed to the same temperature as the water.

As the reaction mixture is surrounded by water, the heating is very even. However, water boils at 100 °C, so you can't use a water bath to heat the reaction mixture to a higher temperature than this.

Sand baths

Sand baths are similar to water baths, but the container is filled with sand. Sand can be heated to a much higher temperature than water, so sand baths are useful for heating reaction mixtures to temperatures above 100 °C.

Heating under reflux

You heat a reaction mixture under **reflux** when you're making volatile organic compounds (substances that evaporate easily) from compounds that need to be heated in order to react. The reaction mixture is heated in a flask that's fitted with a condenser, so that any materials that evaporate will condense and drip back into the mixture. This stops you losing any of the reactants or products from the mixture during the reaction. Figure 4 shows how reflux apparatus would be set up.

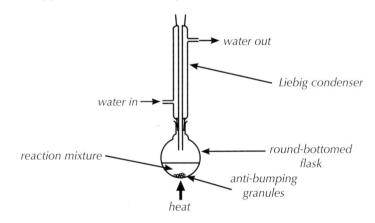

Figure 4: A scientific diagram of reflux apparatus.

Figure 2: An electric heater.

Figure 3: A water bath.

Tip: Organic compounds are generally flammable, so you might use these methods for heating them in synthesis (see page 250).

Tip: Organic compounds are just molecules that contain carbon.

Tip: Once you've synthesised a product under reflux, you might need to purify it. There are lots of techniques for doing this on pages 193-195.

Tip: You also need to know how to synthesise and purify a compound using <u>distillation</u>. See page 194 for more on this.

Filtration

Filtration is used to separate a solid from a liquid.
There are two types of filtration you need to know about:

1. Filtration under reduced pressure

Filtration under reduced pressure is normally used when you want to keep the solid and discard the liquid (filtrate). You use a piece of equipment called a Büchner funnel — a flat-bottomed funnel with holes in the base. The Büchner funnel is attached to the top of a side-arm flask, which is secured with a stand-and-clamp to stop it from falling over. The side-arm flask is attached to a vacuum line, which, when it is switched on, causes the flask to be under reduced pressure — this helps to suck the liquid through the filter.

Here's how you carry out the filtration:

- Place a piece of filter paper, slightly smaller than the diameter of the funnel, on the bottom of the Büchner funnel so that it lies flat and covers all the holes.

- Wet the paper with a little solvent, so that it sticks to the bottom of the funnel, and doesn't slip around when you pour in your mixture.

- Turn the vacuum on, and then pour your mixture into the funnel. As the flask is under reduced pressure, the liquid is sucked through the funnel into the flask, leaving the solid behind.

- Rinse the solid with a little of the solvent that your mixture was in. This will wash off any of the original liquid from the mixture that stayed on your crystals (and also any soluble impurities), leaving you with a more pure solid.

- Disconnect the vacuum line from the side-arm flask and then turn off the vacuum.

- The solid will be a bit wet from the solvent, so leave it to dry completely.

Figure 6: *Apparatus for filtration under reduced pressure.*

2. Filtration using fluted filter paper

Filtration using fluted filter paper is normally used when you want to keep the liquid (the filtrate) and discard the solid. For example, it can be used to remove the solid drying agent from the organic layer of a liquid that has been purified by separation (see page 193). A piece of fluted filter paper is placed in a funnel that feeds into a conical flask. The mixture to be separated is poured gently into the filter paper. The solution will pass through the filter paper into the conical flask, and the solid will be trapped. A pure sample of the solvent present in the solution can be used to rinse the solid left in the filter paper. This makes sure that all the soluble material has passed through the filter paper and collected in the conical flask.

Tip: Filtration is often the first step in purifying an organic compound, either to remove liquid impurities if your product is solid, or solid impurities if your compound is a liquid. It's also an important step in recrystallisation (page 195), to remove the solute from the recrystallised product.

Figure 5: *The apparatus used to carry out a filtration under reduced pressure.*

Tip: If you're doing a filtration using fluted filter paper, take care not to fill the funnel above the top of the filter paper when you're pouring in your mixture.

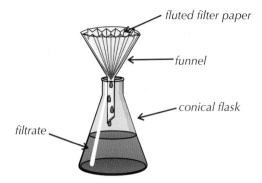

fluted filter paper

funnel

conical flask

filtrate

Tip: Fluted filter paper is a cone with a concertinaed edge. The concertina gives the paper a greater surface area than if the paper were smooth, so the solution is filtered faster.

Figure 7: Filtration using fluted filter paper.

Filter paper normally comes as a flat disc. To make fluted filter paper, follow the steps in Figure 8.

1. Fold the paper in half, then in quarters.

2. Unfold the paper so it's in half.

3. Fold each side into the centre.

4. Unfold the paper again so that it's in half.

5. Concertina the paper, using the folds as guidelines.

6. Unfold the paper, and make it into a cone.

Figure 8: Making fluted filter paper.

4. Data

When you're doing an experiment you need to think about how you're going to record your results and process the data that you've collected.

Types of data

Experiments always involve some sort of measurement to provide data. There are different types of data — and you need to know what they are.

1. Discrete data

You get **discrete data** by counting — a discrete variable can only have certain values on a scale. E.g. the number of bubbles produced in a reaction would be discrete (see Figure 1). You can't have 1.25 bubbles. That'd be daft. Shoe size is another good example of a discrete variable.

2. Continuous data

A **continuous variable** can have any value on a scale. For example, the volume of gas produced or the mass of products from a reaction. You can never measure the exact value of a continuous variable.

3. Categoric data

A **categoric variable** has values that can be sorted into categories. For example, the colours of solutions might be blue, red and green (see Figure 2). Or types of material might be wood, steel, glass.

4. Ordered (ordinal) data

Ordered data is similar to categoric, but the categories can be put in order. For example, if you classified reactions as 'slow', 'fairly fast' and 'very fast' you'd have ordered data.

Tables of data

It's a good idea to set up a table to record the results of your experiment. Make sure that you include enough rows and columns to record all the data you need. You might also need to include a column for processing your data (e.g. working out an average).

Each column should have a heading so that you know what's going to be recorded where. In the column heading, you should include the units — this is to avoid having to write them out repeatedly in every cell.

Figure 1: *An acid-carbonate reaction. The number of bubbles produced is discrete data, but the volume of gas produced is continuous data.*

Figure 2: *Different coloured solutions. Colour is a type of categoric data.*

[KI] / mol dm^{-3}	Duration of clock reaction / s				Mean duration of clock reaction / s
	Run 1	Run 2	Run 3	Run 4	
0.045	32	34	33	33	
0.033	50	50	48	48	
0.021	72	71	89	70	

Figure 3: *A table of results.*

Calculating means

A mean is just an **average** of your repeated results. Calculating an average helps to balance out any random errors in your data (see page 17).

To calculate the mean result for a data point, first remove any anomalous results. Then add up all the other measurements from each repeat and divide by the number of (non-anomalous) measurements.

Tip: Have a look at page 13 for more on anomalous results.

Example — Maths Skills

The average duration of the clock reaction at each concentration of potassium iodide point for the table in Figure 3 is:

- When [KI] = 0.045 mol dm^{-3}: $(32 + 34 + 33 + 33) \div 4 = $ **33 s**
- When [KI] = 0.033 mol dm^{-3}: $(50 + 50 + 48 + 48) \div 4 = $ **49 s**
- When [KI] = 0.021 mol dm^{-3}: The result for Run 3 is anomalously high, so ignore it when calculating the mean. $(72 + 71 + 70) \div 3 = $ **71 s**

Tip: There's more about dealing with data (e.g. using the right number of significant figures and converting units) in the Maths Skills section on pages 275 to 285.

Types of charts and graphs

You'll often be expected to make a graph of your results. Graphs make your data easier to understand — so long as you choose the right type.

Bar charts

You should use a bar chart when one of your data sets is categoric or ordered data, like in Figure 4.

Tip: Use simple scales when you draw graphs — this'll make it easier to plot points.

Figure 4: Bar chart to show the lattice enthalpies of various chloride compounds.

Pie charts

Pie charts are normally used to display categoric data, like in Figure 5.

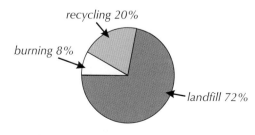

Figure 5: Pie chart to show how plastic waste is disposed of by a country.

Exam Tip
Whatever type of graph you make, you'll only get full marks if you:

1. Choose a sensible scale — don't do a tiny graph in the corner of the paper.

2. Label both axes — including units.

3. Plot your points accurately — using a sharp pencil.

Scatter graphs

Scatter graphs, like the graphs shown in Figures 6 and 7, are great for showing how two sets of continuous data are related (or correlated — see page 13).

Don't try to join up all the points on a scatter graph — you should draw a line of best fit to show the trend of the data instead. A line of best fit can be a straight line, like the example in Figure 6...

Tip: A line of best fit should have about half of the points above it and half of the points below. You should ignore any anomalous results, like the one circled in Figure 6 — there's more about anomalous results coming up on page 13.

Figure 6: *Scatter graph showing the relationship between ΔG and temperature for a reaction.*

...or a curve, like the example in Figure 7.

Exam Tip
If you're asked to <u>sketch</u> a graph in an exam, you only need to show the labelled axes and the general shape of the line. You don't need to plot points and draw the line accurately for a sketch graph.

Figure 7: *Scatter graph to show how the rate of a reaction changes with the concentration of one of the reactants.*

5. Analysing Results

Once you've got your results nicely presented you can start to draw a conclusion. But be careful — you may have a graph showing a lovely correlation, but that doesn't always tell you as much as you might think.

Anomalous results

Anomalous results are ones that don't fit in with the other values — this means they are likely to be wrong. They're often caused by experimental errors, e.g. if a drop in a titration is too big and shoots past the end point, or if a syringe plunger gets stuck whilst collecting gas produced in a reaction. When looking at results in tables or graphs, you need to check if there are any anomalies — you ignore these results when calculating means or drawing a line of best fit.

Tip: Even though you ignore anomalies when you're calculating means and drawing lines of best fit, if possible you should try to find an explanation for why they happened (and include it in your write-up).

Examples — Maths Skills

The table below shows the titre volume of a number of titrations.

Titration Number	1	2	3	4
Titre Volume (cm³)	15.20	15.30	15.70	15.25

Titre 3 isn't concordant with (doesn't match) the other results, so you need to ignore that one and just use the other three.

$$\text{mean} = \frac{15.20 + 15.30 + 15.25}{3} = 15.25 \text{ cm}^3$$

Tip: In titrations, saying that your results are concordant means that they're all within 0.1 cm³ of each other.

The graph below shows how the pH of a reaction mixture changes as an alkali is added.

The result at 4 cm³ doesn't fit with the other results, so you should ignore it when drawing the line of best fit.

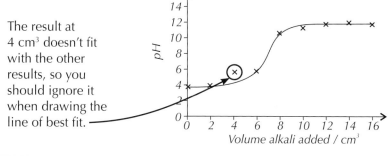

Tip: Saying that one result 'isn't concordant' with the other results is just another way of saying that it's an anomalous result.

Scatter graphs and correlation

Correlation describes the relationship between two variables — usually the independent one and the dependent one. Data can show positive correlation, negative correlation or no correlation. A scatter graph can show you how two variables are correlated:

Positive correlation
As one variable increases the other also increases.

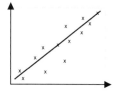

Negative correlation
As one variable increases the other decreases.

No correlation
There is no relationship between the variables.

Correlation and cause

Ideally, only two quantities would ever change in any experiment — everything else would remain constant. But in experiments or studies outside the lab, you can't usually control all the variables. So even if two variables are correlated, the change in one may not be causing the change in the other. Both changes might be caused by a third variable.

> **Tip:** If an experiment really does confirm that changing one variable causes another to change, we say there's a <u>causal link</u> between them.

> **Tip:** Watch out for bias too — for instance, a bottled water company might point these studies out to people without mentioning any of the doubts.

Example

Some studies have found a correlation between drinking chlorinated tap water and the risk of developing certain cancers. So some people argue that this means water shouldn't have chlorine added. But it's hard to control all the variables between people who drink tap water and people who don't. It could be many lifestyle factors. Or, the cancer risk could be affected by something else in tap water — or by whatever the non-tap water drinkers drink instead.

Drawing conclusions

The data should always support the conclusion. This may sound obvious, but it's easy to jump to conclusions. Conclusions have to be specific — not make sweeping generalisations.

Example

The rate of an enzyme-controlled reaction was measured at 10 °C, 20 °C, 30 °C, 40 °C, 50 °C and 60 °C. All other variables were kept constant, and the results are shown in Figure 1.

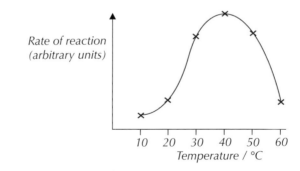

Figure 1: *Graph to show the effect of temperature on the rate of an enzyme-controlled reaction.*

> **Tip:** Whoever funded the research (e.g. a chemical manufacturer) may have some influence on what conclusions are drawn from the results, but scientists have a responsibility to make sure that the conclusions they draw are supported by the data.

A science magazine concluded from this data that this enzyme works best at 40 °C. The data doesn't support this exact claim. The enzyme could work best at 42 °C or 47 °C, but you can't tell from the data because increases of 10 °C at a time were used. The rate of reaction at in-between temperatures wasn't measured. All you know is that it's faster at 40 °C than at any of the other temperatures tested.

Also, the experiment only gives information about this particular enzyme-controlled reaction. You can't conclude that all enzyme-controlled reactions happen faster at a particular temperature — only this one. And you can't say for sure that doing the experiment at, say, a different constant pressure wouldn't give a different optimum temperature.

6. Evaluations and Errors

Now that you've drawn some conclusions from your experiment, you can consider how accurate those conclusions could be.

Evaluations

There are a few terms that you need to understand. They'll be useful when you're evaluating how convincing your results are.

1. Valid results

Valid results answer the original question. For example, if you haven't controlled all the variables your results won't be valid, because you won't be testing just the thing you wanted to.

2. Accurate results

Accurate results are those that are really close to the true answer.

3. Precise results

The smaller the amount of spread of your data around the mean (see page 11), the more **precise** it is. Calculating a mean (average) result from your repeats will increase the precision of your result, because it helps to reduce the effect of random errors on the answer (see page 17).

4. Repeatable results

Your results are **repeatable** if you get the same results when you repeat the experiment using the same method and the same equipment. You really need to repeat your readings at least three times to demonstrate that your results really are repeatable.

Tip: Results that fulfil all of these criteria are sometimes referred to as being reliable.

5. Reproducible results

Your results are **reproducible** if other people get the same results when they repeat your experiment.

Errors

Any measurements you make will have **errors** (or **uncertainties**) in them, due to the limits of the sensitivity of the equipment.

Errors are usually written with a ± sign, e.g. ±0.05 cm. The ± sign tells you the actual value of the measurement is likely to lie somewhere between your reading minus the error value and your reading plus the error value.

The error will be different for different pieces of equipment.

> **Example**
>
> Pieces of equipment such as pipettes, volumetric flasks and thermometers will have errors that depend on how well made they are.
>
> The manufacturers provide these error values — they're usually written on the equipment somewhere (see Figure 1).

Figure 1: *A conical flask where the graduations have an error of ±5%.*

Example

The scale on a 50 cm³ burette usually has marks every 0.1 cm³. You should be able to tell which mark the level's closest to, so any reading you take won't be more than 0.05 cm³ out. So the error on your burette readings is ±0.05 cm³.

Figure 2: *Reading a volume from a burette.*

The level in this burette is between the 44.9 cm³ and 45.0 cm³ marks. It's closer to 45.0 — so the level is between 44.95 and 45.0. So a reading of 45.0 cm³ can't have an error of more than 0.05 cm³.

Example

If a pH meter measures the pH of a solution to 1 decimal place, the real pH could be up to 0.05 smaller or larger. For example, if the display says 6.3, the real pH could be anywhere between 6.25 and 6.35.
So the error on the pH meter is ±0.05.

Percentage error

If you know the **error** (or **uncertainty**) in a reading that you've taken, you can use it to calculate the percentage error in your measurement:

$$\text{percentage error} = \frac{\text{error}}{\text{reading}} \times 100$$

Examples — Maths Skills

The EMF of an electrochemical cell is measured as 0.42 V. The voltmeter has an error of ±0.01 V. Calculate the percentage error on the EMF value.

Percentage error is $\frac{0.01}{0.42} \times 100 = $ **2.4 %**.

In a titration a burette with an error of ±0.05 cm³ is used. The initial reading on the burette is 0.0 cm³. The final reading is 21.2 cm³. Calculate the percentage error on the titre value.

The titre value is 21.2 – 0.0 = 21.2 cm³. The error on each burette reading is ±0.05 cm³. Two readings have been combined to find the titre value, so the total error is 0.05 + 0.05 = ±0.1 cm³.

So, percentage error on the titre value = $\frac{0.1}{21.2} \times 100 = $ **0.47%**

Tip: Percentage error means you can directly compare the degree of error in different measurements as a proportion of the total measurement.

Percentage error is useful because it tells you how significant the error in a reading is in comparison to its size — e.g. an error of ±0.1 g is more significant when you weigh out 0.2 g of a solid than when you weigh out 100.0 g.

You can reduce errors in your measurements by using the most sensitive equipment available. There's not much you can do about this at school or college though — you're stuck with whatever's available.

But there are other ways to lower the uncertainty in experiments. The larger the reading you take with a piece of equipment, the smaller the percentage error on that reading will be. Here's a quick example:

Example

If you measure out 2 g of a solid using a mass balance with an error of ±0.05 g cm³ then the percentage error is $(0.05 \div 2) \times 100 = 2.5\%$.

But if you measure 4 g of the solid using the same mass balance the percentage error is $(0.05 \div 4) \times 100 = 1.25\%$. You've just halved the percentage error.

So you can reduce the percentage error of this experiment by using a greater mass of solid.

You can apply the same principle to other measurements too. For example, if you measure out a small volume of liquid, the percentage error will be larger than if you measured out a larger volume using the same measuring cylinder.

Types of error

Errors in your results can come from a variety of different sources.

Random errors

Random errors cause readings to be spread about the true value due to the results varying in an unpredictable way. You get random error in all measurements and no matter how hard you try, you can't correct them. The tiny errors you make when you read a burette are random — you have to estimate the level when it's between two marks, so sometimes your figure will be above the real one and sometimes below.

Repeating an experiment and finding the mean of your results helps to deal with random errors. The results that are a bit high will be cancelled out by the ones that are a bit low. So your results will be more precise.

Systematic errors

Systematic errors cause each reading to be different to the true value by the same amount, i.e. they shift all of your results. They may be caused by the set-up or the equipment you're using. If the 10.00 cm³ pipette you're using to measure out a sample for titration actually only measures 9.95 cm³, your sample will be 0.05 cm³ too small every time you repeat the experiment.

Tip: 'Calibration' is when you mark a scale on a measuring instrument or check the scale by measuring a known value.

Repeating your results won't get rid of any systematic errors, so your results won't get more accurate. The best way to get rid of systematic errors is to carefully calibrate any equipment you're using, if possible.

7. The Practical Endorsement

Alongside your A-level exams, you have to do a separate 'Practical Endorsement'. This assesses practical skills that can't be tested in a written exam.

What is the Practical Endorsement?

The Practical Endorsement is assessed slightly differently to the rest of your course. Unlike the exams, you don't get a mark for the Practical Endorsement — you just have to get a pass grade.

In order to pass the Practical Endorsement, you have to carry out at least twelve practical experiments and demonstrate that you can:

- use a range of specified apparatus, e.g. you must be able to use melting point apparatus (see page 195),
- carry out a range of specified practical techniques, e.g. you must be able to purify a solid by recrystallisation (see page 195).

The twelve practicals that you do are most likely to be the twelve Required Practicals that form part of the AQA A-level Chemistry course — these cover all the techniques you need to be able to demonstrate for your Practical Endorsement. You may carry out other practicals as well, or instead, which could also count towards your Practical Endorsement. You'll do the practicals in class, and your teacher will assess you as you're doing them.

You'll need to keep a record of all your assessed practical activities. Required Practicals 1 to 6 are covered in the Year 1 material so you will probably already have done some experiments that count towards the Practical Endorsement in Year 1 of the course. This book contains information about Required Practicals 7 to 12 (which are all part of the Year 2 material).

Exam Tip
You could also get asked questions about the Required Practicals in your written exams.

Tip: Throughout this book, information about the Required Practicals and opportunities to carry out Required Practicals are marked up with a big stamp, like this one:

REQUIRED PRACTICAL **9**

Assessment of the Practical Endorsement

When assessing your practical work, your teacher will be checking that you're able to do five things:

1. Follow written methods and instructions

Make sure you read any instructions you are given fully before you start work and that you understand what you're about to do. This will help you to avoid missing out any important steps or using the wrong piece of apparatus.

2. Use apparatus and investigative methods correctly

You'll need to demonstrate that you can select appropriate apparatus for the experiment that you're doing and decide what measurements you need to take with it (see pages 2 and 3 for more). Once you've selected your apparatus and set it up correctly, you'll also need to show that you use it to take accurate measurements.

You'll also need to show that you can identify which variables need to be controlled in an experiment and work out how best to control them (see page 1).

Tip: You won't necessarily need to demonstrate that you can do all five of these things every time you carry out a practical.

3. Use apparatus and materials safely

This means being able to carry out a risk assessment (see pages 4 and 5) to identify the hazards in your experiment and what you can do to reduce the risks associated with those hazards. You'll also have to show that you can work safely in the lab, using appropriate safety equipment to reduce the risks you've identified, and that you adapt your method as you go along if necessary.

4. Make observations and record results

You need to show that you can collect data that's valid, accurate and precise. When you record the data, e.g. in a table, you need to make sure you do so to an appropriate level of precision and you include things like the units. There's more on recording data on page 10.

5. Carry out supporting research and write reports using appropriate references

You need to show that you can write up an investigation properly. As well as reporting your results and drawing a conclusion about your findings, you'll need to describe the method you used and any safety precautions you took. You'll also need to show that you can use computer software to process your data. This might mean drawing a graph of your results using the computer, or using a computer programme to help you quickly and accurately carry out calculations on large amounts of data.

You'll need to write up any research you've done too (e.g. to help you with planning a method or to draw your conclusions) and properly cite any sources that you've used.

Research, references and citations

You can use books or the Internet to carry out research, but there a few things you'll need to bear in mind:

- Not all the information you find on the Internet will be true. It's hard to know where information comes from on forums, blogs and websites that can be edited by the general public, so you should avoid using these. Websites of organisations such as the Royal Society of Chemistry and the National Institute of Standards and Technology (NIST) provide lots of information that comes from reliable scientific sources. Scientific papers and textbooks are also good sources of reliable information.

- It may sound obvious, but when you're using the information that you've found during your research, you can't just copy it down word for word. Any data you're looking up should be copied accurately, but you should rewrite everything else in your own words.

- When you've used information from a source, you need to cite the reference properly. Citations allow someone else to go back and find the source of your information. This means they can check your information and see you're not making things up out of thin air. Citations also mean you've properly credited other people's data that you've used in your work. A citation for a particular piece of information may include the title of the book, paper or website where you found the information, the author and/or the publisher of the document and the date the document was published.

Tip: If you're unsure whether the information on a website is true or not, try and find the same piece of information in a different place. The more sources you can find for the information, the more likely it is to be correct.

Tip: There are lots of slightly different ways of referencing sources, but the important thing is that it's clear where you found the information.

1. Enthalpy Changes

Learning Objective:

- Be able to define the terms enthalpy of formation, ionisation energy, enthalpy of atomisation, bond enthalpy, electron affinity, lattice enthalpy (defined as either lattice dissociation or lattice formation) and enthalpy of hydration.

Specification Reference 3.1.8.1

Some of this stuff may ring a few bells from Year 1. Make sure you understand all the definitions in this topic because they're really important for the rest of the section.

The basics

Enthalpy notation

Enthalpy change, ΔH (delta H), is the heat energy transferred in a reaction at constant pressure. The units of ΔH are kJ mol^{-1}. You write $\Delta H^{\ominus}$ to show that the substances were in their standard states and that the measurements were made under **standard conditions**. Standard conditions are 100 kPa (about 1 atm) pressure and a stated temperature (e.g. $\Delta H^{\ominus}_{298}$). In this book, all the enthalpy changes are measured at 298 K (25 °C). Sometimes the notation will also include a subscript to signify whether the enthalpy change is for a reaction (r), for combustion (c), or for the formation of a new compound (f).

Exothermic and endothermic reactions

Exothermic reactions have a negative ΔH value, because heat energy is given out (the chemicals lose energy). **Endothermic reactions** have a positive ΔH value, because heat energy is absorbed (the chemicals gain energy).

Tip: You covered enthalpy notation in Year 1 so if you need a reminder, get your old notes out.

What is lattice enthalpy?

Ions in lattices are held together by ionic bonds. It takes energy to break apart the bonds, and energy is given out when new bonds form. The energy needed to break a bond between two ions is the same amount of energy that is given out when that bond is formed. These 'lattice enthalpies' have specific values that differ depending on the ions involved (see Figure 1). So, lattice enthalpy is a measure of ionic bond strength. It can be defined in two ways.

Lattice formation enthalpy: the enthalpy change when 1 mole of a solid ionic compound is formed from its gaseous ions.

Compound	Lattice formation enthalpy (kJ mol^{-1})
LiCl	−826
NaCl	−787
KCl	−701
RbCl	−692

Figure 1: *Lattice formation enthalpies of chloride compounds.*

┌─ **Example** ──────────────────

Formation of sodium chloride:

$$Na^+_{(g)} + Cl^-_{(g)}$$

Gaseous sodium and chloride ions come together...

... to form a solid ionic lattice of sodium chloride.

Lattice formation enthalpy, $\Delta H_{lattice}$, for this reaction is −787 kJ mol^{-1}. The negative ΔH value shows that lattice formation is an exothermic process.

Lattice dissociation enthalpy: the enthalpy change when 1 mole of a solid ionic compound is completely dissociated into its gaseous ions.

Exam Tip
In the exam, make sure you use the term 'enthalpy' and not 'energy' otherwise you'll lose a mark.

┌─ **Example** ─────────────────────────────

Dissociation of sodium chloride:

$$Na^+_{(g)} + Cl^-_{(g)}$$

... to form gaseous sodium and chloride ions.

A solid ionic lattice of sodium chloride dissociates...

Lattice dissociation enthalpy, $\Delta H_{lattice}$, for this reaction is +787 kJ mol^{-1}. The positive ΔH value shows that the reaction is endothermic.

└───

Tip: Notice that the lattice formation enthalpy and the lattice dissociation enthalpy are exactly the same size — the only difference is that one's negative and the other one's positive.

Determining lattice enthalpy

Lattice enthalpy can't be measured directly. Instead, you have to combine the enthalpies from a number of other processes to work out the lattice enthalpy — see Figure 2.

Gaseous atoms form from the elements — *The enthalpy change of atomisation.*

↓

Atoms of one element lose electrons to form positive ions — *The ionisation energy.*

↓

Atoms of one element gain electrons to form negative ions — *The electron affinity.*

↓

Positive and negative ions form a solid ionic lattice — *The lattice formation enthalpy.*

Figure 2: *The processes which lead to the formation of a lattice.*

Tip: Although lattice enthalpy can't be measured directly, it can be calculated using a Born-Haber cycle — all will be revealed on page 23.

┌─ **Example** ─────────────────────────────

The processes that lead to the formation of sodium chloride:

Gaseous Na and Cl atoms form from solid Na and gaseous Cl$_2$ — *The enthalpy change of atomisation for sodium and for chlorine.*

↓

Atoms of Na lose one electron to form Na$^+$ ions — *The first ionisation energy of sodium.*

↓

Atoms of Cl gain one electron to form Cl$^-$ ions — *The electron affinity of chlorine.*

↓

Na$^+$ ions and Cl$^-$ ions form solid NaCl — *The lattice formation enthalpy of sodium chloride.*

└───

Figure 3: *A 3D model of a sodium chloride lattice.*

Unfortunately, each specific type of enthalpy change has its own definition and you need to learn them all.

- **Enthalpy change of formation**, ΔH_f, is the enthalpy change when 1 mole of a compound is formed from its elements in their standard states, e.g. $Ca_{(s)} + Cl_{2(g)} \rightarrow CaCl_{2(s)}$

- The **bond dissociation enthalpy**, ΔH_{diss}, is the enthalpy change when all the bonds of the same type in 1 mole of gaseous molecules are broken, e.g. $Cl_{2(g)} \rightarrow 2Cl_{(g)}$

- **Enthalpy change of atomisation of an element**, ΔH_{at}, is the enthalpy change when 1 mole of gaseous atoms is formed from an element in its standard state, e.g. $\frac{1}{2}Cl_{2(g)} \rightarrow Cl_{(g)}$

- **Enthalpy change of atomisation of a compound**, ΔH_{at}, is the enthalpy change when 1 mole of a compound in its standard state is converted to gaseous atoms, e.g. $NaCl_{(s)} \rightarrow Na_{(g)} + Cl_{(g)}$

- The **first ionisation energy**, ΔH_{ie1}, is the enthalpy change when 1 mole of gaseous 1+ ions is formed from 1 mole of gaseous atoms, e.g. $Mg_{(g)} \rightarrow Mg^+_{(g)} + e^-$

- The **second ionisation energy**, ΔH_{ie2}, is the enthalpy change when 1 mole of gaseous 2+ ions is formed from 1 mole of gaseous 1+ ions, e.g. $Mg^+_{(g)} \rightarrow Mg^{2+}_{(g)} + e^-$

- **First electron affinity**, ΔH_{ea1}, is the enthalpy change when 1 mole of gaseous 1– ions is made from 1 mole of gaseous atoms, e.g. $O_{(g)} + e^- \rightarrow O^-_{(g)}$

- **Second electron affinity**, ΔH_{ea2}, is the enthalpy change when 1 mole of gaseous 2– ions is made from 1 mole of gaseous 1– ions, e.g. $O^-_{(g)} + e^- \rightarrow O^{2-}_{(g)}$

- The **enthalpy change of hydration**, ΔH_{hyd}, is the enthalpy change when 1 mole of aqueous ions is formed from gaseous ions, e.g. $Na^+_{(g)} \rightarrow Na^+_{(aq)}$

- The **enthalpy change of solution**, $\Delta H_{solution}$, is the enthalpy change when 1 mole of an ionic substance dissolves in enough solvent to form an infinitely dilute solution.

Exam Tip
You could be asked to give any of these definitions in the exam, so make sure you've learned them all word for word.

Tip: These terms will crop up a lot in this section so don't move on until you understand what each one means — you might want to fold this page over so you can find it again if you need to.

Tip: An infinitely dilute solution is one which contains so much solvent that when you add more liquid, there is no change in concentration.

Practice Questions — Fact Recall

Q1 What is meant by the term enthalpy change?

Q2 Give the symbol for enthalpy change.

Q3 Give two different definitions for lattice enthalpy.

Q4 Define the following:
- a) enthalpy change of formation,
- b) second electron affinity,
- c) enthalpy change of hydration.

Q5 Name the changes in enthalpy defined below:
- a) The enthalpy change when 1 mole of gaseous atoms is formed from an element in its standard state.
- b) The enthalpy change when 1 mole of gaseous 1+ ions is formed from 1 mole of gaseous atoms.

Q6 Write the symbol for the following enthalpy changes:
- a) The enthalpy change of hydration.
- b) The bond dissociation enthalpy.

2. Born-Haber Cycles

Get those rulers and pencils out — it's time to draw some Born-Haber cycles.

Calculating lattice enthalpies

You can't measure a lattice enthalpy directly, so you have to use a **Born-Haber cycle** to figure out what the enthalpy change would be if you took another, less direct, route. There are two routes you can follow to get from the elements in their standard states to the ionic lattice. On the diagram below, the blue arrow shows the direct route and the red arrows show the indirect route.

Learning Objectives:

- Be able to construct Born-Haber cycles to calculate lattice enthalpies and other enthalpy changes.

- Be able to compare lattice enthalpies from Born-Haber cycles with those from calculations based on a perfect ionic model to provide evidence for covalent character in ionic compounds.

Specification Reference 3.1.8.1

The enthalpy change for each route is the same. This is **Hess's law**:

> The total enthalpy change of a reaction is always the same, no matter which route is taken.

So, to calculate the lattice enthalpy change of formation ($\Delta H6$), you use an alternative route around the diagram:

$$\Delta H6 = -\Delta H5 - \Delta H4 - \Delta H3 - \Delta H2 + \Delta H1$$

Notice that you add in a minus sign if you go the wrong way along an arrow.

Figure 1: *German physicist Max Born who, along with Fritz Haber, developed Born-Haber cycles.*

Tip: You can also get the equation above by re-arranging this equation:
$\Delta H1 = \Delta H2 + \Delta H3 + \Delta H4 + \Delta H5 + \Delta H6$.

Tip: The Haber who helped develop Born-Haber cycles is the same Haber who invented the Haber process for synthesising ammonia (see page 155).

— **Example** —————————————

To calculate the lattice enthalpy of NaCl:

$\Delta H6 = -\Delta H5 - \Delta H4 - \Delta H3 - \Delta H2 + \Delta H1$
$\quad = -(-349) - (+496) - (+107) - (+122) + (-411) =$ **−787 kJ mol⁻¹**

Born-Haber cycles for compounds containing Group 2 elements have an extra step compared to the one on the previous page. Here's a Born-Haber cycle for a compound containing a Group 2 element:

Group 2 elements form 2+ ions — so you've got to include the second ionisation energy.

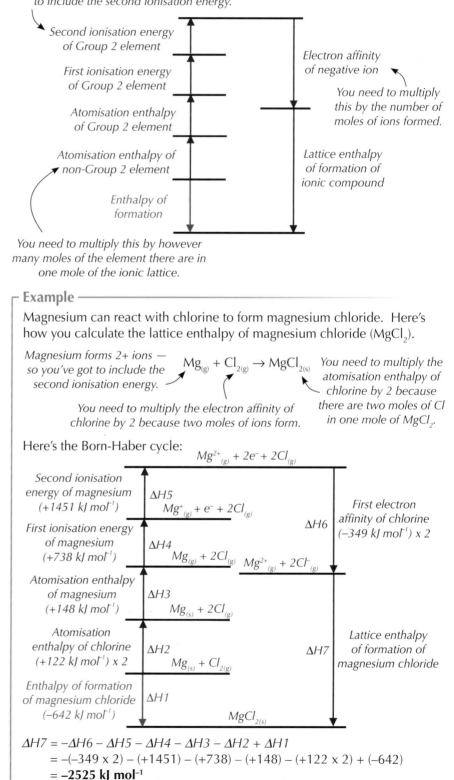

Second ionisation energy of Group 2 element

First ionisation energy of Group 2 element

Atomisation enthalpy of Group 2 element

Atomisation enthalpy of non-Group 2 element

Enthalpy of formation

Electron affinity of negative ion

You need to multiply this by the number of moles of ions formed.

Lattice enthalpy of formation of ionic compound

You need to multiply this by however many moles of the element there are in one mole of the ionic lattice.

Tip: Remember, enthalpy change of formation, ΔH_f, is the enthalpy change when <u>one mole of a compound</u> is formed from its elements in their standard states under standard conditions.

Example

Magnesium can react with chlorine to form magnesium chloride. Here's how you calculate the lattice enthalpy of magnesium chloride ($MgCl_2$).

Magnesium forms 2+ ions — so you've got to include the second ionisation energy.

$$Mg_{(g)} + Cl_{2(g)} \rightarrow MgCl_{2(s)}$$

You need to multiply the atomisation enthalpy of chlorine by 2 because there are two moles of Cl in one mole of $MgCl_2$.

You need to multiply the electron affinity of chlorine by 2 because two moles of ions form.

Here's the Born-Haber cycle:

$$Mg^{2+}_{(g)} + 2e^- + 2Cl_{(g)}$$

Second ionisation energy of magnesium (+1451 kJ mol⁻¹) — ΔH5

$$Mg^+_{(g)} + e^- + 2Cl_{(g)}$$

First ionisation energy of magnesium (+738 kJ mol⁻¹) — ΔH4

$$Mg_{(g)} + 2Cl_{(g)}$$

Atomisation enthalpy of magnesium (+148 kJ mol⁻¹) — ΔH3

$$Mg_{(s)} + 2Cl_{(g)}$$

Atomisation enthalpy of chlorine (+122 kJ mol⁻¹) x 2 — ΔH2

$$Mg_{(s)} + Cl_{2(g)}$$

Enthalpy of formation of magnesium chloride (−642 kJ mol⁻¹) — ΔH1

$$MgCl_{2(s)}$$

First electron affinity of chlorine (−349 kJ mol⁻¹) x 2 — ΔH6

$$Mg^{2+}_{(g)} + 2Cl^-_{(g)}$$

Lattice enthalpy of formation of magnesium chloride — ΔH7

$$\Delta H7 = -\Delta H6 - \Delta H5 - \Delta H4 - \Delta H3 - \Delta H2 + \Delta H1$$
$$= -(-349 \times 2) - (+1451) - (+738) - (+148) - (+122 \times 2) + (-642)$$
$$= \mathbf{-2525 \ kJ \ mol^{-1}}$$

***Figure 2:** Dry magnesium chloride.*

Tip: State symbols are really important here. If you're not sure what symbols should go where, double-check the definitions on page 22.

Calculating other enthalpy changes

You could be asked to calculate any of the enthalpy or energy values used in Born-Haber cycles. Don't worry though, you just construct the diagram and calculate the unknown value in exactly the same way as for lattice enthalpy.

Example

Magnesium can react with oxygen to form magnesium oxide.

Magnesium forms 2+ ions — so you've got to include the second ionisation energy.

$$Mg_{(g)} + \tfrac{1}{2}O_{2(g)} \rightarrow MgO_{(s)}$$

Oxygen forms 2– ions — so you've got to include the second electron affinity.

Here's how to calculate the atomisation enthalpy of magnesium using the Born-Haber cycle for MgO:

Second ionisation energy of magnesium ($+1451$ kJ mol^{-1}) — $\Delta H5$ — $Mg^{2+}_{(g)} + 2e^- + O_{(g)}$

$Mg^+_{(g)} + e^- + O_{(g)}$

First electron affinity of oxygen (-141 kJ mol^{-1}) — $\Delta H6$

First ionisation energy of magnesium ($+738$ kJ mol^{-1}) — $\Delta H4$ — $Mg_{(g)} + O_{(g)}$

$Mg^{2+}_{(g)} + e^- + O^-_{(g)}$

Second electron affinity of oxygen ($+798$ kJ mol^{-1}) — $\Delta H7$

$Mg^{2+}_{(g)} + O^{2-}_{(g)}$

Atomisation enthalpy of magnesium — $\Delta H3$ — $Mg_{(s)} + O_{(g)}$

Atomisation enthalpy of oxygen ($+249$ kJ mol^{-1}) — $\Delta H2$ — $Mg_{(s)} + \tfrac{1}{2}O_{2(g)}$

Lattice enthalpy of formation of magnesium oxide (-3791 kJ mol^{-1}) — $\Delta H8$

Enthalpy of formation of magnesium oxide (-548 kJ mol^{-1}) — $\Delta H1$ — $MgO_{(s)}$

$$\Delta H3 = -\Delta H2 + \Delta H1 - \Delta H8 - \Delta H7 - \Delta H6 - \Delta H5 - \Delta H4$$
$$= -(+249) + (-548) - (-3791) - (+798) - (-141) - (+1451) - (+738)$$
$$= \mathbf{+148\ kJ\ mol^{-1}}$$

Tip: The unknown value you need to find out is in a different position in the cycle to the previous examples. You work it out in the same way as before though. In this example, work your way round the arrows from $[Mg_{(s)} + O_{(g)}]$ to $[Mg_{(g)} + O_{(g)}]$ by the indirect route.

Theoretical and experimental enthalpies

You can work out a theoretical lattice enthalpy by doing some calculations based on the purely ionic model of a lattice. The **purely ionic model of a lattice** assumes that all the ions are spherical, and have their charge evenly distributed around them. But the experimental lattice enthalpy from the Born-Haber cycle is usually different. This is evidence that ionic compounds usually have some covalent character. The positive and negative ions in a lattice aren't usually exactly spherical (see Figure 3). Positive ions polarise neighbouring negative ions to different extents, and the more polarisation there is, the more covalent the bonding will be.

Purely ionic bonding — the ions are spherical and unpolarised.

Partial covalent bonding — the electrons in the negative ion are pulled towards the positive ion.

Figure 3: *Purely ionic and partial covalent bonding.*

Tip: The purely ionic model of a lattice is also known as the <u>perfect ionic model</u>.

Tip: Although lattice enthalpy cannot be directly measured, the value obtained from the Born-Haber cycle is the actual, true value of the lattice enthalpy because all of the other values which have been used to calculate it are real experimental values for that substance.

If the experimental and theoretical lattice enthalpies for a compound are very different, it shows that the compound has a lot of covalent character.

— Example —

Here are both lattice enthalpy values for some magnesium halides.

Compound	Lattice Enthalpy of Formation (kJ mol^{-1})		
	From experimental values in Born-Haber cycle	From theory
Magnesium chloride	-2526	-2326
Magnesium bromide	-2440	-2079
Magnesium iodide	-2327	-1944

The experimental lattice energies are more exothermic than the theoretical values by a fair bit. This tells you that the bonding is stronger than the calculations from the ionic model predict. The difference shows that the ionic bonds in the magnesium halides are quite strongly polarised and so they have quite a lot of covalent character.

Exam Tip
Don't worry — you don't have to memorise any of these enthalpy values. You'll always be given them in the question if you need them.

If the experimental and theoretical lattice enthalpies for a compound are very similar, it shows that the compound has very little covalent character.

— Example —

Here are some more lattice energies, for sodium halides this time:

Compound	Lattice Enthalpy of Formation (kJ mol^{-1})		
	From experimental values in Born-Haber cycle	From theory
Sodium chloride	-787	-766
Sodium bromide	-742	-731
Sodium iodide	-698	-686

The experimental and theoretical values are a pretty close match — so you can say that these compounds fit the 'purely ionic' model very well. This indicates that the structure of the lattice for these compounds is quite close to being purely ionic. There's almost no polarisation so they don't have much covalent character.

Tip: If you're struggling to remember which way round it goes, just think — <u>lots</u> of difference means <u>lots</u> of covalent character, <u>little</u> difference means <u>little</u> covalent character.

Practice Questions — Application

Q1 Complete the following Born-Haber cycle for the formation of CaBr$_2$.

Exam Tip
If you're asked to complete a Born-Haber cycle, it just means fill in the black bits on the diagram — you don't have to write out what each stage is unless it specifically asks you to.

Tip: Calcium is a Group 2 element.

Q2 Look at the table below.

Enthalpy change	ΔH°/ kJ mol^{-1}
Enthalpy change of atomisation of chlorine	+122
Enthalpy change of atomisation of lithium	+159
First ionisation energy of lithium	+520
First electron affinity of chlorine	−349
Lattice enthalpy of formation of lithium chloride	−861

a) Draw the Born-Haber cycle for the formation of LiCl.

b) Use Hess's law to calculate the enthalpy of formation of LiCl.

Q3 Look at the table below.

Enthalpy change	ΔH°/ kJ mol^{-1}
Enthalpy change of atomisation of potassium	+89
Enthalpy change of atomisation of fluorine	+79
First ionisation energy of potassium	+419
First electron affinity of fluorine	−328
Enthalpy of formation of potassium fluoride	−563

a) Draw the Born-Haber cycle for the formation of KF.

b) Use Hess's law to calculate the lattice enthalpy of formation of KF.

c) Explain why theoretical lattice enthalpies are often different from experimental values.

Exam Tip
Always double-check that you've got the plus and minus signs right when you're doing calculations using a Born-Haber cycle. It's really easy to make a mistake and get it wrong in the exam — and you will lose precious marks.

Exam Tip
When completing Born-Haber cycles in the exam, make sure you get the enthalpy changes in the right order. Atomisation always comes before ionisation, and they always come before electron affinity.

■ Be able to use enthalpy cycles to calculate enthalpies of solution for ionic compounds from lattice enthalpies and enthalpies of hydration.

Specification Reference 3.1.8.1

3. Enthalpies of Solution

Lattice enthalpies aren't the only enthalpies you can calculate using Hess's law. You can work out enthalpies of solution too. You'll need to remind yourself of the definitions for lattice dissociation enthalpy (page 21) and enthalpy changes of solution and hydration (page 22) before you start.

Dissolving ionic lattices

When a solid ionic lattice dissolves in water these two things happen:

■ The bonds between the ions break to give gaseous ions — this is endothermic. This enthalpy change is the **lattice enthalpy of dissociation**.

■ Bonds between the ions and the water are made — this is exothermic. The enthalpy change here is called the **enthalpy change of hydration**.

Water can form bonds with the ions because it is a polar molecule. Oxygen is more electronegative than hydrogen, so it draws the bonding electrons toward itself, creating a dipole. Consequently, positive ions form weak bonds with the partial negative charge on the oxygen atom and negative ions form weak bonds with the partial positive charge on the hydrogen atoms (see Figure 1).

Tip: Take a look back at your Year 1 notes if you need a reminder about electronegativity and the $\delta+$ and $\delta-$ charges on polar molecules such as water:

$$\delta- \overset{H\,\delta+}{\underset{O-H\,\delta+}{|}}$$

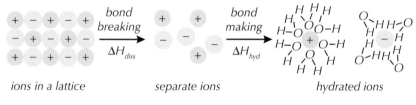

Figure 1: A solid ionic lattice dissolving in water.

The enthalpy change of solution is the overall effect on the enthalpy of bond breaking and bond making.

Calculating enthalpy change of solution

You can work out the enthalpy change of solution using an enthalpy cycle. You just need to know the lattice dissociation enthalpy of the compound and the enthalpies of hydration of the ions. Here's how to draw an enthalpy cycle for calculating the enthalpy change of solution:

① *Put the ionic lattice and the dissolved ions on the top — connect them by the enthalpy change of solution. This is the direct route.*

solid ionic lattice → Enthalpy change of solution → aqueous ions

$\Delta H3$

Lattice dissociation enthalpy $\Delta H1$ $\Delta H2$ Enthalpy of hydration of positive ion

Enthalpy of hydration of negative ion

gaseous ions

② *Connect the ionic lattice to the gaseous ions by the lattice enthalpy of dissociation. This will be a positive number. If you're given a negative value for lattice enthalpy, it'll be the lattice enthalpy of formation. It's the reverse of this that you want (see page 21).*

③ *Connect the gaseous ions to the dissolved ions by the hydration enthalpies of each ion. This completes the indirect route.*

Figure 2: *Copper(II) sulfate (CuSO$_4$) dissolved in water.*

Examples

Here's the enthalpy cycle for working out the enthalpy change of solution for sodium chloride.

From Hess's law: $\Delta H3 = \Delta H1 + \Delta H2$
$$= +787 + (-406 + -364) = \textbf{+17 kJ mol}^{-1}$$

Tip: Take a look back at page 23 for more on Hess's law.

And here's another example. This enthalpy cycle is for working out the enthalpy change of solution for silver chloride.

From Hess's law: $\Delta H3 = \Delta H1 + \Delta H2$
$$= +905 + (-464 + -364) = \textbf{+77 kJ mol}^{-1}$$

Tip: The enthalpy change of solution for silver chloride is much more endothermic than the enthalpy change of solution for sodium chloride. Take a look at page 30 to see why changes in entropy mean that sodium chloride is soluble in water but silver chloride isn't.

Practice Questions — Application

Q1 The cycle below shows the enthalpy change of solution for LiCl.

Calculate the enthalpy change of solution for LiCl.

Q2 a) Draw a cycle to show the enthalpy change of solution for sodium bromide. Use the following values:

Lattice dissociation enthalpy of NaBr = +747 kJ mol⁻¹
Enthalpy of hydration of Na⁺ = –406 kJ mol⁻¹
Enthalpy of hydration of Br⁻ = –336 kJ mol⁻¹

   b) Calculate the enthalpy change of solution for sodium bromide.

Exam Tip
In the exam, there's no need to draw the cycle out unless the question specifically asks for it. However, if you find it easier to calculate values from a cycle, it's a good idea to draw one out anyway.

Practice Question — Fact Recall

Q1 a) What two processes happen when a solid ionic lattice dissolves in water?

   b) State whether each of the processes named in part a) is exothermic or endothermic.

4. Entropy

Left alone, things generally tend towards disorder — that's entropy.

What is entropy?

Entropy tells you how much disorder there is. It's a measure of the number of ways that particles can be arranged and the number of ways that the energy can be shared out between the particles. Substances really like disorder, so the particles move to try to increase the entropy. Entropy is represented by the symbol S. There are a few things that affect entropy, such as:

Physical state

Physical state affects entropy. You have to go back to the good old solid-liquid-gas particle explanation thingy to understand this. Solid particles just wobble about a fixed point — there's hardly any disorder, so they have the lowest entropy. Gas particles whizz around wherever they like. They've got the most disordered arrangements of particles, so they have the highest entropy.

Increasing entropy (disorder)

Figure 1: *Melting ice. When ice melts, its entropy increases.*

Dissolution

Dissolving a solid also increases its entropy — dissolved particles can move freely as they're no longer held in one place:

Increasing entropy

Number of particles

More particles means more entropy. It makes sense — the more particles you've got, the more ways they and their energy can be arranged. So in a reaction like $N_2O_{4(g)} \rightarrow 2NO_{2(g)}$, entropy increases because the number of moles increases:

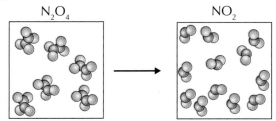

Examples

Evaporation of water

When water evaporates, there is an increase in entropy because there's a change in physical state from liquid to gas.

Water vapour is more chaotic than liquid water.

Reaction of NaHCO₃ and HCl

When sodium hydrogen carbonate reacts with hydrochloric acid there is an increase in entropy.

$$NaHCO_{3(s)} + H^+_{(aq)} \rightarrow Na^+_{(aq)} + CO_{2(g)} + H_2O_{(l)}$$

1 mole solid NaHCO₃   1 mole aqueous H⁺ ions   1 mole aqueous Na⁺ ions   1 mole liquid H₂O   1 mole CO₂ gas

There are more particles in the products — and gases and liquids have more entropy than solids too.

Figure 2: *The evaporation of water, to form clouds, brings about an increase in entropy.*

Calculating entropy changes

Most reactions won't happen unless the entropy change is positive. During a reaction, there's an entropy change (ΔS) between the reactants and products.

This is just the difference between the entropies of the reactants and products.

$$\Delta S = S_{products} - S_{reactants}$$

Exam Tip
You need to be able to calculate entropy changes in your exam so make sure you learn this equation.

Example ——— Maths Skills

Calculate the entropy change for the reaction of ammonia and hydrogen chloride under standard conditions.

$$NH_{3(g)} + HCl_{(g)} \rightarrow NH_4Cl_{(s)}$$

$S^\ominus[NH_{3(g)}] = 192.3 \text{ J K}^{-1}\text{mol}^{-1}$
$S^\ominus[HCl_{(g)}] = 186.8 \text{ J K}^{-1}\text{mol}^{-1}$
$S^\ominus[NH_4Cl_{(s)}] = 94.6 \text{ J K}^{-1}\text{mol}^{-1}$

$$\Delta S = S_{products} - S_{reactants} = 94.6 - (192.3 + 186.8)$$
$$= -284.5 \text{ J K}^{-1}\text{mol}^{-1}$$

This reaction has a negative change in entropy. It's not surprising, as 2 moles of gas have combined to form 1 mole of solid.

Tip: $S^\ominus$ is the standard entropy. The $S^\ominus$ value of a substance is the entropy of one mole of that substance, measured under standard conditions.

Tip: When you calculate an entropy change, don't forget to give the units — they're always J K⁻¹ mol⁻¹.

Substance	Standard entropy of substance, $S^\ominus$ ($J\ K^{-1}\ mol^{-1}$)
$CH_{4(g)}$	186
$O_{2(g)}$	205
$CO_{2(g)}$	214
$H_2O_{(l)}$	69.9
$SO_{2(g)}$	248
$H_2S_{(g)}$	206
$S_{(s)}$	31.6

Figure 3: Standard entropy values for different substances.

Practice Questions — Application

Q1 Solid sodium hydroxide is added to aqueous hydrogen chloride. The reaction produces sodium chloride solution. The solution is heated to produce solid sodium chloride and water vapour.

Describe the entropy changes that take place during these processes.

Q2 Using the data from Figure 3, work out the entropy change for this reaction under standard conditions:

$$CH_{4(g)} + 2O_{2(g)} \rightarrow CO_{2(g)} + 2H_2O_{(l)}$$

Q3 Using the data in Figure 3 work out the entropy change for this reaction under standard conditions:

$$SO_{2(g)} + 2H_2S_{(g)} \rightarrow 3S_{(s)} + 2H_2O_{(l)}$$

Practice Questions — Fact Recall

Q1 a) What is entropy?

b) Give the symbol for entropy change.

Q2 Explain how the following affect the entropy of a system:

a) a substance changing from a liquid to a gas.

b) a solid dissolving in water.

c) a reaction that results in an increased number of gaseous particles.

5. Free-Energy Change

Everyone likes free things, so I can almost guarantee you'll like free-energy.

What is free-energy change?

Free-energy change, ΔG, is a measure used to predict whether a reaction is **feasible**. A feasible reaction is one that, once started, will carry on to completion, without any energy being supplied to it. If ΔG is negative or equal to zero, then the reaction is feasible. Free-energy change takes into account the changes in enthalpy and entropy in the system. And of course, there's a formula for it:

Free-energy change (in J mol⁻¹) — $\Delta G = \Delta H - T\Delta S$ — *Entropy change (in J K⁻¹ mol⁻¹)*

Enthalpy change (in J mol⁻¹) — *Temperature (in K)*

A negative ΔG doesn't guarantee a reaction will happen or tell you about its rate. Even if ΔG shows that a reaction is theoretically feasible, it might have a really high activation energy or be so slow that you wouldn't notice it happening at all. Here's an example of calculating free-energy change.

Example — **Maths Skills**

Calculate the free-energy change for the following reaction at 298 K.

$$MgCO_{3(s)} \rightarrow MgO_{(s)} + CO_{2(g)}$$

$\Delta H^{\ominus} = +117 \text{ kJ mol}^{-1}$
$\Delta S^{\ominus} = +175 \text{ J K}^{-1} \text{ mol}^{-1}$

$\Delta G = \Delta H - T\Delta S = +117 \times 10^3 - [298 \times (+175)]$

$\qquad = \textbf{+64 900 J mol}^{-1}$ (3 s.f.)

ΔG is positive — so the reaction isn't feasible at this temperature.

Effect of temperature

If a reaction is exothermic (negative ΔH) and has a positive entropy change, then ΔG is always negative since $\Delta G = \Delta H - T\Delta S$. These reactions are feasible at any temperature.

If a reaction is endothermic (positive ΔH) and has a negative entropy change, then ΔG is always positive. These reactions are not feasible at any temperature. But for other combinations, temperature has an effect.

If ΔH is positive (endothermic) and ΔS is positive then the reaction will only be feasible above a certain temperature.

Example

The decomposition of calcium carbonate is endothermic but results in an increase in entropy (the number of molecules increases and CO_2 is a gas).

$$CaCO_{3(s)} \rightarrow CaO_{(s)} + CO_{2(g)}$$

The reaction only occurs when $CaCO_3$ is heated — it isn't feasible at 298 K.

If ΔH is negative (exothermic) and ΔS is negative then the reaction will only be feasible below a certain temperature.

Example

The process of turning water from a liquid to a solid is exothermic but results in a decrease in entropy (a solid is more ordered than a liquid). So it will only occur at certain temperatures (i.e. at 0 °C or below).

Learning Objectives:

- Understand that ΔH, whilst important, is not sufficient to explain feasible change and that ΔS accounts for this deficiency.
- Understand that the balance between entropy and enthalpy determines the feasibility of a reaction; know that this is given by the relationship $\Delta G = \Delta H - T\Delta S$.
- Be able to use this equation to determine how ΔG varies with temperature.
- Understand that for a reaction to be feasible, the value of ΔG must be zero or negative.
- Be able to use this relationship to determine the temperature at which a reaction is feasible.

Specification Reference 3.1.8.2

Figure 1: *Calcium carbonate ($CaCO_3$) being heated to produce CaO and CO_2.*

Tip: You might see free-energy referred to as 'Gibbs free-energy'. They're the same thing.

Here are some examples of how to decide if a reaction is feasible at different temperatures.

Examples — **Maths Skills**

Reaction 1: $\Delta H = +10$ kJ mol^{-1}, $\Delta S = +10$ J K^{-1} mol^{-1}

At 300 K:

$\Delta G = \Delta H - T\Delta S$
$= +10 \times 10^3 - (300 \times +10)$
$= +7000$ J mol^{-1}

At 1500 K:

$\Delta G = \Delta H - T\Delta S$
$= +10 \times 10^3 - (1500 \times +10)$
$= -5000$ J mol^{-1}

Tip: The units of ΔH and ΔS must be the same. So, if you're given a value for ΔH in kJ, multiply it by 10^3 to get in J. Or if you want ΔG in kJ mol^{-1}, divide ΔS by 10^3 instead.

So this reaction is feasible at 1500 K, but not at 300 K.

Reaction 2: $\Delta H = -10$ kJ mol^{-1}, $\Delta S = -10$ J K^{-1} mol^{-1}

At 300 K:

$\Delta G = \Delta H - T\Delta S$
$= -10 \times 10^3 - (300 \times -10)$
$= -7000$ J mol^{-1}

At 1500 K:

$\Delta G = \Delta H - T\Delta S$
$= -10 \times 10^3 - (1500 \times -10)$
$= +5000$ J mol^{-1}

Tip: Don't forget — the value of ΔG has to be less than or equal to zero for a reaction to be feasible.

So this reaction is feasible at 300 K, but not at 1500 K.

When ΔG is zero, a reaction is *just* feasible. You can find the temperature when ΔG is zero by rearranging the free-energy equation.

$\Delta G = \Delta H - T\Delta S$, so when $\Delta G = 0$, $T\Delta S = \Delta H$. So:

temperature at which a reaction becomes feasible (in K) $\longrightarrow$ $T = \dfrac{\Delta H}{\Delta S}$ $\longleftarrow$ enthalpy change (in J mol^{-1}) / entropy change (in J K^{-1} mol^{-1})

Substance	Standard entropy of substance, $S^\ominus$ ($J\ K^{-1}\ mol^{-1}$)
$WO_{3(s)}$	76.0
$H_{2(g)}$	65.0
$W_{(s)}$	33.0
$H_2O_{(g)}$	189.0

Figure 2: *Standard entropy values for different substances.*

Tip: For more on the ΔS formula, see page 31.

Example — **Maths Skills**

Tungsten, W, can be extracted from its ore, WO_3, by reduction using hydrogen.

$$WO_{3(s)} + 3H_{2(g)} \rightarrow W_{(s)} + 3H_2O_{(g)} \qquad \Delta H^\ominus = +117 \text{ kJ mol}^{-1}$$

Use the data in Figure 2 to find the minimum temperature at which the reaction becomes feasible.

First, convert the enthalpy change, ΔH, to joules per mole:

$\Delta H = 117 \times 10^3$ J mol$^{-1} = 117\ 000$ J mol^{-1}

Then find the entropy change, ΔS:

$\Delta S = S_{\text{products}} - S_{\text{reactants}}$ $= [33.0 + (3 \times 189.0)] - [76.0 + (3 \times 65.0)]$
$= +329$ J K^{-1} mol^{-1}

Then divide ΔH by ΔS to find the temperature at which the reaction just becomes feasible:

$$T = \frac{\Delta H}{\Delta S} = \frac{117\ 000}{329} = \textbf{356 K}$$

Free-energy graphs

If you're given a graph of free-energy (ΔG) versus temperature (T), you can use it to work out the enthalpy change (ΔH) and entropy change (ΔS) for the reaction. The ΔG vs T graph is a straight line so can be described using the equation of a straight line, $y = mx + c$. You can rearrange the free-energy equation to get it into the same form as the equation of a straight line:

$$\Delta G = \Delta H - T\Delta S$$
$$\Delta G = (-\Delta S \times T) + \Delta H$$
$$y \ \ = (m \times x) + c$$

So on a graph where ΔG is the y-axis and T is the x-axis, the gradient of the line (m) is equal to $-\Delta S$ and the y-intercept (c) is equal to ΔH.

Tip: There are some tips about drawing and using straight line graphs on page 284.

Example — Maths Skills

A graph showing the free-energy change (ΔG) versus temperature for a reaction is shown below. Use the graph to determine the enthalpy change and the entropy change for this reaction.

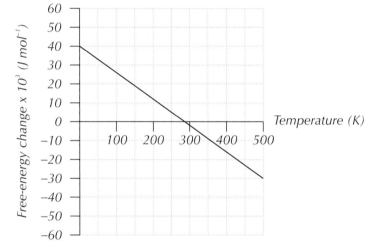

Figure 3: *Graph showing free-energy change versus temperature for a reaction.*

Tip: When you're working out the gradient of a straight line, pick two points on the line where it's easy to read off an x and y value. This usually means points that lie on grid lines.

Tip: ΔG vs T graphs for different reactions can look a little different. This one has a positive y-intercept and a negative gradient. Others might have a negative y-intercept or a positive gradient. Any combination is possible but it will always be a straight line so treat them all in the same way.

By rearranging the equation $\Delta G = \Delta H - T\Delta S$ into the form of the equation of a straight line, we know that:

$\Delta H = y$-intercept (c)
$-\Delta S$ = gradient (m)

The y-intercept of the line is at 40 000 J mol⁻¹:

$\Delta H = $ **+40 kJ mol⁻¹**

The gradient of a straight line is equal to the change in the y-axis divided by the change in the x-axis:

$$m = \Delta y \div \Delta x = (-30\ 000 - 40\ 000) \div (500 - 0)$$
$$= -70\ 000 \div 500 = -140$$

The entropy change is the same size as the gradient but with the opposite sign:

$-\Delta S$ = gradient $(m) = -140$
$\Delta S = $ **+140 J K⁻¹ mol⁻¹**

Tip: This graph is for a reaction with a positive enthalpy change and a positive entropy change. In this situation, the reaction is unfeasible at low temperatures and only becomes feasible above a certain temperature. You can see this from the graph. The free-energy change only becomes negative at higher temperatures. The temperature at which this reaction becomes feasible is 286 K, which is the x-intercept of the graph.

Substance	Standard entropy of substance, $S^\oplus$ ($J\ K^{-1}\ mol^{-1}$)
$Al_2O_{3(s)}$	51.0
$Mg_{(s)}$	32.5
$Al_{(s)}$	28.3
$MgO_{(s)}$	27.0

Figure 4: *Standard entropy values for different substances.*

Tip: Be careful with the scale on the vertical axis here. You need to multiply the values on the graph by 10^3 to get the actual ΔG values in $J\ mol^{-1}$.

Practice Questions — Application

Q1 Using the data from Figure 4 for this reaction under standard conditions: $Al_2O_{3(s)} + 3Mg_{(s)} \rightarrow 2Al_{(s)} + 3MgO_{(s)}$ $\Delta H^\oplus = -130$ kJ mol^{-1}
   a) calculate ΔS.
   b) calculate ΔG.
   c) explain whether the reaction is feasible at 298K.

Q2 Calculate the temperature at which this reaction becomes feasible:
$$CaCO_{3(s)} \rightarrow CaO_{(s)} + CO_{2(g)}$$
$\Delta H^\oplus = +178.0$ kJ mol^{-1} $\qquad\qquad\qquad$ $\Delta S = +165.0$ J K^{-1} mol^{-1}

Q3 Using the graph below of free-energy change versus temperature for a reaction:

   a) determine ΔH.
   b) determine ΔS.
   c) explain whether the reaction is feasible at 400K.

Practice Questions — Fact Recall

Q1 a) What is free-energy change?
   b) Give the symbol for free-energy change.
   c) What are the units of free-energy change?

Q2 Give the formula needed to work out free-energy.

Q3 A reaction is endothermic, has a negative entropy change and so has a positive value for free-energy. Is this reaction feasible?

Q4 Give the formula that you'd use to calculate the temperature at which a reaction becomes feasible.

Section Summary

Make sure you know...

- That enthalpy change is the heat energy transferred in a reaction at constant pressure, and the symbol for it is ΔH.

- That exothermic reactions have negative ΔH values and endothermic reactions have positive ΔH values.

- What lattice enthalpy is and the two different ways that it can be defined.

- The definitions of enthalpy change of formation, bond dissociation enthalpy, enthalpy change of atomisation for elements and for compounds, ionisation energy, electron affinity, enthalpy change of hydration and enthalpy change of solution.

- What a Born-Haber cycle is and how to use one to calculate enthalpy changes from experimental data.

- Why theoretical lattice enthalpies are often different from experimental values.

- How to determine the amount of covalent character in an ionic lattice by comparing its theoretical and experimental lattice enthalpy values.

- The different enthalpy changes that take place when a solid ionic lattice dissolves.

- How to calculate the enthalpy change of solution for an ionic compound from lattice dissociation enthalpy and enthalpy of hydration values.

- That entropy, S, is a measure of disorder.

- How entropy is affected by physical state, dissolution and number of particles.

- Why an increase in entropy may (or may not) mean a reaction is feasible.

- How to calculate the total entropy change for a reaction.

- That it's the balance between entropy and enthalpy that determines the feasibility of a reaction.

- What free-energy change is and how to calculate it using $\Delta G = \Delta H - T\Delta S$.

- That the feasibility of some reactions depends on temperature, and how to calculate the temperature at which a reaction becomes feasible.

- How to determine enthalpy change and entropy change from a graph of free-energy change versus temperature.

Exam-style Questions

1   A graph of free-energy change versus temperature for a certain reaction is shown below.

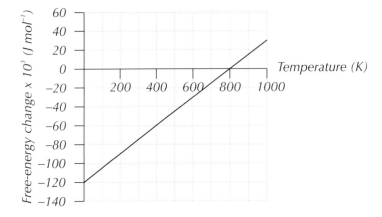

Which statement about this reaction is true?

A   The enthalpy change is positive and the entropy change is positive.

B   The enthalpy change is positive and the entropy change is negative.

C   The enthalpy change is negative and the entropy change is positive.

D   The enthalpy change is negative and the entropy change is negative.

(1 mark)

2   Strontium fluoride is a solid ionic lattice which dissolves in water and can be used as an optical coating for lenses.

2.1   Draw a Born-Haber cycle for the enthalpy change of solution of $SrF_{2(s)}$. Label each enthalpy change.

(2 marks)

2.2   Calculate the enthalpy change of solution for SrF_2, using the data in the table below.

(2 marks)

Enthalpy change	ΔH°/ kJ mol^{-1}
Lattice dissociation enthalpy of $SrF_{2(s)}$	+2492
Enthalpy change of hydration of Sr^{2+} ions	−1480
Enthalpy change of hydration of F^- ions	−506

3   Rubidium chloride is an ionic compound that dissolves easily in water and can be used as a cell marker in laboratories. The table below shows thermodynamic data for rubidium chloride.

Enthalpy change	$\Delta H^\circ / kJ\ mol^{-1}$
Enthalpy change of atomisation of rubidium	+81
First ionisation energy of rubidium	+403
Enthalpy change of hydration of Rb^+ ions	−296
Enthalpy change of atomisation of chlorine	+122
First electron affinity of chlorine	−349
Enthalpy change of hydration of Cl^- ions	−364
Enthalpy change of formation of rubidium chloride	−435

3.1   Define the term enthalpy change of atomisation of an element.

(1 mark)

3.2   Complete the Born-Haber cycle for the formation of rubidium chloride by filling in the blank lines. You should include chemical symbols and state symbols.

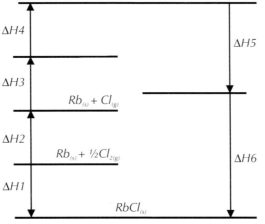

(3 marks)

3.3   Use the data in the table to calculate the lattice enthalpy change of formation of rubidium chloride.

(3 marks)

3.4   The theoretical value for the lattice enthalpy change of formation of rubidium chloride is very close to the experimental value calculated using a Born-Haber cycle. What does this tell you about the bonding character of rubidium chloride?

(2 marks)

3.5 State the value of the lattice dissociation enthalpy of rubidium chloride.

(1 mark)

3.6 Name the enthalpy change for rubidium chloride which is equal to the sum of its lattice dissociation enthalpy, the enthalpy change of hydration of Rb^+ ions and the enthalpy change of hydration of Cl^- ions.

(1 mark)

3.7 Calculate the enthalpy change you named in **3.6**
(If you have not been able to answer **3.5** use the value of $+300$ kJ mol^{-1}. This value is incorrect.)

(1 mark)

4 When methane undergoes incomplete combustion, carbon monoxide and water are produced as shown:

$$2CH_{4\,(g)} + 3O_{2\,(g)} \rightarrow 2CO_{(g)} + 4H_2O_{(g)} \qquad \Delta H^\circ = -1034 \text{ kJ mol}^{-1}$$

The standard entropies for the products and reactants are given in the table below.

	$CH_{4\,(g)}$	$O_{2\,(g)}$	$CO_{(g)}$	$H_2O_{(g)}$
$S^\circ / J\,K^{-1}\,mol^{-1}$	$+186$	$+205$	$+198$	$+189$

4.1 Use the balanced equation to explain whether you would expect entropy to decrease or increase during this reaction.

(2 marks)

4.2 The water vapour produced in the reaction condenses to form liquid water. Explain how the entropy of the system would change during this process.

(1 mark)

4.3 Calculate the entropy change for this reaction.

(3 marks)

4.4 Give the equation for calculating the free-energy change ΔG.

(1 mark)

4.5 Use the enthalpy change of reaction and your answer to **4.3** to explain why this reaction is feasible at any temperature. (If you have not been able to answer **4.3** use $+611$ kJ mol^{-1} for the entropy change. This value is incorrect.)

(2 marks)

5   Manganese can be extracted from its ore manganese(IV) oxide, MnO_2, by reduction using carbon at 1473 K. The reaction is shown in the equation below.

$$MnO_{2(s)} + C_{(s)} \rightarrow Mn_{(s)} + CO_{2(g)} \qquad \Delta H^\circ = +127 \text{ kJ mol}^{-1}$$

	$MnO_{2(s)}$	$C_{(s)}$	$Mn_{(s)}$	$CO_{2(g)}$
$S^\circ / J\,K^{-1}mol^{-1}$	53.0	5.70	32.0	214

5.1   Calculate the free-energy change for the extraction of manganese from its ore.

(4 marks)

5.2   Explain how the free-energy change of a reaction relates to the feasibility of that reaction.

(1 mark)

5.3   Give the equation which links the temperature at which a reaction becomes feasible, T, the enthalpy change for the reaction, ΔH, and the entropy change of the system, ΔS.

(1 mark)

5.4   Calculate the temperature at which the reduction of manganese oxide using carbon becomes feasible.

(2 marks)

The standard enthalpy of change formation of MnO_2 is -521 kJ mol^{-1}.

5.5   Define the term standard enthalpy change of formation.

(1 mark)

5.6   State whether the formation of manganese(IV) oxide from manganese and oxygen will be endothermic or exothermic.

(1 mark)

Learning Objective:

- Be able to measure the rate of reaction by a continuous monitoring method (Required Practical 7).

Specification Reference 3.1.9.2

1. Monitoring Reactions

Being able to work out the rate of a chemical reaction is a really important part of chemistry. You'll have come across reaction rates before, but now it's time to cover things in a bit more detail.

Reaction rates

The reaction rate is the change in the amount of reactants or products per unit time (normally per second). If the reactants are in solution, the rate will be change in concentration per second and the units will usually be mol dm^{-3} s^{-1}.

Measuring the progress of a reaction

If you want to find the rate of a reaction, you need to be able to follow the reaction as it's occurring. You can follow a reaction all the way through to its end by recording the amount of product (or reactant) you have at regular time intervals — this is called **continuous monitoring**.

The results can be used to work out how the rate changes over time. Although there are quite a few ways to follow reactions, not every method works for every reaction. You've got to pick a property that changes as the reaction goes on. Here are a few examples:

Gas volume

If a gas is given off, you could collect it in a gas syringe and record how much you've got at regular time intervals (see Figure 1).

Tip: Before carrying out any experiment, you should do a thorough risk assessment. You should then take any necessary safety precautions to minimise the risks associated with the experiment.

Tip: You need to make sure that your system is airtight. If any gas is allowed to escape, then the measurements you take will be lower than the true values. This means that you won't get accurate results.

Airtight seal so all the gas produced goes into the syringe.

The gas collects in the syringe and its production can be measured over time.

Bubbles of gas given off.

Reactants

Figure 1: *The experimental set-up for a reaction where the rate of reaction is monitored by collecting a gas.*

Tip: The more regularly you take readings, the more clearly you'll be able to see the trend in the rate of reaction against time.

You can find the rate of reaction in terms of concentration per unit of time by drawing a concentration-time graph (see pages 47-48). But before you do that, you need to find the concentration of a reactant or product at each time point. This is often quite hard to measure, so you'll usually have to collect some other data, and then convert that into concentration data.

In experiments where you're collecting gases, you'll need to use the ideal gas equation (see page 277) to work out how many moles of gas you've got, then use the molar ratio to work out the concentration of an aqueous reactant.

Example — Maths Skills

A scientist is following the reaction between 500 cm³ 2.00 mol dm⁻³
hydrochloric acid and 25 g of solid sodium carbonate,
by monitoring the volume of gas produced at r.t.p..
She takes measurements at 15 second intervals. Her results are recorded
in the table below. Calculate the concentration of HCl at each time point.

Tip: At r.t.p, $T = 298$ K and $p = 100$ kPa. You'll need these values later...

Time / seconds	0	15	30	45	60	75
Volume of gas produced / cm³	0.0	140	282	423	565	682

1. First, it's a good idea to write out the chemical equation of the reaction, so you can see exactly what reaction you're dealing with.

$$2HCl_{(aq)} + Na_2CO_{3(s)} \rightarrow 2NaCl_{(aq)} + CO_{2(g)} + H_2O_{(l)}$$

Tip: The ideal gas equation is $pV = nRT$. You need to use it to find out the number of moles (n). You'll need to rearrange the equation to be in terms of n. This is: $n = pV \div RT$. Make sure everything's in the right units too. Look at page 277 if you need a reminder about this.

2. From the reaction above, you can see that the gas produced is carbon dioxide. So, now work out how many moles of carbon dioxide have been produced at each time point, using the ideal gas equation. For example, using the data for the time interval at 15 seconds:

$$\text{moles of } CO_2 = pV \div RT = (100\,000 \times 1.4 \times 10^{-4}) \div (8.31 \times 298)$$
$$= \textbf{5.65... × 10}^{-3} \textbf{ moles}$$

3. Now, work out how many moles of HCl you had initially, using the equation: concentration = moles ÷ volume. You're told in the question that the concentration of HCl is 2.0 mol dm⁻³, and you've got 500 cm³ of it.

$$2.0 = \text{moles} \div (500 \div 1000)$$
$$\text{moles} = 2 \times 0.5 = \textbf{1.0 mole}$$

Tip: Remember to read the question thoroughly — it may tell you vital information that you'll need to answer the question.

4. From the balanced equation, you can see that for every one mole of CO_2 produced, two moles of HCl are used up. This means you can work out the number of moles of HCl lost at each time point. So, at 15 seconds:

$$\text{number of moles of HCl} = \text{initial moles of HCl} - (2 \times \text{moles of } CO_2)$$
$$= 1 - (2 \times 5.65... \times 10^{-3}) = \textbf{0.988... moles}$$

Tip: You couldn't work out the concentration of sodium carbonate as it's a solid — hydrochloric acid is aqueous so its concentration is easy to work out, using the information given in the question.

5. Given that the volume of solution doesn't change throughout the experiment, you can work out the concentration of HCl at each time point. So...

$$\text{Concentration of HCl at 15 seconds} = 0.988... \div (500 \div 1000)$$
$$= \textbf{1.98 mol dm}^{-3}$$

6. Repeating steps 2. to 5. with each data point gives you concentration/time data. You can use this to plot a concentration-time graph (see page 47), which you can use to work out the rate of reaction.

Tip: To make sure you really understand what's going on in this example, try working through steps 2. to 5. for each time interval — make sure you can get all the answers shown in this table.

Time / seconds	0	15	30	45	60	75
Concentration of HCl / mol dm⁻³	2.00	1.98	1.95	1.93	1.91	1.89

Figure 2: *A pH meter is an electronic probe that you can use to accurately measure pH.*

Tip: Make sure you don't mix up colorimeters (which measure absorbance) and calorimeters (which measure enthalpy changes).

Changes in pH
If the reaction produces or uses up H^+ ions, the pH of the solution will change. So you could measure the pH of the solution at regular intervals and calculate the concentration of H^+ (see page 99).

> **Example**
>
> In the reaction between propanone and iodine, H^+ ions are produced, so you can monitor the progress of the reaction by monitoring the decrease in pH.

Colour change
Sometimes you can track the colour change of a reaction using a gadget called a colorimeter. A colorimeter measures the absorbance (the amount of light of particular wavelengths absorbed) of the solution. The more concentrated the colour of the solution, the higher the absorbance is.

> **Example**
>
> In the reaction between propanone and iodine, the brown colour fades.
>
> $$CH_3COCH_{3(aq)} + I_{2(aq)} \rightarrow \underbrace{CH_3COCH_2I_{(aq)} + H^+_{(aq)} + I^-_{(aq)}}$$
>
> $\quad$ *colourless* $\qquad$ *brown* $\qquad\qquad$ *colourless*
>
> You collect and convert absorbance data into concentration like this:
>
> 1. Plot a **calibration curve** — a graph of known concentrations of I_2 plotted against absorbance (you'll need to collect this data yourself by measuring the absorbances of some standard solutions of I_2 of various concentrations).
>
>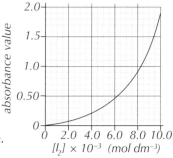
>
> 2. During the experiment, take a small sample from your reaction solution at regular intervals and read the absorbance.
>
> 3. Use your calibration curve to convert the absorbance at each time point into a concentration.
>
> 4. So here for example, if the absorbance value at time t seconds was 1.3, then the concentration of iodine at this time would be 9.0×10^{-3} mol dm^{-3}.

Figure 3: *A student using a colorimeter as part of a colorimetry experiment. A digital display shows the absorbance value of a sample at any given moment.*

Loss of mass
If a gas is given off, the system will lose mass. You can measure this at regular intervals with a balance, as shown in Figure 4.

Tip: The 'loss of mass' method and the 'gas volume' method will both tend to work on the same reactions — they both rely on the production of a gas.

A gas is formed and lost from the reaction container.

reactants

balance

stopwatch

Figure 4: *The experimental set-up for a reaction where the rate of reaction is monitored by measuring the mass lost from a reaction vessel.*

You can use mole calculations to work out how much gas you've lost, and therefore how many moles of reactants are left.

┌─ Example ─ **Maths Skills** ──────────────────────────────────

A student places 5.2 g of zinc in a conical flask containing 225 cm³ of 1.0 mol dm⁻³ hydrochloric acid. The initial mass of the reaction vessel and all its contents is 389 g. He monitors the loss in mass of the container over the course of a minute. His results are in the table below. Calculate the concentration of HCl at each time point.

Time / seconds	0	10	20	30	40	50	60
Mass of reaction vessel / g	389.00	388.97	388.95	388.93	388.91	388.89	388.87

Tip: As you can see, this method takes quite a long time. The initial rates method (see pages 54-57) and clock reactions (see pages 58-59) are often used instead of continuous monitoring, to cut down on the amount of maths you need to do.

1. Start by working out the mass lost at each time interval. This just involves subtracting the mass of the vessel at each time from its initial mass.

Time / seconds	0	10	20	30	40	50	60
Mass lost / g	0	0.03	0.05	0.07	0.09	0.11	0.13

2. Now write out the chemical equation for the reaction.

$$2HCl_{(aq)} + Zn_{(s)} \rightarrow ZnCl_{2(aq)} + H_{2(g)}$$

Tip: Make sure your equation at this point is balanced — if it's not, it could throw off all your calculations.

3. From the reaction above, you can see that the only gas produced is hydrogen, so all the loss in mass is due to the production of H_2. You can work out how many moles of hydrogen are lost at each time interval, using the equation: moles = mass ÷ M_r. So, after 10 seconds:

$$\text{moles of } H_2 = 0.03 \div (2 \times 1)$$
$$= \textbf{0.015 moles}$$

4. Now, work out how many moles of HCl you had initially using the equation: concentration = moles ÷ volume. This will allow you to work out the concentration of HCl at each time point.

$$1.0 = \text{moles} \div (225 \div 1000)$$
$$\text{moles} = 1.0 \times 0.225 = \textbf{0.225 moles}$$

Tip: Dividing the volume by 1000 at this stage converts the volume from cm³ into dm³.

5. From the balanced equation, you can see that for every one mole of H_2 produced, two moles of HCl are used up. So, using the data value at 10 seconds:

$$\text{number of moles of HCl} = \text{initial moles of HCl} - (2 \times \text{moles of } H_2)$$
$$= 0.225 - (2 \times 0.015) = \textbf{0.195 moles}$$

Tip: These mole calculations were covered in the first year of the course. Look back at your Year 1 notes if you need a reminder on how to do them.

6. So, given that the volume of solution doesn't change throughout the experiment, you can work out the concentration of HCl at each time point. For example...

$$\text{Concentration HCl at 10 seconds} = 0.195 \div (225 \div 1000)$$
$$= \textbf{0.87 mol dm}^{-3}$$

7. Repeating this with each data point gives you concentration/time data. You can use this to plot a concentration-time graph (see page 47), which you can use to work out the rate of reaction.

Time / seconds	0	10	20	30	40	50	60
Concentration HCl / mol dm^{-3}	1.0	0.87	0.78	0.69	0.60	0.51	0.42

Practice Questions — Application

Q1 Suggest a technique you could use to follow the progress of each of the following reactions.

a) The reaction between chromate(VI) ions (CrO_4^{2-}) and an acid to form dichromate(VI) ions ($Cr_2O_7^{2-}$) and water.

b) The reaction between zinc metal and hydrochloric acid.

c) The reaction between thiosulfate ($S_2O_3^{2-}$) and acid to produce sulfur dioxide gas, water and a yellow precipitate of solid sulfur.

Q2 A student is monitoring the rate of a reaction between an acid and a metal by collecting gas in a gas syringe. How would her calculated rate be affected if there was a leak in the system?

Q3 A student is using a balance to monitor the loss of mass over the course of the following reaction between zinc sulfide and 250 cm^3 of 1.50 mol dm^{-3} hydrochloric acid.

$$ZnS_{(s)} + 2HCl_{(aq)} \rightarrow ZnCl_{2(aq)} + H_2S_{(g)}$$

She records the mass of the reaction vessel at various time intervals. Calculate the concentration of HCl at each time interval shown below.

Time / seconds	0	10	20	30	40	50	60
Mass of vessel / g	411.02	410.42	409.84	409.25	408.65	408.08	407.51

Q4 A student is following the reaction between 100 cm^3 1.00 mol dm^{-3} sulfuric acid and 15 g of solid sodium carbonate, by monitoring the volume of gas produced at r.t.p.. She takes measurements at 15 second intervals. Her results are recorded in the table below. Calculate the concentration of H_2SO_4 at each time point.

Time / seconds	0	15	30	45	60	75
Volume of gas produced / cm^3	0.00	3.20	6.51	9.94	13.0	15.9

Practice Questions — Fact Recall

Q1 What is meant by the term 'continuous monitoring'?

Q2 Draw and label the set-up you would use to measure the volume of gas produced over the course of a reaction.

Q3 What does a colorimeter measure?

Q4 Describe how you could follow the rate of reaction for a reaction where a gas is lost from the reaction container.

Tip: Think carefully about the reactants and products present in each of these reactions. It may help you to write out a chemical equation.

Tip: You'll need the ideal gas equation for this question. It's $pV = nRT$.

2. Reaction Rates and Graphs

Once you've converted the data you've collected from continuously monitoring a reaction into concentration data, you can plot a concentration-time graph. You can use the gradient of the line of this graph to work out the reaction rate.

Learning Objective:
- Be able to use concentration-time graphs to deduce the rate of reaction.

Specification Reference 3.1.9.2

Finding the rate from a straight-line graph

If you draw a graph of the amount of reactant or product against time for a reaction, the rate at any point is given by the gradient at that point on the graph. You can work out the gradient at any point using the equation:

$$\text{gradient} = \text{change in } y \div \text{change in } x$$

Exam Tip
In the exam, you might have to draw a line of best fit going through the data points on your graph before you can start working out the gradient and rate — so make sure you know how to draw one (see page 284).

Example — **Maths Skills**

The graph below shows data collected from an experiment where the decomposition of a reactant X was monitored over time. Work out the rate of the reaction.

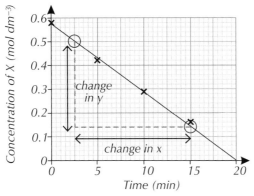

1. To find the rate of this reaction, you can use the gradient of the line. Because this is a straight-line graph, the gradient is the same at all points on the line.

2. Try to pick two points on the line that are easy to read — ideally these are points where the line passes exactly through the corners of the grid squares.

3. Now use the equation, gradient = change in y ÷ change in x, to work out the gradient of the graph.
   - change in y = 0.14 – 0.50 = –0.36 mol dm^{-3}
   - change in x = 15 – 2.5 = 12.5 minutes
   - gradient = –0.36 ÷ 12.5 = –0.029 mol dm^{-3} min^{-1}

4. The gradient is negative, but you can ignore the sign when you use it for the rate. So the rate of reaction is 0.029 mol dm^{-3} min^{-1}.

Tip: Straight-line graphs are pretty simple — the gradient is the same across the entire data set, so the reaction rate is the same too. This means you only have to work out a single rate as it's always the same.

Tip: To help you work out the changes in x and y, you should draw a vertical line down from one point, and a horizontal line across from the other to make a triangle.

Finding the rate from a curve

If the graph's a curve, you have to draw a tangent to the curve and find the gradient of that. The gradient, and so the rate, at a particular point in the reaction is the same as the gradient of the tangent at that point.
A tangent is a line that just touches a curve and has the same gradient as the curve does at that point. Figure 1 shows how a graph of the concentration of a reactant against time might look.

Tip: If you're not sure whether you've calculated the gradient of a straight-line correctly, you can check your answer by working out the gradient at another point too. If your answer is right, they should be the same.

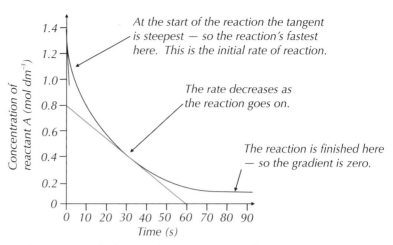

Tip: Concentration-time graphs pop up loads throughout this section, so make sure you really understand how to use them to work out rates before moving on to the next topic.

At the start of the reaction the tangent is steepest — so the reaction's fastest here. This is the initial rate of reaction.

The rate decreases as the reaction goes on.

The reaction is finished here — so the gradient is zero.

Figure 1: Graph showing the concentration of a reactant against time.

Example — Maths Skills

The graph below shows how the concentration of a solution changes over time. Calculate the rate of the reaction at 3 minutes.

Exam Tip
Drawing a tangent is pretty much impossible without a ruler — so make sure you remember to bring one into your exam.

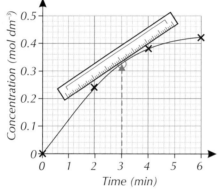

1. Find the point on the curve that you need to look at. The question asks you to find the rate of reaction at 3 minutes, so find 3 on the x-axis and go up to the curve from there.

2. Place a ruler at that point so that it's just touching the curve. Position the ruler so that you can see the whole curve.

Tip: In many cases, it's useful to measure the gradient at various points along the curve. This gives you a more detailed idea of how the rate changes over time.

3. Adjust the ruler until the space between the ruler and the curve is equal on both sides of the point.

4. Draw a line along the ruler to make the tangent. Extend the line right across the graph — it'll help to make your gradient calculation easier as you'll have more points to choose from.

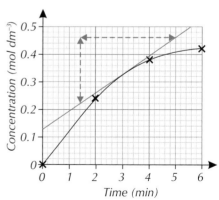

Tip: Working out the gradient of a tangent is exactly the same as working out the gradient of a straight line, so look back at the last page for more details on how to do this.

5. Calculate the gradient of the tangent to find the rate:
   - gradient = change in y ÷ change in x
   $$= (0.46 - 0.22) \div (5.0 - 1.4)$$
   $$= 0.24 \text{ mol dm}^{-3} \div 3.6 \text{ mins} = 0.067 \text{ mol dm}^{-3}\text{min}^{-1}$$
   - So, the rate of reaction at 3 mins was 0.067 mol dm^{-3} min^{-1}.

Q1 The graph below shows the results of a reaction between a metal and hydrochloric acid, where the mass of the reaction vessel was measured throughout the reaction.

a) Calculate the rate of reaction.

b) How does the rate of reaction vary over the 4 minutes?

Q2 A student is measuring the volume of carbon dioxide gas formed by a reaction between limestone and hydrochloric acid. Her results are shown in the following table.

Time / minutes	Concentration of acid / mol dm⁻³
0	5.0
1	3.1
2	2.6
3	2.5
4	2.4
5	2.4

a) Plot the data in the table on a graph.

b) Draw a line of best fit on the graph drawn in part a).

c) Calculate the rate of the reaction at 2 minutes.

Q3 The following graph shows the data collected from a pH experiment.

a) Calculate the rate of the reaction at: i) 2 minutes, ii) 6 minutes.

b) A student says that the rate of the reaction is 0 mol dm⁻³ min⁻¹. Comment on this statement.

Exam Tip
Always remember to include your units when you're working out the rate. It could cost you valuable marks in the exam if you miss them out...

Tip: There's a lot to remember when it comes to drawing graphs. You've got to think about the size of the graph, what goes on which axis, the scale, not to mention making sure you plot the data points correctly. Look at page 284 for some tips on how to draw graphs.

- Know that the rate of a chemical reaction is related to the concentration of reactants by a rate equation of the form:
  Rate = $k[A]^m[B]^n$
  where m and n are the orders of reaction with respect to reactants A and B, and k is the rate constant.

- Be able to define the terms 'order of reaction' and 'rate constant'.

- Know that the rate equation is an experimentally determined relationship.

- Be able to derive the rate equation for a reaction from the orders with respect to each of the reactants.

- Be able to perform calculations using the rate equation.

Specification Reference 3.1.9.1, 3.1.9.2

Exam Tip
m and n could take any value but in the exam you'll only have to deal with rate equations where m and n are 0, 1 or 2.

Tip: In this example there are only two reactants but rate equations can be written for equations with any number of reactants. E.g. if there were three reactants the equation would be:
Rate = $k[A]^m[B]^n[C]^x$

3. Rate Equations

Rate equations tell us a bit more about what affects the rate. You'll have to get your head around something called the rate constant, and you'll meet reaction orders too. It's not the simplest topic, but once you understand the theory, the maths really isn't too hard at all.

The rate equation

Rate equations look ghastly, but all they're really telling you is how the rate is affected by the concentrations of reactants. For a general reaction: A + B $\rightarrow$ C + D, the rate equation is:

$$Rate = k[A]^m[B]^n$$

The square brackets mean the concentration of whatever's inside them. So [A] means 'the concentration of A' and [B] means 'the concentration of B'. The units of rate are usually mol dm^{-3} s^{-1}. m and n are the **orders of reaction** and k is the **rate constant** (but more on these below...).

Reaction orders

m and n are the orders of the reaction with respect to reactant A and reactant B. m tells you how the concentration of reactant A affects the rate and n tells you the same for reactant B.

- If [A] changes and the rate stays the same, the order of reaction with respect to A is 0 (or zero order with respect to A). So if [A] doubles, the rate will stay the same. If [A] triples, the rate will stay the same.

- If the rate is proportional to [A], then the order of reaction with respect to A is 1 (or first order with respect to A). So if [A] doubles, the rate will double. If [A] triples, the rate will triple.

- If the rate is proportional to [A]^2, then the order of reaction with respect to A is 2 (or second order with respect to A). So if [A] doubles, the rate will be $2^2 = 4$ times faster. If [A] triples, the rate will be $3^2 = 9$ times faster.

The overall order of the reaction is $m + n$. So, if m was 2 and n was 1 the overall order of the reaction would be 2 + 1 = 3.

┌─ **Example** ── **Maths Skills** ──────────────

The rate equation of the following reaction is rate = $k[NO_{(g)}]^2[H_{2(g)}]^1$.
$$2H_{2(g)} + 2NO_{(g)} \rightarrow 2H_2O_{(l)} + N_{2(g)}$$

- From this rate equation, you can see that the rate of reaction depends on the concentrations of H_2 and NO present in the reaction mixture.

- The reaction is second order with respect to NO, so if you double the concentration of NO in the reaction mixture, then the reaction rate will be four times faster.

- The reaction is first order with respect to H_2, so if you double the concentration of H_2 in the reaction mixture, the rate will double too.

- The overall order of the reaction is 2 + 1 = 3.

You can only find orders of reactions, and so rate equations, by doing experiments, such as the ones shown on pages 42-44. You can't tell what the rate equation will be from the balanced chemical equation.

The rate constant

k is the rate constant — it's a constant that links the concentration of reactants to the rate of a reaction. The bigger it is, the faster the reaction. The rate constant is always the same for a certain reaction at a particular temperature — but if you increase the temperature, the rate constant rises too. When you increase the temperature of a reaction, the rate of reaction increases. The concentrations of the reactants and the orders of reaction haven't changed though. So it must be an increase in the value of k which has increased the rate of reaction.

Tip: The link between the rate constant and temperature is explained in more detail by the Arrhenius equation. It's covered on pages 64-68.

Writing rate equations

You need to know how to write rate equations for reactions and use them to calculate the rate constant. This example shows you how:

Figure 1: Students measuring the rate of a reaction which produces a gas as a product.

> **Example — Maths Skills**
>
> **The chemical equation below shows the acid-catalysed reaction between propanone and iodine.**
>
> $$CH_3COCH_{3(aq)} + I_{2(aq)} \xrightarrow{H^+_{(aq)}} CH_3COCH_2I_{(aq)} + H^+_{(aq)} + I^-_{(aq)}$$
>
> **a) This reaction is first order with respect to propanone, first order with respect to $H^+_{(aq)}$ and zero order with respect to iodine. Write the rate equation for this reaction.**
>
> In this example there are three things that you need to think about — the orders of reaction of propanone (CH_3COCH_3), iodine (I_2) and hydrogen ions (H^+). (Even though H^+ is a catalyst, rather than a reactant, it can still be in the rate equation because it affects the rate of reaction.) So the rate equation will be in the form Rate $= k[A]^m[B]^n[C]^x$.
>
> You're told the reaction orders with respect to each reactant in the question so just use that information to construct the rate equation:
>
> $$\text{Rate} = k[CH_3COCH_3]^1[H^+]^1[I_2]^0$$
>
> But $[X]^1$ is usually written as $[X]$, and $[X]^0$ equals 1 so is usually left out of the rate equation. So you can simplify the rate equation to:
>
> $$\text{Rate} = k[CH_3COCH_3][H^+]$$
>
> This rate equation shows that the rate of reaction is proportional to the concentrations of propanone and H^+. So doubling the concentration of either propanone or H^+ will double the rate of the reaction. The overall order of this reaction is 2 — it's a second order reaction.
>
> **b) At a certain temperature, k was found to be 520 $mol^{-1}\,dm^3\,s^{-1}$ when $[CH_3COCH_3] = [I_2] = [H^+] = 1.50 \times 10^{-3}\,mol\,dm^{-3}$. Calculate the rate at this temperature.**
>
> Calculating the rate is as simple as popping in the values the question into the rate equation you worked out in part a).
>
> $\text{Rate} = k[CH_3COCH_3][H^+] = 520 \times 1.50 \times 10^{-3} \times 1.50 \times 10^{-3} = 1.17 \times 10^{-3}$
>
> You can find the units for the rate by putting the other units into the rate equation.
>
> The units for the rate are ~~$mol^{-1}\,dm^3\,s^{-1}$~~ $\times$ ~~$mol\,dm^{-3}$~~ $\times mol\,dm^{-3} = mol\,dm^{-3}\,s^{-1}$.
>
> So the answer is: rate $= \mathbf{1.17 \times 10^{-3}\,mol\,dm^{-3}\,s^{-1}}$

Tip: When simplifying rate equations think about the index laws from maths — the same rules apply here. Anything to the power of zero is one (e.g. $[X]^0 = 1$) and anything to the power of one doesn't change (e.g. $[X]^1 = [X]$). Look at pages 282-283 for more about this.

Tip: Look at the Maths Skills section if you need more information on how to work out the units for the rate constant (page 281).

Calculating the rate constant

If you know the orders of a reaction, you can use the rate equation and experimental data to work out the rate constant, k. The units of k vary, so you'll need to work them out too.

┌─ **Example** ── **Maths Skills** ─────────────────────────────┐

The reaction below is second order with respect to NO and zero order with respect to CO and O_2.

$$NO_{(g)} + CO_{(g)} + O_{2(g)} \rightarrow NO_{2(g)} + CO_{2(g)}$$

At a certain temperature, the rate is 1.76×10^{-3} mol dm^{-3} s^{-1}, when $[NO_{(g)}] = [CO_{(g)}] = [O_{2(g)}] = 2.00 \times 10^{-3}$ mol dm^{-3}. Find the value of the rate constant, k, at this temperature.

- To answer this question you first need to write out the rate equation:

$$\text{Rate} = k[NO]^2[CO]^0[O_2]^0$$
$$= k[NO]^2$$

- Next insert the concentration and the rate, which were given to you in the question:

$$\text{Rate} = k[NO]^2$$
$$1.76 \times 10^{-3} = k \times (2.00 \times 10^{-3})^2$$

- Rearrange the equation and calculate the value of k:

$$k = \frac{1.76 \times 10^{-3}}{(2.00 \times 10^{-3})^2} = 440$$

- Find the units of k by putting the other units in the rate equation:

$$\text{Rate} = k[NO]^2 \quad \text{so} \quad \text{mol dm}^{-3} \text{ s}^{-1} = k \times (\text{mol dm}^{-3})^2$$

- Rearrange the equation to get k:

$$k = \frac{\text{mol dm}^{-3} \text{ s}^{-1}}{(\text{mol dm}^{-3})^2}$$

- Cancel out units wherever possible. In this example you can cancel out a mol dm^{-3} from the top and bottom lines of the fraction:

$$k = \frac{\cancel{\text{mol dm}^{-3}} \text{ s}^{-1}}{(\cancel{\text{mol dm}^{-3}})(\text{mol dm}^{-3})} = \frac{\text{s}^{-1}}{\text{mol dm}^{-3}}$$

- Get rid of the fraction using index laws:

$$k = \frac{\text{s}^{-1}}{\text{mol dm}^{-3}} = \text{mol}^{-1} \text{ dm}^3 \text{ s}^{-1}$$

- So the answer is:

$$k = 440 \text{ mol}^{-1} \text{ dm}^3 \text{ s}^{-1}$$

└──┘

Q1 A student is trying to determine the rate equation for the reaction:

$$2Fe^{3+}_{(aq)} + 2I^-_{(aq)} \rightarrow 2Fe^{2+}_{(aq)} + I_{2(aq)}$$

He says, "because the equation involves the reaction of two moles of iron(III) ions and 2 moles of iodide ions, the rate equation must be rate = $k[Fe^{3+}]^2[I^-]^2$".

a) Do you agree with the student? Explain your answer.

b) According to the student's rate equation, how would halving the concentration of iodide ions affect the rate of reaction?

Q2 The following reaction occurs under certain conditions:

$$2H_{2(g)} + 2NO_{(g)} \rightarrow 2H_2O_{(g)} + N_{2(g)}$$

This reaction is first order with respect to H_2 and second order with respect to NO.

a) Construct the rate equation for this reaction.

b) What is the overall order of this reaction?

c) How would you expect the rate of reaction to change if the concentration of NO were doubled?

d) At a certain temperature, k was found to be 221 mol^{-2} dm^6 s^{-1} when $[H_2] = [NO] = 1.54 \times 10^{-3}$ mol dm^{-3}.
    Calculate the rate at this temperature.

Q3 The reaction below is second order with respect to NO and first order with respect to Cl_2:

$$2NO_{(g)} + Cl_{2(g)} \rightarrow 2NOCl_{(g)}$$

The rate of reaction is 5.85×10^{-6} mol dm^{-3} s^{-1} at 50 °C, when the concentration of both NO and Cl_2 is 0.400 mol dm^{-3}.

a) Write the rate equation for this reaction.

b) Calculate the value of the rate constant (k) for this reaction at 50 °C.

c) How would you expect the value of k to change if the temperature were increased?

d) Calculate the expected rate of reaction if 0.500 mol dm^{-3} NO were mixed with 0.200 mol dm^{-3} Cl_2 at 50 °C.

Exam Tip
When answering calculation questions like these always remember to give the units for your answer.

Exam Tip
In the exam, you should give your answers to the same number of significant figures as used in the question. Here, the values in the question are given to 3 s.f. so you should give your answer to 3 s.f. as well (see page 276).

Tip: This isn't the last you'll see of rate equations. Oh no — there's lots more on reaction orders to come, and the rate equation is really useful for working out reaction mechanisms (see page 62). So make sure you really understand the basics covered on the last few pages, and that you can answer all the questions before moving on to the next topic.

Practice Questions — Fact Recall

Q1 What does the rate equation tell you?

Q2 Write out the rate equation for the following, general reaction:
    A + B → C + D

Q3 In the rate equation Rate = $k[X]^a[Y]^b$, what do the following represent:

a) k?

b) $[Y]$?

c) a?

Q4 How do you work out the units of the rate constant?

- Be able to use initial concentration-time data to deduce the initial rate of a reaction.
- Be able to use rate-concentration data to deduce the order (0, 1 or 2) with respect to a reactant.

Specification Reference 3.1.9.2

Tip: Graphs and gradients are covered in a bit more detail on pages 284-285.

Tip: A tangent is a line that just touches a curve and has the same gradient as the curve does at that point.

Tip: Look back at pages 42-44 for different ways to measure the rate of reaction using continuous monitoring.

4. The Initial Rates Method

Rate equations are really useful, but to work out the rate equation you need to know the orders of a reaction. These can be determined experimentally by monitoring the initial rate of a reaction as you change the concentration of one of the reactants.

Finding the initial rate

The initial rate of a reaction is the rate right at the start of the reaction. You can find this from a concentration–time graph. You can collect data for a concentration–time graph by setting up a reaction and then monitoring the amount of a reactant or product over time (see pages 42-44 for lots of ways to do this). The amount of reactant decreases with time because it gets used up in the reaction. Once the reaction is complete, plotting the concentration of reactant against time gives a concentration–time graph.

Once you have a concentration–time graph, you can find the initial rate of reaction by calculating the gradient of the curve at time = 0. Just draw a tangent to the curve at time = 0 and draw in horizontal and vertical lines to make a triangle with the tangent as its longest side. Label the horizontal line x and the vertical line y. The gradient of the line is the change in y divided by the change in x and this represents the initial rate of reaction — see Figure 1.

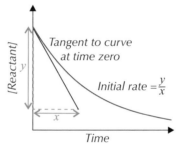

Figure 1: Graph showing how to calculate the initial rate of reaction.

Example — Maths Skills

The data on the graph below was obtained by continuously monitoring the concentration of H^+ ions over the course of a reaction between a metal and an acid. Calculate the initial rate of the reaction.

- To work out the initial rate, you need to work out the gradient of the curve right at the start of the reaction.

- Draw a tangent to the curve at time = 0.
- Then you just need to work out the gradient of the tangent using exactly the same method as the one you saw, back on page 48.

  gradient = change in y ÷ change in x

  $$= (0.3 - 3.0) \div (0.7 - 0.0)$$
  $$= -2.7 \text{ mol dm}^{-3} \div 0.7 \text{ mins} = -3.857... \text{ mol dm}^{-3} \text{ min}^{-1}$$

- So the initial rate of reaction was 3.9 mol dm^{-3} min^{-1}.

Tip: Remember, you can ignore the sign of the gradient when using it to work out the rate.

Using the initial rates method

You can use a process called the **initial rates method** to work out the order of reaction for each reactant. Here's how it works:

- Carry out the reaction and monitor its progress. Unlike with continuous monitoring, you don't have to monitor the reaction all the way through to the end — you just need to collect enough data to allow you to work out an initial rate. Use this data to draw a concentration-time graph.

- Repeat the experiment using a different initial concentration of one of the reactants. Keep the concentrations of other reactants and other conditions the same. Draw another concentration-time graph.

- Use your graphs to calculate the initial rate for each experiment using the method above.

- Now look at how the different initial concentrations affect the initial rate — use this to work out the order for that reactant.

- Repeat the process for each reactant (different reactants may have different orders).

The examples below and on the next page show you how to deduce the orders of reaction, with respect to each reactant, from experimental concentration and initial rates data. Once you know the orders, you can work out the rate equation.

Exam Tip
Missing off the units from your answer is a sure-fire way of losing precious marks. Don't let this trip you up...

Tip: When deciding how much data to collect, you could wait for a set amount of product to form or for a set amount of reactant to be used up.

Tip: Look back at page 45 for how to use experimental data, from continuous monitoring techniques, to calculate the concentration of reactants.

┌─ Example ─ **Maths Skills** ─

The table below shows the results of a series of initial rate experiments for the reaction $2NO_{(g)} + Cl_{2(g)} \rightarrow 2NOCl_{(g)}$. Write down the rate equation for the reaction. The temperature remained constant throughout.

Experiment number	[NO] / mol dm^{-3}	[Cl$_2$] / mol dm^{-3}	Initial rate / mol dm^{-3} s^{-1}
1	0.125	0.125	1.79×10^{-7}
2	0.250	0.125	7.16×10^{-7}
3	0.250	0.250	1.43×10^{-6}

- Look at experiments 1 and 2 — when [NO] doubles (and the concentration of Cl$_2$ stays constant) the rate is four times faster, and $4 = 2^2$. So the reaction is second order with respect to NO.

- Look at experiments 2 and 3 — when [Cl$_2$] doubles (but the concentration of NO stays constant), the rate is two times faster, and $2 = 2^1$. So the reaction is first order with respect to Cl$_2$.

So the rate equation is: Rate = $k[NO]^2[Cl_2]$

Tip: Look back at page 50 if you need a reminder about how to link a change in concentration and a change in rate to the reaction order with respect to a certain reactant.

Tip: You can also work out reaction orders by looking at the shapes of concentration-time graphs and rate-concentration graphs. This is covered later in this section.

In the exam you could get a question where more than one concentration changes. These are a bit trickier. The example below shows you what to do.

Example — Maths Skills

The table below shows the results of a series of initial rate experiments for the reaction $NO_{(g)} + CO_{(g)} + O_{2(g)} \rightarrow NO_{2(g)} + CO_{2(g)}$. The experiments were carried out at a constant temperature. Write down the rate equation for the reaction and use it to calculate k at this temperature.

Experiment number	[NO] / mol dm^{-3}	[CO] / mol dm^{-3}	[O$_2$] / mol dm^{-3}	Initial rate / mol dm^{-3} s^{-1}
1	2.0×10^{-2}	1.0×10^{-2}	1.0×10^{-2}	0.17
2	6.0×10^{-2}	1.0×10^{-2}	1.0×10^{-2}	1.53
3	2.0×10^{-2}	2.0×10^{-2}	1.0×10^{-2}	0.17
4	4.0×10^{-2}	1.0×10^{-2}	2.0×10^{-2}	0.68

- Look at experiments 1 and 2 — when [NO] triples (and all the other concentrations stay constant) the rate is nine times faster, and $9 = 3^2$. So the reaction is second order with respect to NO.

- Look at experiments 1 and 3 — when [CO] doubles (but all the other concentrations stay constant), the rate stays the same. So the reaction is zero order with respect to CO.

- Look at experiments 1 and 4 — the rate of experiment 4 is four times faster than experiment 1. The reaction is second order with respect to [NO], so the rate will quadruple when you double [NO]. But in experiment 4, [O$_2$] has also been doubled. As doubling [O$_2$] hasn't had any additional effect on the rate, the reaction must be zero order with respect to O$_2$.

Now that you know the order with respect to each reactant you can write the rate equation, Rate = k[NO]^2.

You can then calculate k at this temperature by putting the concentrations and the initial rate from one of the experiments into the rate equation.

So, using experiment 1: $0.17 = k(2.0 \times 10^{-2})^2$

$$k = 0.17 \div (2.0 \times 10^{-2})^2 = 425$$

To work out the units of k, substitute the units of each variable into the equation for k.

$$k = \frac{\cancel{mol\,dm^{-3}}\,s^{-1}}{\cancel{mol\,dm^{-3}} \times mol\,dm^{-3}}$$

And get rid of the fraction using index laws:

$$\frac{s^{-1}}{mol\,dm^{-3}} = mol^{-1}\,dm^3\,s^{-1}$$

Meaning the rate constant, $k = 425\ mol^{-1}\,dm^3\,s^{-1}$.

Exam Tip
You would usually only change one concentration at a time but you could get a question where more than one concentration changes — don't get confused, the principle is the same.

Tip: It doesn't matter which experiment you use to calculate k. The value of k should be the same for all of them because they have all been done at the same temperature.

Tip: You might not always be given the rate of the reaction at different concentrations. Instead, you could be given the time taken for the reaction to reach a certain point. The time taken is proportional to the rate — that means you can use 1 ÷ time as a measure of the rate.

Q1 The data shown on the graph below was obtained experimentally from the decomposition of SO_2Cl_2.
Work out the initial rate of the reaction.

Q2 A student is carrying out a reaction to try and work out the rate equation of the following reaction:

$$I_2 + 2S_2O_3^{2-} \rightarrow 2I^- + S_4O_6^{2-}$$

His results are in the table below.

Trial number	$[I_2]$ /mol dm^{-3}	$[S_2O_3^{2-}]$ / mol dm^{-3}	Reaction time / s
1	0.040	0.040	312
2	0.080	0.040	156
3	0.040	0.020	624

Work out the rate equation for this reaction.

Q3 The table below shows the results of a series of initial rate experiments for the reaction: $2A + B + C \rightarrow AB + AC$

Experiment number	[A] / mol dm^{-3}	[B] / mol dm^{-3}	[C] / mol dm^{-3}	Initial rate / mol dm^{-3} s^{-1}
1	1.2	1.2	1.2	0.25
2	1.2	2.4	1.2	1.00
3	1.2	2.4	3.6	3.00
4	0.6	2.4	1.2	0.50

a) Write down the rate equation for this reaction.
b) Calculate the rate constant (k).

Tip: The reaction in question 2 is an example of a clock reaction. They're covered in more detail in the next topic.

Tip: Remember — the rate is proportional to 1/time, so you can use 1/time as a measure of the rate.

Exam Tip
It can be a good idea to check the value of your rate constant by making sure you get the same value for it when you use the data from each experiment.

Practice Questions — Fact Recall

Q1 How do you find out the initial rate of a reaction from a concentration-time graph?

Q2 Briefly outline how to carry out the initial rates method to work out the order of reaction with respect to each reactant.

5. Clock Reactions

Clock reactions are an example of an initial rates method. They involving measuring how long it takes for a certain amount of product to form. These pages cover everything you'll need to know about clock reactions, and you'll even get to meet the king of all clock reactions, the iodine clock reaction.

Clock reactions

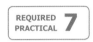

The method described in the last topic for working out initial rates is a bit of a faff — lots of measuring and drawing graphs. In clock reactions, the initial rate can be easily estimated.

In a clock reaction, you measure how the time taken for a set amount of product to form changes as you vary the concentration of one of the reactants. As part of a clock reaction, there will be a sudden increase in the concentration of a certain product as a limiting reactant is used up. There's usually an easily observable endpoint, such as a colour change, to tell you when the desired amount of product has formed. The quicker the clock reaction finishes, the faster the initial rate of the reaction. You need to make the following assumptions:

- The concentration of each reactant doesn't change significantly over the time period of your clock reaction.

- The temperature stays constant.

- When the endpoint is seen, the reaction has not proceeded too far.

As long as these assumptions are reasonable for your experiment, you can assume that the rate of reaction stays constant during the time period of your measurement. So the rate of your clock reaction will be a good estimate for the initial rate of your reaction.

Figure 1: *Using a colorimeter to measure a colour change. In clock reactions, there is often a sudden, clear colour change, so a colorimeter isn't always needed.*

Tip: These are ionic equations — they only show the reacting particles. You met them in Year 1 of the course.

Tip: When carrying out clock reactions, the data you collect will be in units of time, rather than units of rate. You can use 1/time as a measure of the rate.

The iodine clock reaction

The most famous clock reaction is the iodine clock reaction.

In an iodine clock reaction, the reaction you're monitoring is:

$$H_2O_{2(aq)} + 2I^-_{(aq)} + 2H^+_{(aq)} \rightarrow 2H_2O_{(l)} + I_{2(aq)}$$

- A small amount of sodium thiosulfate solution and starch are added to an excess of hydrogen peroxide and iodide ions in acid solution. (Starch is used as an indicator — it turns blue-black in the presence of iodine.)

- The sodium thiosulfate that is added to the reaction mixture reacts instantaneously with any iodine that forms:

$$2S_2O_3^{2-}_{(aq)} + I_{2(aq)} \rightarrow 2I^-_{(aq)} + S_4O_6^{2-}_{(aq)}$$

- To begin with, all the iodine that forms in the first reaction is used up straight away in the second reaction. But once all the sodium thiosulfate is used up, any more iodine that forms will stay in solution, so the starch indicator will suddenly turn the solution blue-black. This is the end of the clock reaction.

- Varying iodide or hydrogen peroxide concentration while keeping the others constant will give different times for the colour change.

You may have to carry out an iodine-clock reaction in the lab.
Here's the method of how to do it...

1. Rinse a clean 25.0 cm³ pipette with sulfuric acid. Then, use this pipette to transfer 25.0 cm³ sulfuric acid, of known concentration (e.g. 0.25 mol dm⁻³), to a clean 250 cm³ beaker. This beaker is your reaction vessel.

2. Using a clean pipette or measuring cylinder, add 20.0 cm³ of distilled water to the beaker containing the sulfuric acid.

3. Using a dropping pipette, add a few drops (or about 1 cm³) of starch solution to the same beaker.

4. Measure out 5.0 cm³ of potassium iodide solution of a known concentration (e.g. 0.1 mol dm⁻³), using either a 5.0 cm³ pipette or a burette, rinsed with potassium iodide solution. Transfer this volume to the reaction vessel.

5. Next, using a pipette rinsed with sodium thiosulfate solution, or a clean measuring cylinder, add 5.0 cm³ sodium thiosulfate to the reaction vessel. Swirl the contents of the beaker so all the solutions are evenly mixed.

6. Finally, rinse a 10.0 cm³ pipette with hydrogen peroxide solution. Then, use the pipette to transfer 10.0 cm³ hydrogen peroxide solution to the reaction vessel and simultaneously start a stop watch. Stir the contents of the beaker throughout the reaction, using a glass rod.

7. Stop the stop watch when the contents of the beaker turn from colourless to blue-black, this marks the endpoint. Record this time in a results table, along with the quantities of sulfuric acid, water, potassium iodide and sodium thiosulfate solutions you used in that experiment.

8. Repeat the experiment varying the volume of potassium iodide solution. Use varying amounts of distilled water in each experiment so the overall volume of the reaction mixture remains constant.

You can then use this data to work out the reaction order, with respect to potassium iodide, using the method on pages 55-56. Varying the concentration of other reagents allows you to find the order of reaction with respect to them too.

Tip: Before you start this experiment, you'll need standard solutions of potassium iodide, hydrogen peroxide and sodium thiosulfate. If you're not given these, check your Year 1 notes for some information on how to make up standard solutions from solids and liquids.

Tip: Make sure you carry out a full risk assessment before doing any experiments. This will help prevent any nasty accidents.

Tip: You need to vary the volumes of KI solution and H_2O in each run. So, you could do 5 runs using, e.g.:

Vol. KI$_{(aq)}$	Vol. H_2O
5 cm³	20 cm³
10 cm³	15 cm³
15 cm³	10 cm³
20 cm³	5 cm³
25 cm³	0 cm³

Practice Questions — Fact Recall

Q1 State what is meant by a clock reaction.

Q2 What assumptions do you have to make when carrying out a clock reaction?

Q3 What colour change is seen in an iodine clock reaction, when starch is used as an indicator?

Learning Objective:

- Be able to use rate-concentration graphs to deduce the order (0, 1 or 2) with respect to a reactant.

Specification Reference 3.1.9.2

6. Rate-concentration Graphs

You can work out the order of reaction, with respect to a certain reactant, from the shape of its concentration-time graph, and its rate-concentration graph. Read on to find out more...

Working out reaction orders from graphs

You can work out the reaction order with respect to a particular reactant using a rate-concentration graph. You can make a rate-concentration graph using a concentration-time graph. Here's how:

- Find the gradient (which is the rate) at various points along the concentration-time graph (see page 47 for a reminder of how to do this). This gives you a set of points for the rate-concentration graph.

- Then just plot the points and join them up with a line or smooth curve.

The shape of the rate-concentration graph tells you the order:

Zero order

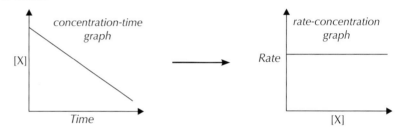

Tip: If something is in [square brackets] it's a concentration. So [X] means the concentration of reactant X.

A horizontal line on a rate-concentration graph means that changing the concentration doesn't change the rate, so the reaction is zero order.

First order

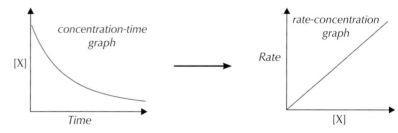

If the rate-concentration graph is a straight line through the origin, then the reaction is first order. The rate is proportional to [X]. For example, if the concentration of X triples, the rate will triple. If it halves, the rate will halve.

Second order

Tip: In theory, a curved rate-concentration graph could mean a higher order than 2. But you won't be asked about any with a higher order than 2 in the exam — so if you see a curve, always say order 2.

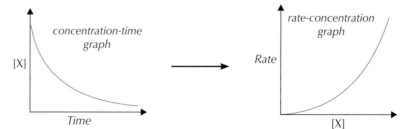

A curved rate-concentration graph means that the reaction is second order. The rate is proportional to $[X]^2$. For example, if the concentration of X triples, the rate will be nine times as fast (because $3^2 = 9$).

Q1 Below are the rate-concentration graphs produced as the concentrations of three different reactants (A, B and C) changed during a reaction.

a) Deduce the reaction orders with respect to reactants A, B and C.

b) State how you would expect the rate of reaction to change if the concentration of:

(i) reactant A was halved.

(ii) reactant B was tripled.

(iii) reactant C was doubled.

Q2 The following reaction occurs between nitrogen monoxide (NO) and oxygen (O_2):

$$2NO_{(g)} + O_{2(g)} \rightarrow 2NO_{2(g)}$$

This reaction is second order with respect to NO and first order with respect to O_2.

a) Sketch a graph showing the rate of reaction against the concentration of NO.

b) State how you would expect the rate of reaction to change if the concentration of O_2 was doubled.

Q1 Describe how you would produce a rate-concentration graph from a concentration-time graph.

Q2 What is the gradient of the straight-line rate-concentration graph produced by a reactant that is zero order?

Q3 Sketch the shape of the rate-concentration graph for a reactant that is first order.

Exam Tip
It's easy to get concentration-time graphs and rate-concentration graphs confused. But make sure you learn the different shapes of each graph, for zero, first and second order reactions. They may well come up in your exam...

Tip: There's more about orders on page 50, so look back there if you need more information.

Tip: If you're asked to sketch a graph, you don't need to plot any actual data. Just make sure you show the correct shape, label the axes and give any other information that the question asks for.

- Know that the orders of reactions with respect to reactants can be used to provide information about the mechanism of a reaction.
- Be able to use the orders with respect to reactants to provide information about the rate-determining/limiting step of a reaction.

Specification Reference 3.1.9.2

7. The Rate-determining Step

Reaction mechanisms show step by step how a chemical reaction takes place. The most important step is the rate-determining step.

What is the rate-determining step?

Mechanisms can have one step or a series of steps. In a series of steps, each step can have a different rate. The overall rate is decided by the step with the slowest rate — the **rate-determining step**.

The rate equation is handy for working out the mechanism of a chemical reaction. You need to be able to pick out which reactants from the chemical equation are involved in the rate-determining step. This isn't too hard — if a reactant appears in the rate equation, it must affect the rate. So this reactant, or something derived from it, must be in the rate-determining step. If a reactant doesn't appear in the rate equation, then it won't be involved in the rate-determining step and neither will anything derived from it.

An important point to remember about rate-determining steps and mechanisms is that the rate-determining step doesn't have to be the first step in a mechanism. Also, the reaction mechanism can't usually be predicted from just the chemical equation.

Tip: The rate-determining step is also known as the rate-limiting step.

Orders of reaction and the rate-determining step

The order of a reaction with respect to a reactant shows the number of molecules of that reactant that are involved in the rate-determining step. So, if a reaction's second order with respect to X, there'll be two molecules of X in the rate-determining step.

Tip: Look back at your Year 1 notes for more about this reaction between ozone and chlorine radicals.

┌─ **Example** ─────────────────────────────────

The mechanism for the reaction between chlorine free radicals (Cl•) and ozone (O_3) consists of two steps:

$Cl•_{(g)} + O_{3(g)} \rightarrow ClO•_{(g)} + O_{2(g)}$ *This step is slow — it's the rate determining step.*
$ClO•_{(g)} + O_{3(g)} \rightarrow Cl•_{(g)} + 2O_{2(g)}$ *This step is fast.*

Cl• and O_3 are both in the rate determining step so must both be in the rate equation. So, the rate equation will be:

$$Rate = k[Cl•]^m[O_3]^n$$

There's only one Cl• and one O_3 molecule in the rate-determining step, so the orders, *m* and *n*, are both 1. So the rate equation is:

$$Rate = k[Cl•][O_3]$$

Tip: See pages 50-53 for more on rate equations.

Reaction mechanisms

If you know which reactants are in the rate-determining step, you can work out the reaction mechanism.

Tip: Catalysts can appear in rate equations, so they can be in rate-determining steps too.

┌─ **Examples** ─────────────────────────────────

2–bromo–2–methylpropane can react with the nucleophile OH⁻ to give 2–methyl propan–2–ol and bromide ions (Br⁻).

There are two possible mechanisms for this reaction. Here's one...

$$H_3C-\overset{\overset{\displaystyle CH_3}{|}}{\underset{\underset{\displaystyle CH_3}{|}}{C}}-Br \ + \ OH^- \ \longrightarrow \ H_3C-\overset{\overset{\displaystyle CH_3}{|}}{\underset{\underset{\displaystyle CH_3}{|}}{C}}-OH \ + \ Br^-$$

... and here's the other one:

$$\underset{\underset{CH_3}{|}}{\overset{\overset{CH_3}{|}}{H_3C-C-Br}} \longrightarrow \underset{\underset{CH_3}{|}}{\overset{\overset{CH_3}{|}}{H_3C-\overset{+}{C}}} + Br^-$$

This step is slow — it's the rate-determining step.

$$\underset{\underset{CH_3}{|}}{\overset{\overset{CH_3}{|}}{H_3C-\overset{+}{C}}} + OH^- \longrightarrow \underset{\underset{CH_3}{|}}{\overset{\overset{CH_3}{|}}{H_3C-C-OH}}$$

This step is fast.

The actual rate equation was worked out using rate experiments. It is:

$$Rate = k[(CH_3)_3CBr]$$

OH^- isn't in the rate equation, so it can't be involved in the rate-determining step. The second mechanism is correct because OH^- isn't in the rate-determining step.

Nitrogen monoxide can react with oxygen to produce nitrogen dioxide:

$$2NO + O_2 \rightarrow 2NO_2$$

The reaction mechanism for this reaction is made up of two steps:

$$Step\ 1 — NO + NO \rightarrow N_2O_2$$
$$Step\ 2 — N_2O_2 + O_2 \rightarrow 2NO_2$$

The rate equation for this reaction is:

$$Rate = k[NO]^2[O_2]$$

So you know that the rate-determining step must involve 2 molecules of NO and 1 molecule of O_2. Neither step 1 nor step 2 contains all the molecules you'd expect from the rate equation. But in step 2 there's an intermediate molecule, N_2O_2, that's derived from 2 molecules of NO. So step 2 is the rate-determining step.

Exam Tip
In the exam, you could be given reactions with three or even four steps, but don't be put off — you work it out in exactly the same way.

Practice Questions — Application

Q1 The reaction $NO_2 + CO \rightarrow NO + CO_2$ has a two-step mechanism:

$$Step\ 1: 2NO_2 \rightarrow NO + NO_3$$
$$Step\ 2: NO_3 + CO \rightarrow NO_2 + CO_2$$

The rate equation for this reaction is rate $= k[NO_2]^2$.

a) What is the rate-determining step? Explain your answer.

b) A one-step mechanism was also proposed for this reaction. How can you tell that this reaction isn't a one-step mechanism?

Q2 The rate-determining step for a reaction between three reactants (A, B and C) is $2A + B + C \rightarrow X + Y$. Predict the rate equation for this reaction.

Tip: Working out mechanisms is a little bit of trial and error. You have to keep going until you find a mechanism that both fits the rate equation, and is likely to happen in real life.

Practice Questions — Fact Recall

Q1 What is the rate-determining step of a chemical reaction?

Q2 A reaction is second order with respect to oxygen. How many molecules of oxygen are involved in the rate-determining step?

- Know that the rate constant, k, varies with temperature as shown by the equation:
  $k = Ae^{\frac{-E_a}{RT}}$
  where A is a constant, known as the Arrhenius constant, E_a is the activation energy, and T is the temperature in K.

- Be able to explain the qualitative effect of changes in temperature on the rate constant k.

- Be able to perform calculations using the equation
  $k = Ae^{\frac{-E_a}{RT}}$.

- Understand that the equation
  $k = Ae^{\frac{-E_a}{RT}}$ can be rearranged into the form
  $\ln k = -E_a/RT + \ln A$
  and know how to use this rearranged equation with experimental data to plot a straight-line graph with a slope $-E_a/R$.

  **Specification
  Reference 3.1.9.1**

8. The Arrhenius Equation

You met the rate constant (k) back on page 50, and you saw briefly how it increases with temperature. Now it's time to cover this idea in a bit more detail, with the help of a really yucky looking equation.

What is the Arrhenius equation?

The **Arrhenius equation** (that nasty-looking thing in the purple box) shows how the rate constant (k) varies with temperature (T) and activation energy (E_a, the minimum amount of kinetic energy particles need to react).

This is probably the worst equation you're going to meet. Luckily, it'll be given to you in your exams if you need it, so you don't have to learn it off by heart. But you do need to know what all the different bits mean, and how it works.

Here it is:

$$k = Ae^{\frac{-E_a}{RT}}$$

Where:

- k = rate constant
- E_a = activation energy (J mol^{-1})
- T = temperature (K)
- R = gas constant (8.31 J K^{-1} mol^{-1})
- A = the Arrhenius constant (another constant)

The rate constant and activation energy

The Arrhenius equation is a really useful tool for helping us to work out what happens to the rate constant if various conditions, such as the temperature or activation energy, change.

As the activation energy, E_a, gets bigger, k gets smaller. You can test this out by trying different numbers for E_a in the equation... ahh go on, have a go.

┌─ **Examples** ── **Maths Skills** ────────────────────

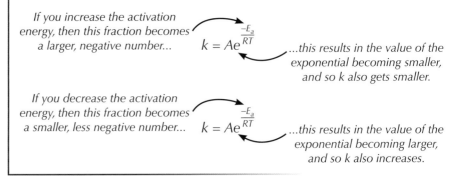

If you increase the activation energy, then this fraction becomes a larger, negative number... $k = Ae^{\frac{-E_a}{RT}}$ *...this results in the value of the exponential becoming smaller, and so k also gets smaller.*

If you decrease the activation energy, then this fraction becomes a smaller, less negative number... $k = Ae^{\frac{-E_a}{RT}}$ *...this results in the value of the exponential becoming larger, and so k also increases.*

So, a large E_a will mean a slow rate. This makes sense when you think about it. If a reaction has a high activation energy, then not many of the reactant particles will have enough energy to react. So only a few of the collisions will result in the reaction actually happening, and the rate will be slow.

The rate constant and temperature

The equation also shows that as the temperature rises, k increases. (You can test this out by trying different numbers for T as well. Will the fun never cease?)

Examples — Maths Skills

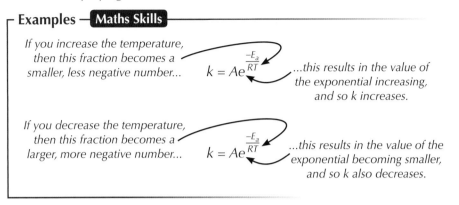

If you increase the temperature, then this fraction becomes a smaller, less negative number... $k = Ae^{\frac{-E_a}{RT}}$ ...this results in the value of the exponential increasing, and so k increases.

If you decrease the temperature, then this fraction becomes a larger, more negative number... $k = Ae^{\frac{-E_a}{RT}}$ ...this results in the value of the exponential becoming smaller, and so k also decreases.

The temperature dependence makes sense too. Higher temperatures mean reactant particles move around faster and with more energy so they're more likely to collide and more likely to collide with at least the activation energy, so the reaction rate is higher.

Using the Arrhenius equation

You might be given four of the five values in the Arrhenius equation and asked to use the equation to find the value of the fifth. All you need to do is rearrange the equation to make the unknown the subject, and then substitute the values you know into the equation. Here are some examples to show you how it's done...

Examples — Maths Skills

The decomposition of N_2O_5 at 308 K has a rate constant of 1.35×10^{-4} s^{-1}. The Arrhenius constant for this reaction is 4.79×10^{13} s^{-1}. Calculate the activation energy of this reaction. ($R = 8.31$ J K^{-1} mol^{-1})

- First it's a good idea to get the Arrhenius equation into a simpler form so it's easier to use. That means getting rid of the nasty exponential bit — so you need to take the natural log (ln) of everything in the equation:

$$k = Ae^{\frac{-E_a}{RT}} \longrightarrow \ln(k) = \ln(Ae^{\frac{-E_a}{RT}})$$

$$= \ln(A) + \ln(e^{\frac{-E_a}{RT}})$$

$$= \ln(A) - \frac{E_a}{RT}$$

- Now re-arrange the equation to get E_a on the left hand side:

$$\frac{E_a}{RT} = \ln(A) - \ln(k)$$

- And another quick re-arrangement to get E_a on its own:

$$E_a = (\ln(A) - \ln(k)) \times RT$$

- Now you can just pop the numbers from the question into this formula:

$$E_a = (\ln(4.79 \times 10^{13}) - \ln(1.35 \times 10^{-4})) \times (8.31 \times 308)$$
$$= (31.5... - (-8.91...)) \times (8.31 \times 308) = 103\ 429.54 \text{ J mol}^{-1}$$
$$= 103 \text{ kJ mol}^{-1} \text{ (3 s.f.)}$$

Tip: If you're asked what happens to a variable or constant in the Arrhenius equation when something changes, just use this method to work out what will happen. The only thing that can't change is R, the gas constant — this is a defined physical constant that can't change. Though k and A are known as constants, they're only constant for a given reaction under certain conditions.

Figure 1: *Svante August Arrhenius, the Swedish chemist after whom the Arrhenius equation is named.*

Tip: 'e' and 'ln' are inverses, so you can use them to 'get rid' of each other.

Tip: This example uses the log law that states: $\ln(ab) = \ln(a) + \ln(b)$, but you can look at pages 282-283 for lots more on how to use logs.

Tip: There are buttons on your calculator for 'e' and for 'ln'. They make life much easier when it comes to dealing with calculations involving the Arrhenius equation.

Tip: The Arrhenius constant is temperature-dependent, so it won't always have the same value for the same reaction.

Tip: Rearranging equations can be quite tricky. Always check your answer at the end. It's a good idea to make sure all the variables that were in the starting equation have ended up in the final one, and that you've not lost or gained any along the way.

Tip: The logarithmic version of the Arrhenius equation,
$$\ln(k) = -\frac{E_a}{RT} + \ln(A)$$
is in the form,
$y = mx + c$, the equation for a straight-line graph.

Tip: The units of the x-axis are K^{-1}. The y-axis doesn't have any units — no natural logarithms have units.

Tip: Values of $1/T$ can often be quite small, and it can get confusing writing out lots of 0s all the time. Sometimes axes are written with units in standard form. If this is the case, you'll need to watch out for the units on the x-axis — they might show that there are actually some extra decimal places to put in.

The same reaction is set up at a different temperature, and the rate constant is found to have a value of 2.4×10^{-3} s^{-1}. Given that the Arrhenius constant for this reaction is 6.22×10^{13} s^{-1}, but all other conditions remain the same, calculate the temperature at which this reaction occurs.

- First of all, rearrange your equation so it's in terms of your unknown. In this case, it's T.

$$k = Ae^{\frac{-E_a}{RT}} \longrightarrow \ln(k) = \ln(A) - \frac{E_a}{RT} \qquad \textit{First take the natural log (ln)...}$$

$$\frac{E_a}{RT} = \ln(A) - \ln(k) \qquad \textit{...then subtract ln(k) from, and add } E_a/RT \textit{ to, both sides...}$$

$$\frac{E_a}{R} = T(\ln(A) - \ln(k)) \qquad \textit{...then multiply by T...}$$

$$T = \frac{E_a}{R(\ln(A) - \ln(k))} \qquad \textit{...and finally divide by (ln(A) – ln(k)).}$$

- Then just go about substituting everything you know into your new equation (the activation energy will be your answer from the last question).

$$T = \frac{103\,429.54}{8.31 \times (\ln(6.22 \times 10^{13}) - \ln(2.4 \times 10^{-3}))} = 329 \text{ K (3 s.f.)}$$

Arrhenius plots

Putting the **Arrhenius equation** into logarithmic form generally makes it a bit easier to use. By creating a graph of ln k against $1/T$, known as an Arrhenius plot, you can use the relationship in the logarithmic form of the Arrhenius equation to find out certain variables. For example, the line of best fit on an Arrhenius plot will be a straight line with a gradient of $-E_a/R$, and the y-intercept will be equal to ln A.

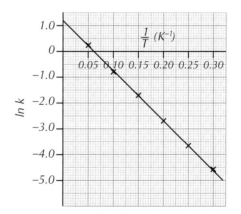

Figure 2: An example of an Arrhenius plot. The value of $-E_a/R$ is given by the gradient, and ln A is equal to the y-intercept.

To gather the data for an Arrhenius plot, you'll need to carry out the same experiment a few times, each time at a different temperature, and work out the rate at the same point for each one.

Example ─ Maths Skills

The rate constants for a reaction at a variety of temperatures are shown in the table below. Use the data to create an Arrhenius plot, and therefore work out the activation energy and the Arrhenius constant.

T / K	k / s⁻¹	1/T / K⁻¹	ln k
150	4.59×10^{-48}	0.0067	−109
200	2.44×10^{-36}	0.0050	−82.0
250	5.90×10^{-29}	0.0040	−65.0
300	9.60×10^{-24}	0.0033	−53.0
350	1.05×10^{-20}	0.0029	−46.0
400	4.25×10^{-18}	0.0025	−40.0

Tip: If you need to work out the values of $1/T$ and ln k, draw out a table with four columns, like the one on the left. This makes sure you don't miss out any values, and you don't get your T's and k's muddled up.

- If you're given data for T and k, and asked to plot an Arrhenius plot, the first thing you need to do is to work out the values of $1/T$ and ln k for each T and k value respectively.

- Now, plot your values of $1/T$ and ln k on a suitable set of axes, and draw a line of best fit through the data set.

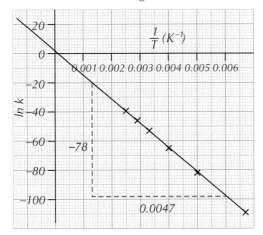

Tip: When you're drawing your line of best fit through you data set, if you can, extend it so it goes through the y-axis. This can sometimes help when you're working out the Arrhenius constant.

Tip: Look back at pages 47-49 if you need a reminder on how to calculate the gradient of a straight line.

- To find the value of E_a, find the gradient of the straight-line.

  gradient = change in y ÷ change in x

  = −78 ÷ 0.0047 = −16 595.7...

- You know that gradient = $-E_a/R$, so just substitute in the value of R, and solve to find the activation energy.

  $-E_a/R = -16\ 595.7...$

  $-E_a = -16\ 595.7... \times 8.31$

  $E_a = 137\ 910.6...$ J mol⁻¹ = **140 kJ mol⁻¹** (2 s.f.)

Tip: If the x-axis on your Arrhenius plot extends to 0, you can work out A by looking at the y-intercept — this is just where the line of best fit crosses the y-axis, and is equal to ln (A).
So in this example:
ln $(A) = 2.0$
$A = e^{2.0} = 7.4$ s⁻¹ (2 s.f.)

- To find out A, substitute your value of E_a back into the equation $k = Ae^{\frac{-E_a}{RT}}$, along with a value from the table of T and k.

  So, using the data point at 150 K: $A = \dfrac{k}{e^{-E_a/RT}}$

  $A = 4.59 \times 10^{-48} \div e^{(-137\ 910.6... \div (8.31 \times 150))}$

  $A = $ **5.1 s⁻¹** (2 s.f.)

Tip: The units of A are the same as the units of k (which you're given in the question).

Figure 2: *A sulfuric acid plant in Cleveland.*

Practice Questions — Application

Q1 In part of the industrial manufacture of sulfuric acid, SO_2 is converted into SO_3. In the Contact process, this step is catalysed by a vanadium(V) oxide catalyst.
The rate constant for the reaction can be expressed by the Arrhenius equation:

$$k = Ae^{\frac{-E_a}{RT}}$$

a) With reference to the Arrhenius equation, would you expect the rate constant of the catalysed reaction to be greater, smaller or the same as the uncatalysed reaction?

b) A manufacturer tries decreasing the temperature at which they run the Contact process to save money. With reference to the Arrhenius equation, explain how will this affect the rate constant.

Q2 The activation energy of the following reaction is 180 kJ mol⁻¹.

$$2NH_{3(g)} \rightarrow N_{2(g)} + 3H_{2(g)}$$

a) Given that the rate constant of this reaction is 1.10×10^{-5} mol⁻¹ dm³ s⁻¹ at 600 K, calculate the Arrhenius constant for this reaction.

b) A catalyst is added to the reaction vessel which increases the rate constant to 2.02×10^{-5} mol⁻¹ dm³ s⁻¹. Given that all other variables stay the same, calculate the activation energy of the catalysed reaction.

Q3 The rate of reaction at different temperatures are recorded below.

T (K)	k
555	3.50×10^{-7}
630	3.00×10^{-5}
665	2.20×10^{-4}
700	1.15×10^{-3}
790	3.94×10^{-2}

a) Construct an Arrhenius plot for the data above.

b) Work out the activation energy of this reaction.

c) Work out the Arrhenius constant for this reaction.

Practice Questions — Fact Recall

Q1 Write out the Arrhenius equation, defining all the variables in it.

Q2 What happens to the rate of a reaction when the temperature is increased?

Q3 What is the logarithmic form of the Arrhenius equation?

Q4 What should go on the x- and y- axes on an Arrhenius plot?

Tip: Be careful when working out the Arrhenius constant. The value of the *y*-intercept is when *x* = 0. But sometimes you'll find your axes don't meet at (0, 0). If this is the case, then you can't use the *y*-intercept to work out the value of ln A (unless you redraw your axes) — you'll need to use the substitution method instead.

Tip: When you're using real experimental data, you may find your calculated value of *A* varies a little bit, depending on which data point you use, but as long as it's within the same order of magnitude, you can be reasonably happy you've got the right answer.

9. Gas Equilibria

When we're dealing with equilibrium reactions involving gases, it's easier to think in terms of pressure than in terms of concentrations. A gaseous equilibrium system will have a total pressure, but there will also be individual pressures for each of the individual gases. These are called partial pressures.

Partial pressures

You've met equilibrium reactions before — they're just reactions that can go in both a forwards direction, and a reverse direction.

Example

The reaction between hydrogen and iodine vapour is an example of a gas equilibrium reaction.

$$H_{2(g)} + I_{2(g)} \rightleftharpoons 2HI_{(g)}$$

The forwards reaction is: $H_{2(g)} + I_{2(g)} \rightarrow 2HI_{(g)}$

And the backwards reaction is: $2HI_{(g)} \rightarrow H_{2(g)} + I_{2(g)}$

In a mixture of gases, each individual gas exerts its own pressure — this is called its partial pressure. So, in the example above, hydrogen, iodine and hydrogen iodide gases will all exert a pressure on the system. The size of the pressure exerted by each gas doesn't have to be the same. If gases are present in equal quantities, their partial pressures will be the same.

     The total pressure of a gas mixture is the sum of all the partial pressures of the individual gases. Partial pressures are often written as p_X — this just means the partial pressure of X.

Example

So, in the reaction between hydrogen and iodine vapour to make hydrogen iodide, the total pressure can be expressed as:

Total pressure = $p_{H_2} + p_{I_2} + p_{HI}$

You can put this fact into use when dealing with pressure calculations, such as the one below.

Example — **Maths Skills**

When 3.00 moles of the gas PCl_5 is heated, it decomposes into PCl_3 and Cl_2:
$$PCl_{5(g)} \rightleftharpoons PCl_{3(g)} + Cl_{2(g)}$$

In a sealed vessel at 500 K, the equilibrium mixture contains chlorine with a partial pressure of 263 kPa. If the total pressure of the mixture is 714 kPa, what is the partial pressure of PCl_5?

From the equation you know that PCl_3 and Cl_2 are produced in equal amounts, so the partial pressures of these two gases are the same at equilibrium — they're both 263 kPa.

Total pressure = $p_{PCl_5} + p_{PCl_3} + p_{Cl_2}$

    $714 = p_{PCl_5} + 263 + 263$

So the partial pressure of $PCl_5 = 714 - 263 - 263 = 188$ kPa

---

Tip: Look back at your Year 1 notes for a reminder on reversible reactions and equilibria.

Figure 1: John Dalton, the English chemist, who came up with the theory that the total pressure of a mixture of gases is equal to the sum of the partial pressures of the gases in the mixture. This theory is also known as Dalton's Law.

Mole fractions

A 'mole fraction' is just the proportion of a gas mixture that is a made up of particular gas. So if you have four moles of gas in total and two of them are gas A, the mole fraction of gas A is ½. There are two formulas you need to know.

Mole fraction of a gas in a mixture $=$ $\dfrac{\text{number of moles of gas}}{\text{total number of moles of gas in the mixture}}$

Partial pressure of a gas in a mixture $=$ mole fraction of gas × total pressure of the mixture

Exam Tip
You won't be given these equations in the exam — make sure you learn them off by heart so you can handle any K_p calculations the examiners could throw at you.

Here are some examples to show you how to use these equations.

Examples — Maths Skills

When 2.00 mol of PCl$_5$ is heated in a sealed vessel, the equilibrium mixture contains 1.25 mol of chlorine.
What is the mole fraction of PCl$_5$?

Tip: You need to use a balanced chemical equation when working out mole fractions — you have to take into account the ratios of the number of moles of each gas when working out the mole fraction of a particular reactant or product.

- First, write out a chemical equation so you can see what's happening:
$$PCl_{5(g)} \rightleftharpoons PCl_{3(g)} + Cl_{2(g)}$$

- From the equation, PCl$_3$ and Cl$_2$ are produced in equal amounts, so there'll be 1.25 moles of PCl$_3$ too.

- 1.25 moles of PCl$_5$ must have decomposed so, $(2.00 - 1.25) = 0.75$ moles of PCl$_5$ must be left at equilibrium.

- This means that the total number of moles of gas at equilibrium $= 0.75 + 1.25 + 1.25 = 3.25$.

- So the mole fraction of PCl$_5$ = $\dfrac{0.75}{3.25} = 0.2307...$

- So the mole fraction of PCl$_5$ is 0.231 (to 3 s.f.)

Tip: Lots of gases made up of only one element are diatomic, e.g. N$_2$, O$_2$, Cl$_2$, H$_2$ etc. So, make sure you remember to divide by the M_r of the whole gas molecule, rather than just the A_r of the element when you're doing calculations with moles.

A mixture of 8.02 g of nitrogen and 2.42 g of oxygen is contained inside a sealed vessel. Given that the total pressure of the mixture is 921 kPa, what is the partial pressure of the oxygen?

- First, work out the number of moles of each gas present in the vessel:
    moles of N$_2$ = $8.02 \div (14 \times 2) = 0.286...$
    moles of O$_2$ = $2.42 \div (16 \times 2) = 0.0756...$

- Add the values of each of these together to find out the total number of moles present in the mixture:
    $0.286... + 0.0756... = 0.362...$

Tip: Try not to round your intermediate answers. Rounding too early could lead to an error in your final answer.

- The question asks for the partial pressure of oxygen, so you need to work out the mole fraction of oxygen, using the trusty equation, mole fraction = no. moles of gas ÷ total moles of gas in the system
    $= 0.0756... \div 0.362... = 0.208...$

- Finally, substitute the mole fraction of oxygen, along with the total pressure that you were given in the question, into the equation for partial pressure:

partial pressure = mole fraction × total pressure

$$= 0.208... \times 921 = 192 \text{ kPa (3 s.f.)}$$

The gas equilibrium constant, K_p

K_p is the equilibrium constant for a reversible reaction where some, or all, of the reactants and products are gases. The expression for K_p is just like the one for K_c, except you use partial pressures instead of concentrations.

Tip: K_c and K_p work in pretty much exactly the same way — K_p is just specifically for gases. Look back at your Year 1 notes for more on K_c.

For the equilibrium
$$aA_{(g)} + bB_{(g)} \rightleftharpoons dD_{(g)} + eE_{(g)} \qquad K_p = \frac{(p_D)^d (p_E)^e}{(p_A)^a (p_B)^b}$$

Tip: Solid, liquid and aqueous substances don't appear in the expression for K_p. They also don't contribute to the total pressure of a system (see page 69).

Example

Write an expression for K_p for the following reaction.

$$O_{3(g)} + H_2O_{(g)} \rightleftharpoons H_{2(g)} + 2O_{2(g)}$$

There are two moles of O_2 in the balanced equation, so the partial pressure of O_2 needs to be raised to the power of 2.

The reactants go on the bottom of the expression.

$$K_p = \frac{(p_{O_2})^2 \times p_{H_2}}{p_{O_3} \times p_{H_2O}}$$

The products go on the top of the expression.

Tip: Make sure your chemical equation is balanced — otherwise you'll get your expression for K_p wrong.

To calculate K_p you put the partial pressures in the expression. Then you work out the units like you did for K_c.

Example — **Maths Skills**

Calculate K_p for the decomposition of PCl_5 gas at 500 K. The partial pressures of each gas are: p_{PCl_5} = 188 kPa, p_{PCl_3} = 263 kPa, p_{Cl_2} = 263 kPa

- Start by writing out a balanced chemical equation:
$$PCl_{5(g)} \rightleftharpoons PCl_{3(g)} + Cl_{2(g)}$$

- Now, write an expression for K_p. Remember, the reactants go on the bottom of the expression, and the products go on the top. Then just substitute in all the partial pressure values you were given in the question.

$$K_p = \frac{p_{Cl_2} \times p_{PCl_3}}{p_{PCl_5}} = \frac{263 \times 263}{188} = 368$$

- To find the units, substitute all the partial pressure units into your expression for K_p, then cancel down as much as you can.

$$K_p = \frac{kPa \times kPa}{kPa} = kPa \qquad \text{So } K_p = 368 \text{ kPa}$$

Tip: K_p is temperature dependent (see page 73). So, a particular value of K_p is only valid at a given temperature.

Figure 2: *A molecular model of benzene (C_6H_6). In the hydrogenation of benzene, hydrogen is added to the aromatic ring to create a saturated alkane — cyclohexane.*

Practice Questions — Application

Q1 Ammonia is reacted with oxygen.
The products are nitrogen gas and water vapour.
The reaction is a reversible reaction.

a) Write out a balanced chemical equation for this reaction.

b) Write out an expression for the total pressure of the system.

c) p_{oxygen} = 85 kPa, $p_{ammonia}$ = 42 kPa,
$p_{nitrogen}$ = 21 kPa, and $p_{water\ vapour}$ = 12 kPa.
Calculate the total pressure of the system.

d) What is the mole fraction of water vapour at the partial pressures given in c)?

Q2 A sealed container holds 4.00 g of helium gas (He) and 2.81 g of oxygen gas. Given that the total pressure of the container is 8.12 kPa, what is the partial pressure of oxygen?

Q3 The following equation shows the reaction between benzene and hydrogen to create cyclohexane:

$$C_6H_{6(g)} + 3H_{2(g)} \rightleftharpoons C_6H_{12(g)}$$

a) Write an equation for K_p for the reaction above.

b) At equilibrium, the partial pressures of the three gases are all equal. Given that $K_p = 4.80 \times 10^{-13}$ kPa^{-3}, what is the partial pressure of hydrogen?

Q4 When 24.32 mol of hydrogen fluoride is heated in a sealed vessel, the equilibrium mixture contains 9.340 mol of fluorine gas.

a) If the total pressure of the mixture is 2313 kPa, what is the partial pressure of hydrogen?

b) Calculate the gas equilibrium constant for this reaction.

Practice Questions — Fact Recall

Q1 What is meant by the term 'partial pressure'?

Q2 What equation links the mole fraction of a gas, the number of moles of that gas and the total number of moles of gas in a mixture?

Q3 Write an expression for K_p for the equation: $aA_{(g)} + bB_{(g)} \rightleftharpoons dD_{(g)} + eE_{(g)}$.

10. Changing Gas Equilibria

It's time to see how changing temperature, pressure or adding a catalyst affects equilibrium in gases. You'll need to use Le Chatelier's principle, which you met in Year 1.

Le Chatelier's Principle

You met Le Chatelier's principle in the first year of the course. It's a theory that states that, if a reversible reaction at equilibrium is subjected to a change in temperature, pressure or concentration, then the equilibrium position shifts to counteract the change. The effects of Le Chatelier's principle apply to gas equilibria too. Like K_c, K_p is affected by changes in temperature but not by changes in pressure.

Temperature

If you increase the temperature, the equilibrium shifts in the endothermic (positive ΔH) direction. If you decrease the temperature, the equilibrium shifts in the exothermic (negative ΔH) direction. Changing the temperature of a system will change K_p, depending on which way the equilibrium shifts.

Example

The reaction below is exothermic in the forward direction.
$$2SO_{2(g)} + O_{2(g)} \rightleftharpoons 2SO_{3(g)} \quad \Delta H = -197 \text{ kJ mol}^{-1}$$

- If the temperature is increased, the equilibrium shifts to the left to try and absorb the extra heat and counteract the change. This means that less product is formed.

$$K_p = \frac{(p_{SO_3})^2}{(p_{SO_2})^2 \times p_{O_2}}$$

If there's less product, the partial pressure of SO_3 will be reduced...

... and the partial pressures of SO_2 and O_2 will increase.

So, as the temperature increases, p_{SO_3} will decrease and p_{SO_2} and p_{O_2} will increase, so K_p will decrease.

- If the temperature is decreased, the equilibrium shifts to the right to try and make up for the decrease in heat. This means more product is formed, so K_p will increase.

Pressure

Le Chatelier's principle states that if you increase the pressure, the equilibrium shifts to the side with fewer moles of gas, and if you decrease the pressure, the equilibrium shifts to the side with more moles of gas. However, these changes don't affect K_p. Instead, if you change the pressure, the position of equilibrium shifts in such a way the partial pressures of reactants and products at the new equilibrium position keep K_p constant.

Example

The equilibrium of the reaction below shifts in response to changes in pressure.
$$2SO_{2(g)} + O_{2(g)} \rightleftharpoons 2SO_{3(g)} \quad \Delta H = -197 \text{ kJ mol}^{-1}$$

- If the pressure is increased, the equilibrium shifts to the right, the side with fewer moles of gas, to counteract the change. This means that the partial pressure of SO_3 increases.

Learning Objectives:
- Predict the qualitative effects of changes in temperature and pressure on the position of equilibrium.
- Predict the qualitative effects of changes in temperature on the value of K_p.
- Understand that, whilst a catalyst can affect the rate of attainment of an equilibrium, it does not affect the value of the equilibrium constant.

Specification Reference 3.1.10

Tip: Exothermic reactions release heat and endothermic reactions absorb heat. If a reversible reaction is exothermic in one direction, it will always be endothermic in the other direction.

Tip: If you change the pressure of a system, there's only a shift in equilibrium position of reactions where there is an unequal number of moles of gas on each side of the reaction.

Tip: You'll need to make sure you're using a balanced chemical equation when looking at how the number of moles changes as the reactants change to products.

Figure 1: *Sulfur burning in oxygen to produce sulfur dioxide (SO₂).*

$$K_p = \frac{(p_{SO_3})^2}{(p_{SO_2})^2 \times p_{O_2}}$$

The partial pressure of SO_3 will increase, so this value gets bigger...

...and the increase in the overall pressure cause the partial pressures of SO_2 and O_2 to increase, so that K_p remains constant.

- Similarly, if the pressure is decreased, the equilibrium shifts to the left to try and make up for the drop in pressure — so at equilibrium, there's more SO_2 and O_2, and less SO_3. But the partial pressures of all of the gases in the mixture change so as to keep K_p the same.

Catalysts

As with K_c, catalysts have no effect on the position of equilibrium or on the value of K_p. This is because a catalyst will increase the rate of both the forward and backward reactions by the same amount. As a result, the equilibrium position will be the same as the uncatalysed reaction, but equilibrium will be reached faster. So catalysts can't increase the amount of product produced, but they do decrease the time taken to reach equilibrium.

Tip: To work out how K_p is affected by changes in temperature, it's often helpful to write out the expression for K_p. You can then see how increasing amounts of products or reactants affect K_p much more easily.

Practice Questions — Application

Q1 The reaction between hydrogen and iodine to produce hydrogen iodide is a reversible reaction.

$$H_{2(g)} + I_{2(g)} \rightleftharpoons 2HI_{(g)}$$

A student says, "altering the pressure of a reaction affects the equilibrium position. Therefore, changing the pressure of this reaction would move equilibrium." Comment on the statement.

Q2 Nitrogen dioxide reacts to produce dinitrogen tetroxide as part of a reversible reaction. The forward reaction is exothermic.

$$2NO_{2(g)} \rightleftharpoons N_2O_{4(g)}$$

a) What will happen to the equilibrium position if there is a decrease in pressure? Explain your answer.

b) A student is investigating the effect on K_p of changing the temperature of the system. How would K_p change if the student decreased the temperature of the system?

Practice Questions — Fact Recall

Q1 What does Le Chatelier's principle state?

Q2 How would an increase in temperature affect the equilibrium position of a reaction that is exothermic in the forward direction?

Q3 What happens to K_p when there is a change in pressure for a reaction where there are a different number of moles of gas in the reactants and products?

Q4 How do catalysts affect the position of equilibrium and the value of K_p?

Section Summary

Make sure you know...

- That the reaction rate is the change in the amount of reactants or products per unit time.
- That continuous monitoring involves following a reaction through to completion, by monitoring the amount of product or reactant you have at regular intervals.
- That measuring gas volumes, loss of mass, changes in pH or colour are all ways to follow a reaction.
- How to find the rate of a reaction from a straight-line concentration-time graph by calculating the gradient.
- How to find the rate of a reaction at a given time from a curved concentration-time graph, by calculating the gradient of a tangent to the curve.
- That rate equations take the general form rate = $k[A]^m[B]^n$ where m and n are the orders of reaction with respect to A and B respectively.
- What is meant by the term 'order of reaction', and how the concentration of reactants with order 0, 1 and 2, affects the rate of reaction.
- That the overall order is the sum of the individual orders of reaction in a rate equation.
- That rate equations and orders of reactions can only be determined experimentally.
- Know that the rate constant of a reaction is a measure of how fast the reaction is going.
- How to write rate equations for reactions, given appropriate information.
- How to calculate the rate constant, its units, and related values, given information about the rate, and the concentration and relative orders of reactants in a reaction.
- How to find the initial rate of a reaction from a concentration-time graph.
- How to use the initial rates method to work out the orders of reaction, with respect to reactants in a chemical reaction, using concentration and rates.
- How clock reactions work.
- What the shapes of zero, first and second order concentration-time and rate-concentration graphs look like.
- That the rate-determining step of a reaction is the slowest step in a reaction mechanism.
- How to determine the rate-determining step from a rate equation.
- How to use the rate equation to suggest a possible reaction mechanism for a given chemical reaction.
- The variables and constants that make up the Arrhenius equation.
- How to use the Arrhenius equation to explain how the rate varies when the activation energy and temperature of a system are altered.
- How to use the Arrhenius equation to find the rate and related quantities.
- How to construct and use an Arrhenius plot to work out the activation energy and Arrhenius constant.
- That the partial pressure of a gas is how much pressure it exerts on a system, and that the total pressure of a gaseous system is equal to the sum of the partial pressures of its constituent gases.
- How to use partial pressures to work out the total pressure of a system.
- How to work out the mole fraction of a gas, and how to use mole fractions in calculations involving pressure.
- How to work out the expression for the gas equilibrium constant, K_p, for a given chemical reaction involving gases.
- How to calculate K_p for a chemical reaction, given the partial pressures of the constituent gases.
- How K_p is affected by changes in temperature, but not by changes in pressure or the addition of a catalyst.
- The effect of changes in temperature and pressure on the position of a gas equilibrium.

Exam-style Questions

1   What is the overall order of the following reaction?

$$3ClO^-_{(aq)} \rightarrow ClO^-_{3\ (aq)} + 2Cl^-_{(aq)} \qquad\qquad rate = k[ClO^-]^2$$

   A   1

   B   2

   C   3

   D   4

(1 mark)

2   Which of these techniques would **not** produce data that would be suitable for working out the rate of the reaction?

   A   Measuring the loss of mass from a reaction container, every 10 seconds, until the reaction is complete.

   B   Measuring the mass of a reaction container, containing a reaction which involves the production of a gas, at the start and end of a reaction.

   C   Recording the absorbance of a sample of a reaction mixture, that involves the formation of a coloured solution, every 20 seconds.

   D   Measuring the pH of a reaction mixture, where H^+ ions are produced, at regular intervals throughout a reaction.

(1 mark)

3   Increasing the value of which of the following variables will result in a decrease in rate?

   A   The Arrhenius constant.

   B   The temperature.

   C   The activation energy.

   D   The pressure.

(1 mark)

4   Calculate the partial pressure of water vapour in the following reaction, given that p_{CO} = 109 kPa, p_{CO_2} = 623 kPa, p_{H_2} = 468 kPa and K_p = 31.4.

$$CO_{(g)} + H_2O_{(g)} \rightleftharpoons CO_{2(g)} + H_{2(g)}$$

   A   77.7 kPa

   B   83.9 kPa

   C   840 kPa

   D   85.2 kPa

(1 mark)

5 A student is investigating the rate of a reaction between a sample of zinc metal and hydrochloric acid. She measures the mass lost from a reaction container at regular intervals until the reaction is complete. She converts the mass loss into concentration data, with respect to HCl.

5.1 Suggest another way that the student could monitor this reaction.

(1 mark)

5.2 The data that the student recorded is shown in the table below.
Use the data to plot a graph.

Time / min	0	1	2	3	4	5	6	7	8
Concentration of HCl / mol dm^{-3}	5.9	5.1	4.5	4.0	3.6	3.3	3.1	2.9	2.8

(4 marks)

5.3 Calculate the initial rate of the reaction.

(2 marks)

6 The Arrhenius equation, shown below, describes the relationship between the rate constant, the activation energy and the temperature.

$$k = Ae^{\frac{-E_a}{RT}}$$

6.1 Find the activation energy of a reaction that has a rate constant of 1.28×10^{-5} mol^{-1} dm^3 s^{-1} at 600 K. The Arrhenius constant is 2.21 mol^{-1} dm^3 s^{-1} and the gas constant is 8.31 J K^{-1} mol^{-1}.

(2 marks)

6.2 When a catalyst is added to a reaction, the rate constant of the reaction increases. With reference to the Arrhenius equation, explain why this is.

(2 marks)

6.3 A student is carrying out an investigation into the Arrhenius equation for a certain reaction. He calculates the rate constant for the reaction at various temperatures. His results are shown in the table below.

Temperature / K	k / mol dm^{-3} s^{-1}
286	7.49×10^{-5}
294	2.03×10^{-4}
299	3.71×10^{-4}
313	1.50×10^{-3}
322	3.52×10^{-3}
334	1.11×10^{-2}

Calculate the activation energy and the Arrhenius constant for this reaction.

(8 marks)

7 The Haber Process, as shown below, is used in the manufacture of ammonia gas.

$$N_{2(g)} + 3H_{2(g)} \rightarrow 2NH_{3(g)} \qquad \Delta H = -92 \text{ kJ mol}^{-1}$$

7.1 In a certain reaction container, $p_{H_2} = 19$ kPa, $p_{NH_3} = 8920$ kPa and $K_p = 52.7$ kPa^{-2}. Calculate the partial pressure of nitrogen in this reaction.

(2 marks)

7.2 An iron catalyst is used when ammonia is manufactured on an industrial scale. Explain how the presence of a catalyst affects the value of K_p.

(1 mark)

7.3 The temperature of the reaction container in **7.1** is increased. Explain how this affects the position of equilibrium and the value of K_p.

(2 marks)

8 Under certain conditions the following reaction occurs between nitrogen monoxide (NO) and hydrogen (H_2):

$$2NO_{(g)} + 2H_{2(g)} \rightarrow N_{2(g)} + 2H_2O_{(g)}$$

The table below shows the results of a series of initial rate experiments for this reaction.

Experiment	[NO] / mol dm^{-3}	[H$_2$] / mol dm^{-3}	Initial rate / mol dm^{-3} s^{-1}
1	3.0×10^{-3}	6.0×10^{-3}	4.50×10^{-3}
2	3.0×10^{-3}	3.0×10^{-3}	2.25×10^{-3}
3	6.0×10^{-3}	1.5×10^{-3}	4.50×10^{-3}

8.1 Determine the orders of reaction with respect to NO and H_2.

(2 marks)

8.2 Write out the rate equation for this reaction.

(1 mark)

8.3 Using the data above, calculate the rate constant (k) for this reaction and give its units.

(3 marks)

8.4 What would the rate of reaction be if 4.5×10^{-3} mol dm^{-3} NO were mixed with 2.5×10^{-3} mol dm^{-3} H_2 under the same conditions as the experiment above?

(2 marks)

8.5 Using the rate equation, explain why a one-step mechanism is not possible for this reaction.

(2 marks)

8.6 By writing reaction equations, suggest a possible two step mechanism for this reaction. The first step is the slowest step.

(2 marks)

1. Electrode Potentials

Learning Objectives:
- Be able to write and apply the conventional representation of cells.
- Know the IUPAC convention for writing half-equations for electrode reactions.
- Be able to calculate the EMF of a cell.
- Know how to measure the EMF of electrochemical cells (Required Practical 8).

Specification Reference 3.1.11.1

In redox reactions, electrons move from one atom to another. When electrons move, you get electricity. So redox reactions can be used to make electricity.

Electrochemical cells

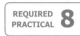

Electrochemical cells can be made from two different metals dipped in salt solutions of their own ions and connected by a wire (the external circuit). There are always two reactions within an electrochemical cell — one's an oxidation and one's a reduction — so it's a **redox** process.

┌─ **Example** ──────────────────

The diagram below shows an electrochemical cell made using copper and zinc.

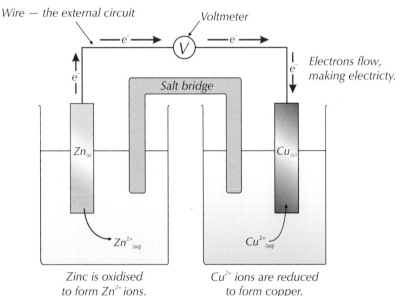

Wire — the external circuit

Voltmeter

Electrons flow, making electricty.

Salt bridge

$Zn_{(s)}$ $Cu_{(s)}$

$Zn^{2+}_{(aq)}$ $Cu^{2+}_{(aq)}$

Zinc is oxidised to form Zn^{2+} ions.   *Cu^{2+} ions are reduced to form copper.*

A copper electrode is dipped in a solution of Cu^{2+} ions and a zinc electrode is dipped in a solution of Zn^{2+} ions. Zinc loses electrons more easily than copper. So in the **half-cell** on the left, zinc (from the zinc electrode) is oxidised to form $Zn^{2+}_{(aq)}$ ions. This releases electrons into the external circuit. In the other half-cell, the same number of electrons are taken from the external circuit, reducing the Cu^{2+} ions to copper atoms.

The solutions are connected by a **salt bridge**, e.g. a strip of filter paper soaked in $KNO_{3(aq)}$. This allows ions to flow between the half-cells and balance out the charges — it completes the circuit.

└──────────────────

Electrons flow through the wire from the most reactive metal to the least. A voltmeter in the external circuit shows the voltage between the two half-cells. This is the **cell potential** or **EMF**, E_{cell}.

Tip: Always be careful when carrying out experiments involving electricity. Carry out proper risk assessment before you start.

***Figure 1:** A zinc/copper electrochemical cell.*

Tip: When you set up a cell, you need to clean the surfaces of the metal electrodes before you begin. Rub them with emery paper and then clean off any grease or oil using propanone.

Tip: EMF stands for electromotive force.

You can also have half-cells involving solutions of two aqueous ions of the same element.

Tip: An electrode has to be a <u>solid</u> that <u>conducts electricity</u>. If a half-cell doesn't contain anything like this, you can use something else (like platinum) as an electrode.

Tip: <u>Inert</u> means it won't react with anything. (The electrode has to be inert or it could react with the solution it's in.)

Tip: The electrode the electrons <u>flow to</u> is the <u>positive</u> electrode. The electrode the electrons <u>flow from</u> is the <u>negative</u> electrode.

┌─ **Example** ─────────────────────────────

You can make an electrochemical half-cell using solutions of Fe^{2+} and Fe^{3+} ions. A platinum electrode is dipped into the solution.

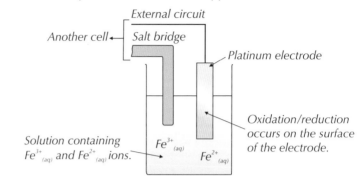

External circuit

Another cell ← *Salt bridge*

Platinum electrode

Oxidation/reduction occurs on the surface of the electrode.

Solution containing $Fe^{3+}_{(aq)}$ and $Fe^{2+}_{(aq)}$ ions.

$Fe^{3+}_{(aq)}$

$Fe^{2+}_{(aq)}$

Platinum is used as the electrode because it is inert and conducts electricity. The conversion from Fe^{2+} to Fe^{3+}, or vice versa, happens on the surface of the electrode.

The direction of the conversion depends on the other half-cell in the circuit. If the other cell contains a metal that is less reactive than iron, then Fe^{2+} will be oxidised to Fe^{3+} at the electrode. But if the other cell contains a more reactive metal, Fe^{3+} will be reduced to Fe^{2+} at the electrode.

└──

Electrode potentials

The reactions that occur at each electrode in a cell are reversible.

┌─ **Example** ─────────────────────────────

The reactions that occur at each electrode in the zinc/copper cell are:

$$Zn^{2+}_{(aq)} + 2e^- \rightleftharpoons Zn_{(s)}$$
$$Cu^{2+}_{(aq)} + 2e^- \rightleftharpoons Cu_{(s)}$$

The reversible arrows show that both reactions can go in either direction.

└──

Tip: These reactions are called half-reactions and, even though they're reversible, they're always written with the reduction reaction going in the forward direction, with the electrons being added on the left-hand side.

Which direction each reaction goes in depends on how easily each metal loses electrons (i.e. how easily it's oxidised). How easily a metal is oxidised is measured using **electrode potentials**. A metal that's easily oxidised has a very negative electrode potential, while one that's harder to oxidise has a less negative (or positive) electrode potential.

┌─ **Example** ─────────────────────────────

The table below shows the electrode potentials for the copper and zinc half-cells:

Half-cell	Electrode potential / V
$Zn^{2+}_{(aq)}/Zn_{(s)}$	−0.76
$Cu^{2+}_{(aq)}/Cu_{(s)}$	+0.34

The zinc half-cell has a more negative electrode potential, so in a zinc/copper cell, zinc is oxidised (the reaction goes backwards), while copper is reduced (the reaction goes forwards).

└──

Figure 2: *Analogue or digital voltmeters can be used to measure electrode potentials.*

Tip: There's more on how electrode potentials are measured coming up.

Drawing electrochemical cells

It's a bit of a faff drawing pictures of electrochemical cells. There's a shorthand way of representing them though. You just take the oxidised and reduced forms of the species from each of the half-cells and arrange them in a row (see Figure 3). This is called the 'conventional representation'.

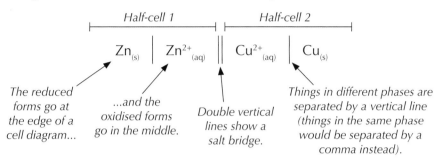

The reduced forms go at the edge of a cell diagram...

...and the oxidised forms go in the middle.

Double vertical lines show a salt bridge.

Things in different phases are separated by a vertical line (things in the same phase would be separated by a comma instead).

Figure 3: *The conventional representation of a zinc/copper cell.*

Tip: The term 'phase' just means whether a substance is a solid, a liquid, an aqueous solution or a gas.

You always put the half-cell that has the more negative electrode potential on the left. In Figure 3, the zinc half-cell is on the left because it has an electrode potential of –0.76 V, while the potential of the copper half-cell is +0.34 V.

The zinc/copper electrochemical cell is quite simple. Some cells are a bit trickier to draw, e.g. they might have platinum electrodes or involve more reagents. If you need to draw a cell diagram for any cell, just follow these steps and you'll be fine:

1. Use the electrode potentials to work out which half-cell goes on the left and which goes on the right.

2. Write out the left-hand half-equation as an oxidation reaction. Then write out the right-hand half-equation as a reduction reaction.

3. Write out the reactants and products of the oxidation reaction, followed by the reactants and products of the reduction reaction.

4. Add in a salt bridge by drawing two vertical lines between the half-cells.

5. Draw a vertical line between any reagents that are in different phases. Put a comma between any reagents that are in the same phase.

6. If either of your half-cells has a separate electrode (like a platinum electrode, Pt), put that on the outside and separate it from the half-cell with a vertical line.

Tip: Remember, the one with the more negative electrode potential goes on the left.

Tip: If you write out the half-equations like this, you'll always end up with the reduced forms on the outside and the oxidised forms in the middle.

Tip: You might see some cells which are a bit more complicated and have some more reagents going around. Don't worry though, you won't need to draw these reagents in representations of cells.

Example

The two half-equations below show the reactions taking place in an electrochemical cell:

$$Sn^{2+}_{(aq)} + 2e^- \rightarrow Sn_{(s)} \quad \text{electrode potential} = -0.14\,V$$
$$Fe^{3+}_{(aq)} + e^- \rightarrow Fe^{2+}_{(aq)} \quad \text{electrode potential} = +0.77\,V$$

A platinum rod is used as the electrode in the iron half-cell. Draw the conventional representation of this cell.

1. The Sn^{2+}/Sn reaction has a more negative electrode potential so it will go on the left. The Fe^{3+}/Fe^{2+} reaction will go on the right.

2. Oxidation: $Sn_{(s)} \rightarrow Sn^{2+}_{(aq)} + 2e^-$ *(left)*
   Reduction: $Fe^{3+}_{(aq)} + e^- \rightarrow Fe^{2+}_{(aq)}$ *(right)*

3. Write out the reactants and products of the oxidation equation, followed by the reactants and products of the reduction equation:

$$Sn_{(s)} \quad Sn^{2+}_{(aq)} \quad Fe^{3+}_{(aq)} \quad Fe^{2+}_{(aq)}$$

4. Put in the salt bridge between the half-cells:

|←— Half-cell 1 —→| |←— Half-cell 2 —→|

$$Sn_{(s)} \quad Sn^{2+}_{(aq)} \;\|\; Fe^{3+}_{(aq)} \quad Fe^{2+}_{(aq)}$$

5. Add in the phase boundaries:

$$Sn_{(s)} \;|\; Sn^{2+}_{(aq)} \;\|\; Fe^{3+}_{(aq)}, \; Fe^{2+}_{(aq)}$$

Vertical lines for different phases.   *Comma for same phase.*

6. Finally, add in the platinum electrode that's part of the right-hand cell:

$$Sn_{(s)} \;|\; Sn^{2+}_{(aq)} \;\|\; Fe^{3+}_{(aq)}, \; Fe^{2+}_{(aq)} \;|\; Pt$$

Tip: The platinum electrode goes on the left if it's for the half-cell on the left. It goes on the right if it's for the half-cell on the right.

Writing half-equations from cell diagrams

You won't always be asked to draw a cell diagram from the half-equations. Sometimes, you might be given a cell diagram and asked to write half-equations for one or both of the electrodes.

┌─ **Example** ─────────────────────────────

A conventional representation of an aluminium/lead cell is given below:

$$Al_{(s)} \;|\; Al^{3+}_{(aq)} \;\|\; Pb^{2+}_{(aq)} \;|\; Pb_{(s)}$$

Write half-equations for the reactions occurring at the positive and negative electrodes of this cell.

The positive electrode is the one on the right-hand side (Pb^{2+}/Pb) and the negative electrode is the one on the left-hand side (Al/Al^{3+}).

Reduction always happens at the positive electrode, so the half-equation for the reaction occurring at the positive electrode is:

$$Pb^{2+}_{(aq)} + 2e^- \rightleftharpoons Pb_{(s)}$$

Oxidation always happens at the negative electrode, so the half-equation for the reaction occurring at the negative electrode will be:

$$Al_{(s)} \rightleftharpoons Al^{3+}_{(aq)} + 3e^-$$

Tip: Each half-equation should just look like one half of the cell diagram (with the arrow and the electrons put back in).

Calculating the cell potential

$E^\ominus$ is the symbol for standard electrode potential. If you follow the conventions for drawing electrochemical cells, you can calculate the standard cell potential ($E^\ominus_{cell}$) (see page 79) using this formula:

$$E^\ominus_{cell} = E^\ominus_{\text{right-hand side}} - E^\ominus_{\text{left-hand side}}$$

Tip: If you don't have a cell diagram you can still use this formula. You just work out which half-cell would go on the left — it's always the one with the more negative electrode potential.

The cell potential will always be a positive voltage, because the more negative $E^\ominus$ value is being subtracted from the more positive $E^\ominus$ value.

┌─ **Example** ─────────────────────────────

Tip: See page 84 for more on how electrode potentials for half-cells are measured.

For the Zn/Cu cell:

$$E^\ominus_{cell} = E^\ominus_{\text{right-hand side}} - E^\ominus_{\text{left-hand side}}$$
$$= +0.34 - (-0.76)$$
$$= +1.10 \, V$$

Example

The cell below has an EMF of +2.00 V:

$$Al_{(s)} \mid Al^{3+}_{(aq)} \parallel Cu^{2+}_{(aq)} \mid Cu_{(s)}$$

The standard electrode potential of the copper half-cell is +0.34 V. Calculate the standard electrode potential of the aluminium half-cell.

$$E^{\ominus}_{cell} = E^{\ominus}_{right\text{-}hand\ side} - E^{\ominus}_{left\text{-}hand\ side}$$
$$E^{\ominus}_{left\text{-}hand\ side} = E^{\ominus}_{right\text{-}hand\ side} - E^{\ominus}_{cell}$$
$$= 0.34 - 2.00$$
$$= -1.66\ V$$

Exam Tip
Because the Al/Al^{3+} half-cell is on the left-hand side, you know it should have a more negative electrode potential than the Cu^{2+}/Cu half-cell. You can use this idea to check your answers in the exam.

Practice Questions — Application

Q1 An electrochemical cell containing a calcium half-cell and a silver half-cell was set up.

Half-cell	Electrode potential / V
Ca$^{2+}_{(aq)}$/Ca$_{(s)}$	−2.87
Ag$^+_{(aq)}$/Ag$_{(s)}$	+0.80

a) (i) Write a half-equation for the reaction at the positive electrode.
(ii) Write a half-equation for the reaction at the negative electrode.

b) Draw a conventional representation of this cell.

c) Calculate the cell potential.

Q2 The conventional representation of an iron/thallium electrochemical cell is shown below:

$$Pt \mid Fe^{2+}_{(aq)},\ Fe^{3+}_{(aq)} \parallel Tl^{3+}_{(aq)},\ Tl^+_{(aq)} \mid Pt$$

a) Write half-equations for the reactions occurring at the positive and negative electrodes.

b) Calculate the electrode potential of the Tl^{3+}/Tl$^+$ electrode given that the overall cell potential is +0.48 V and the Fe^{3+}/Fe^{2+} electrode potential is +0.77 V.

Q3 In an electrochemical cell with a Mg$^{2+}_{(aq)}$/Mg$_{(s)}$ half-cell and a Fe$^{3+}_{(aq)}$/Fe$^{2+}_{(aq)}$ half-cell (using a Pt electrode), oxidation occurs in the Mg$^{2+}_{(aq)}$/Mg$_{(s)}$ half-cell and reduction occurs in the Fe$^{3+}_{(aq)}$/Fe$^{2+}_{(aq)}$ half-cell.

a) Which half-cell has the more negative electrode potential?

b) Draw the conventional representation of this cell.

Exam Tip
You don't have to memorise values for electrode potentials. You'll always be told them in the question.

Exam Tip
If you're drawing a cell diagram in the exam, use the state symbols you're given in the question to work out whether things should be separated by vertical lines or commas.

Tip: You don't need to include the platinum electrode in the half-equations because it's not actually involved in the redox reaction.

Practice Questions — Fact Recall

Q1 a) Suggest a metal that could be used for the electrode in half-cells involving solutions of two aqueous ions of the same element.

b) Why is this type of electrode suitable?

Q2 Does oxidation or reduction occur in the half-cell with the more positive electrode potential?

Q3 Give two important conventions that you have to follow when you're drawing electrochemical cells using the conventional representation.

- Know the importance of the conditions when measuring the electrode potential, *E*.

- Understand how cells are used to measure electrode potentials by reference to the standard hydrogen electrode.

- Know that standard electrode potential, $E^{\ominus}$, refers to conditions of 298 K, 100 kPa and 1.00 mol dm^{-3} solution of ions.

Specification Reference 3.1.11.1

Tip: See your Year 1 notes on Le Chatelier's Principle for more about how changes in temperature, pressure and concentration affect the position of equilibria.

Tip: A platinum electrode is needed because you can't have a gas electrode.

Figure 2: *A nugget of platinum. Platinum is used as the electrode in the standard hydrogen electrode.*

Exam Tip
Make sure you learn the standard conditions — you might well be asked about them in the exam.

2. Standard Electrode Potentials

Electrode potentials are influenced by things like temperature and pressure. So if you want to compare electrode potentials, they need to be standardised. This is done using a standard hydrogen electrode.

Factors affecting the electrode potential

Half-cell reactions are reversible. So just like any other reversible reaction, the equilibrium position is affected by changes in temperature, pressure and concentration. Changing the equilibrium position changes the cell potential. To get around this, **standard conditions** are used to measure electrode potentials — using these conditions means you always get the same value for the electrode potential and you can compare values for different cells.

The standard hydrogen electrode

You measure the electrode potential of a half-cell against a **standard hydrogen electrode**. In the standard hydrogen electrode, hydrogen gas is bubbled through a solution of aqueous H^+ ions. A platinum electrode is used as a platform for the oxidation/reduction reactions — see Figure 1.

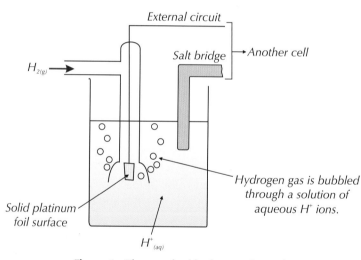

Figure 1: *The standard hydrogen electrode*

When measuring electrode potentials using the standard hydrogen electrode it's important that everything is done under standard conditions:

1. Any solutions of ions must have a concentration of 1.00 mol dm^{-3}.
2. The temperature must be 298 K (25 °C).
3. The pressure must be 100 kPa.

Measuring standard electrode potentials

The standard electrode potential of a half-cell is the voltage measured under standard conditions when the half-cell is connected to a standard hydrogen electrode — see Figure 3 (next page).

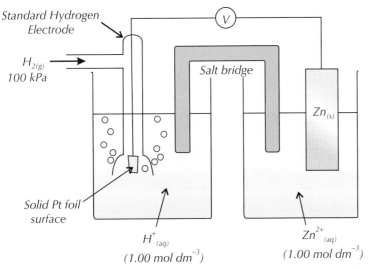

Standard Hydrogen Electrode

$H_{2(g)}$ 100 kPa

Salt bridge

$Zn_{(s)}$

Solid Pt foil surface

$H^+_{(aq)}$ (1.00 mol dm^{-3})

$Zn^{2+}_{(aq)}$ (1.00 mol dm^{-3})

Figure 3: A zinc electrode connected to a standard hydrogen electrode. This system could be used to measure the standard electrode potential of the zinc electrode.

The electrochemical cell in Figure 3 can be written as:

$$Pt \mid H_{2(g)} \mid H^+_{(aq)} \mid\mid Zn^{2+}_{(aq)} \mid Zn_{(s)}$$

The standard hydrogen electrode is always shown on the left — it doesn't matter whether or not the other half-cell has a more positive value.

Standard hydrogen electrodes can be used to calculate standard electrode potentials because the standard hydrogen electrode half-cell has an electrode potential of 0.00 V. The whole cell potential is:

$$E^{\ominus}_{cell} = E^{\ominus}_{right\text{-}hand\ side} - E^{\ominus}_{left\text{-}hand\ side}$$

The cell on the left-hand side is the standard hydrogen electrode so:

$$E^{\ominus}_{left\text{-}hand\ side} = 0.00\ V$$

So the voltage reading will be equal to $E^{\ominus}_{right\text{-}hand\ side}$. This reading could be positive or negative, depending which way the electrons flow.

Practice Question — Application

Q1 When a $Pb^{2+}_{(aq)}/Pb_{(s)}$ half-cell was connected to a standard hydrogen electrode via a voltmeter, the reading on the voltmeter was –0.13 V.

   a) Draw the conventional representation of this cell.

   b) What is the standard electrode potential of the Pb^{2+}/Pb half-cell?

   c) Is oxidation or reduction occurring in the Pb^{2+}/Pb half-cell?

Practice Questions — Fact Recall

Q1 Give three factors that can influence electrode potentials.

Q2 Describe how a standard hydrogen electrode is set up and give the standard conditions used when measuring electrode potentials.

Q3 a) What is the electrode potential of the standard hydrogen electrode?

   b) Why is it this value?

Q4 Define the term "standard electrode potential".

Tip: Notice how the H_2 gas is at a pressure of 100 kPa and the H⁺ and Zn²⁺ solutions both have concentrations of 1.00 mol dm⁻³. These are the standard conditions.

Tip: If you've forgotten what cell potential is, have a read of page 79.

Tip: The standard hydrogen electrode has an electrode potential of 0.00 V by definition — it's that because scientists say it is.

Tip: Remember, oxidation happens in the half-cell with the more negative electrode potential — see page 80 for more on this.

Learning Objectives:

- Know that standard electrode potentials can be listed as an electrochemical series.

- Be able to use $E^\ominus$ values to predict the direction of simple redox reactions.

Specification Reference 3.1.11.1

Exam Tip

Don't panic — you don't have to memorise any of these values. You'll always be told them in the question if you need to use them.

3. Electrochemical Series

The standard electrode potentials of different reactions are different (unsurprisingly). If you write a list of electrode potentials in order, you get an electrochemical series, which you can use to predict the direction of a reaction.

What is an electrochemical series?

An **electrochemical series** is basically a big long list of electrode potentials for different electrochemical half-cells. They look something like this:

Half-reaction	$E^\ominus$ / V
$Mg^{2+}_{(aq)} + 2e^- \rightleftharpoons Mg_{(s)}$	−2.38
$Al^{3+}_{(aq)} + 3e^- \rightleftharpoons Al_{(s)}$	−1.66
$Zn^{2+}_{(aq)} + 2e^- \rightleftharpoons Zn_{(s)}$	−0.76
$Ni^{2+}_{(aq)} + 2e^- \rightleftharpoons Ni_{(s)}$	−0.25
$2H^+_{(aq)} + 2e^- \rightleftharpoons H_{2(g)}$	0.00
$Sn^{4+}_{(aq)} + 2e^- \rightleftharpoons Sn^{2+}_{(aq)}$	+0.15
$Cu^{2+}_{(aq)} + 2e^- \rightleftharpoons Cu_{(s)}$	+0.34
$Fe^{3+}_{(aq)} + e^- \rightleftharpoons Fe^{2+}_{(aq)}$	+0.77
$Ag^+_{(aq)} + e^- \rightleftharpoons Ag_{(s)}$	+0.80
$Br_{2(aq)} + 2e^- \rightleftharpoons 2Br^-_{(aq)}$	+1.07
$Cr_2O_7^{2-}{}_{(aq)} + 14H^+_{(aq)} + 6e^- \rightleftharpoons 2Cr^{3+}_{(aq)} + 7H_2O_{(l)}$	+1.33
$Cl_{2(aq)} + 2e^- \rightleftharpoons 2Cl^-_{(aq)}$	+1.36
$MnO_4^-{}_{(aq)} + 8H^+_{(aq)} + 5e^- \rightleftharpoons Mn^{2+}_{(aq)} + 4H_2O_{(l)}$	+1.52

Figure 1: *A table showing an electrochemical series.*

The electrode potentials are written in order, starting from the most negative and going down to the most positive. The half-equations are always written as reduction reactions — but the reactions are reversible and can go the opposite way. When two half-equations are put together in an electrochemical cell, the one with the more negative electrode potential goes in the direction of oxidation (backwards) and the one with the more positive electrode potential goes in the direction of reduction (forwards).

Electrochemical series and reactivity

An electrochemical series shows you what's reactive and what's not.

The more reactive a metal is, the more it wants to lose electrons to form a positive ion. More reactive metals have more negative standard electrode potentials.

Exam Tip

If you're given the electrode potential of a half-cell and asked to say how reactive something is, make sure you identify whether it's a metal or a non-metal first — they're very different.

┌─ **Example** ─────────────────────────────

Magnesium is more reactive than zinc — so it's more eager to form 2+ ions than zinc is. The list of standard electrode potentials shows that Mg^{2+}/Mg has a more negative value than Zn^{2+}/Zn — it's −2.38 V for Mg^{2+}/Mg and −0.76 V for Zn^{2+}/Zn. In terms of oxidation and reduction, magnesium would reduce Zn^{2+} (or Zn^{2+} would oxidise magnesium).

The more reactive a non-metal, the more it wants to gain electrons to form a negative ion. More reactive non-metals have more positive standard electrode potentials.

Chlorine is more reactive than bromine — so it's more eager to form a negative ion than bromine is. The list of standard electrode potentials shows that $Cl_2/2Cl^-$ is more positive than $Br_2/2Br^-$ — it's +1.36 V for $Cl_2/2Cl^-$ and +1.09 V for $Br_2/2Br^-$. In terms of oxidation and reduction, chlorine would oxidise Br^- (or Br^- would reduce chlorine).

Calculating cell potentials

You can use the information in an electrochemical series to calculate the standard cell potential, or EMF, when two half-cells are connected together. All you have to do is work out which half-reaction is going in the direction of oxidation and which half-reaction is going in the direction of reduction. Then just substitute the $E^\ominus$ values into this equation:

$$E^\ominus_{cell} = E^\ominus_{reduced} - E^\ominus_{oxidised}$$

This is the standard electrode potential of the half-cell which goes in the direction of reduction (the one with the more positive electrode potential).

This is the standard electrode potential of the half-cell which goes in the direction of oxidation (the one with the more negative electrode potential).

Figure 2: Chlorine will displace bromide ions — this confirms that chlorine is more reactive.

── Example ──

Calculate the EMF of an Mg/Ag electrochemical cell using the two redox reaction equations shown below:

$$Mg^{2+}_{(aq)} + 2e^- \rightleftharpoons Mg_{(s)} \qquad E^\ominus = -2.38\ V$$
$$Ag^+_{(aq)} + e^- \rightleftharpoons Ag_{(s)} \qquad E^\ominus = +0.80\ V$$

The Mg/Mg^{2+} half-cell has the more negative electrode potential, so this half-reaction will go in the direction of oxidation. The Ag/Ag^+ half-cell has the more positive electrode potential and so will go in the direction of reduction.

$$E^\ominus_{cell} = E^\ominus_{reduced} - E^\ominus_{oxidised} = 0.80 - (-2.38) = +3.18\ V$$

Tip: Don't forget — cell potential is the voltage between two half-cells. See page 79 for more.

Predicting the direction of reactions

You can use electrode potentials to predict whether a redox reaction will happen and to show which direction it will go in. Just follow these steps:

1. Find the two half-equations for the redox reaction, and write them both out as reduction reactions.

2. Use an electrochemical series to work out which half-equation has the more negative electrode potential.

3. Write out the half-equation with the more negative electrode potential going in the backwards direction (oxidation) and the half-equation with the more positive electrode potential going in the forwards direction (reduction).

4. Combine the two half-equations and write out a full redox equation.

Tip: Once you know these steps, you can apply them to predict the direction of any redox reaction.

This is the feasible direction of the reaction and will give a positive overall $E^\ominus$ value. The reaction will not happen the other way round.

Example

Work out the direction of the reaction when a Zn/Zn²⁺ half-cell is connected to a Cu²⁺/Cu half-cell.

1. Write down the two half-equations for the redox reaction as reduction reactions:

$$Zn^{2+}_{(aq)} + 2e^- \rightleftharpoons Zn_{(s)} \quad \text{and} \quad Cu^{2+}_{(aq)} + 2e^- \rightleftharpoons Cu_{(s)}$$

Tip: These values for the electrode potentials came from the electrochemical series on page 86.

2. Find out the electrode potentials for the two half-equations:

$$Zn^{2+}_{(aq)} + 2e^- \rightleftharpoons Zn_{(s)} \qquad E^{\circ} = -0.76\,V$$
$$Cu^{2+}_{(aq)} + 2e^- \rightleftharpoons Cu_{(s)} \qquad E^{\circ} = +0.34\,V$$

3. The zinc half-reaction has the more negative electrode potential, so write it out going backwards and the copper half-reaction going forwards.

$$Zn_{(s)} \rightarrow Zn^{2+}_{(aq)} + 2e^-$$
$$Cu^{2+}_{(aq)} + 2e^- \rightarrow Cu_{(s)}$$

Tip: Have a look back at your Year 1 notes if you're unsure how to combine half-equations.

4. Write out the combined full equation:

$$Zn_{(s)} + Cu^{2+}_{(aq)} \rightarrow Zn^{2+}_{(aq)} + Cu_{(s)}$$

This full equation is the outcome of the reaction. Zinc metal will reduce copper(II) ions and copper(II) ions will oxidise zinc metal. The overall reaction has a cell potential of +1.10 V, so is feasible.

$$E^{\ominus}_{cell} = E^{\ominus}_{reduced} - E^{\ominus}_{oxidised} = 0.34 - (-0.76) = +1.10\,V$$

Zinc(II) ions will not oxidise copper metal as this would give an electrode potential of –1.10 V.

You could be given a reaction and asked whether it is feasible or not. Answer the question in a similar way to the one above. Work out the EMF of the cell. If the EMF has a positive value, the reaction is feasible. If the EMF has a negative value, the reaction is not feasible.

Example

Work out whether the following redox reaction is feasible or not:

$$Cu_{(s)} + Ni^{2+}_{(aq)} \rightarrow Cu^{2+}_{(aq)} + Ni_{(s)}$$

$$Ni^{2+}_{(aq)} + 2e^- \rightleftharpoons Ni_{(s)} \qquad E^{\ominus} = -0.25\,V$$
$$Cu^{+}_{(aq)} + 2e^- \rightleftharpoons Cu_{(s)} \qquad E^{\ominus} = +0.34\,V$$

In the full-equation above, Ni is reduced and Cu is oxidised.
Work out the EMF of the cell:

$$E^{\ominus}_{cell} = E^{\ominus}_{reduced} - E^{\ominus}_{oxidised} = -0.25 - (+0.34) = -0.59\,V$$

The EMF of the cell has a negative value, so the reaction is not feasible.

For these questions use the electrochemical series on page 86.

Q1 For each of the combinations below state which species is more reactive and explain how you know, in terms of electrode potential.

a) Aluminium and nickel.

b) Bromine and chlorine.

c) Silver and copper.

Q2 Calculate the EMF for the following reactions:

a) $Al_{(s)} + 3Ag^+_{(aq)} \rightarrow Al^{3+}_{(aq)} + 3Ag_{(s)}$

b) $Cu_{(s)} + Cl_{2(aq)} \rightarrow Cu^{2+}_{(aq)} + 2Cl^-_{(aq)}$

Q3 Predict the direction of the redox reactions of the following half-cells:

a) $Mg^{2+}_{(aq)}/Mg_{(s)}$ and $Ni^{2+}_{(aq)}/Ni_{(s)}$

b) $2Br^-_{(aq)}/Br_{2(aq)}$ and $Fe^{3+}_{(aq)}/Fe^{2+}_{(aq)}$

Q4 Predict whether or not these reactions will happen:

a) $Sn^{2+}_{(aq)} + Cu^{2+}_{(aq)} \rightarrow Sn^{4+}_{(aq)} + Cu_{(s)}$

b) $Sn^{2+}_{(aq)} + Zn^{2+}_{(aq)} \rightarrow Sn^{4+}_{(aq)} + Zn_{(s)}$

Q5 Will Ag^+ ions react with Sn^{2+} ions in solution? Explain your answer.

Exam Tip
Sometimes you have to multiply one of the half-equations by something to make the full equation balance — but you don't need to multiply its $E^\ominus$ value when you calculate the EMF of the cell.

Exam Tip
In the exam, don't assume you'll always be given a reaction that will happen — you're just as likely to be given one that won't.

Practice Questions — Fact Recall

Q1 What is an electrochemical series?

Q2 In what direction are half-equations written in electrochemical series?

Q3 A half-reaction has a very positive electrode potential.
Is it more likely to go in the direction of oxidation or reduction?

Q4 a) Do very reactive metals generally have very negative or very positive electrode potentials?

b) Do very reactive non-metals generally have very negative or very positive electrode potentials?

- Appreciate that electrochemical cells can be used as a commercial source of electrical energy.

- Appreciate that cells can be non-rechargeable (irreversible), rechargeable or fuel cells.

- Be able to describe the simplified electrode reactions in a lithium cell.
  Positive electrode:
  $Li^+ + CoO_2 + e^- \rightarrow Li^+[CoO_2]^-$.
  Negative electrode:
  $Li \rightarrow Li^+ + e^-$.

- Be able to use given electrode data to deduce the reactions occurring in non-rechargeable and rechargeable cells and to deduce the EMF of a cell.

- Understand the electrode reactions in an alkaline hydrogen-oxygen fuel cell and appreciate that a fuel cell does not need to be electrically recharged.

- Explain how the electrode reactions in a cell can be used to generate an electric current.

- Appreciate the benefits and risks to society associated with the use of these cells.

Specification Reference 3.1.11.2

4. Electrochemical Cells

The last few topics told you all about electrochemical cells. This one's all about what electrochemical cells are actually used for.

Batteries

The batteries that we use to power things like watches, digital cameras and mobile phones are all types of electrochemical cell. Some types of cell are rechargeable while others can only be used until they run out.

Non-rechargeable cells

Non-rechargeable cells use irreversible reactions. A common type of non-rechargeable cell is a dry cell alkaline battery. You'll probably find some of these in the TV remote control, torch or smoke alarms in your house. They're useful for gadgets that don't use a lot of power or are only used for short periods of time.

--- Example ---

Zinc-carbon dry cell batteries have a zinc positive electrode and a mixture of manganese dioxide and carbon for a negative electrode. In between the electrodes is a paste of ammonium chloride, which acts as an electrolyte.

The half-equations are:

$$Zn_{(s)} \rightarrow Zn^{2+}_{(aq)} + 2e^- \qquad E^{\ominus} = -0.76\,V$$
$$2MnO_{2(s)} + 2NH_4^+{}_{(aq)} + 2e^- \rightarrow Mn_2O_{3(s)} + 2NH_{3(aq)} + H_2O_{(l)} \qquad E^{\ominus} = +0.75\,V$$

The EMF of this type of cell is:

$$E^{\ominus}_{cell} = E^{\ominus}_{right\text{-}hand\ side} - E^{\ominus}_{left\text{-}hand\ side} = +0.75 - (-0.76) = +1.51\,V$$

The half-equations have non-reversible arrows because it is not practical to reverse them in a battery. They can be made to run backwards under the right conditions, but trying to do this in a battery can make it leak or explode. This is because the zinc electrode forms the casing of the battery, so becomes thinner as the zinc is oxidised.

Rechargeable cells

Rechargeable cells use reversible reactions. Rechargeable batteries are found in loads of devices, such as mobile phones, laptops and cars.

--- Example ---

Lithium cells are used in phones and laptops. One type of lithium cell is made up of a lithium cobalt oxide ($LiCoO_2$) electrode and a graphite electrode. The electrolyte is a lithium salt in an organic solvent.

The half-equations are: $\quad Li^+{}_{(aq)} + CoO_{2(s)} + e^- \rightleftharpoons Li^+[CoO_2]^-{}_{(s)} \qquad E^{\circ} = +0.56\,V$
$$Li_{(s)} \rightleftharpoons Li^+{}_{(aq)} + e^- \qquad\qquad E^{\circ} = -3.04\,V$$

So the reactions which happen when the battery supplies power are:

At the negative electrode: $\quad Li_{(s)} \rightarrow Li^+{}_{(aq)} + e^-$
At the positive electrode: $\quad Li^+{}_{(aq)} + CoO_{2(s)} + e^- \rightarrow Li^+[CoO_2]^-{}_{(s)}$

The EMF of this type of cell is:

$$E^{\ominus}_{cell} = E^{\ominus}_{right\text{-}hand\ side} - E^{\ominus}_{left\text{-}hand\ side} = +0.56 - (-3.04) = +3.60\,V$$

Two other types of rechargeable battery are NiCad (nickel-cadmium) and lead-acid. To recharge batteries, a current is supplied to force electrons to flow in the opposite direction around the circuit and reverse the reactions. This is possible because none of the substances in a rechargeable battery escape or are used up. The reactions that take place in non-rechargeable batteries are difficult or impossible to reverse in this way.

Fuel cells

In most cells the chemicals that generate the electricity are contained in the electrodes and the electrolyte that form the cell. In a **fuel cell** the chemicals are stored separately outside the cell and fed in when electricity is required.

Figure 1: A lithium battery being recharged.

Example

One example is the alkaline hydrogen-oxygen fuel cell, which can be used to power electric vehicles. Here's how this type of fuel cell works:

electron flow — power source — +

positive electrode — negative electrode

H_2 ↑ e^- — e^- O_2

Hydrogen fed into the positive electrode. → H_2 — O_2 ← Oxygen fed into the negative electrode.

Electrolyte — OH^- ions in solution

Water out ← H_2O ↑ e^- — e^- O_2

Anion-exchange membranes: allows OH^- through but not O_2 or H_2.

Figure 2: A bus powered by a hydrogen-oxygen fuel cell.

Hydrogen and oxygen gases are fed into two separate platinum-containing electrodes. These electrodes are usually made by coating a porous ceramic material with a thin layer of platinum. This is cheaper than using solid platinum rods and it provides a larger surface area so the reactions go faster.

The electrodes are separated by an anion-exchange membrane that allows anions (OH^- ions) and water to pass through it, but stops hydrogen and oxygen gas passing through it. The electrolyte is an aqueous alkaline (KOH) solution. Hydrogen is fed to the positive electrode.

The reaction that occurs at the positive electrode is:
$$H_{2(g)} + 2OH^-_{(aq)} \rightarrow 2H_2O_{(l)} + 2e^-$$
The electrons flow from the positive electrode through an external circuit to the negative electrode. The OH^- ions pass through the anion-exchange membrane towards the positive electrode. Oxygen is fed to the negative electrode.

The reaction that occurs at the negative electrode is:
$$O_{2(g)} + 2H_2O_{(l)} + 4e^- \rightarrow 4OH^-_{(aq)}$$
The overall effect is that H_2 and O_2 react to make water:
$$2H_{2(g)} + O_{2(g)} \rightarrow 2H_2O_{(l)}$$

Tip: An electrolyte is a substance that contains free ions and can conduct electricity.

Tip: These equations are for fuel cells working in <u>alkaline</u> conditions. That means the electrolyte is a base (e.g. KOH).

You can make fuel cells with <u>acidic</u> electrolytes (e.g. H_3PO_4) too. Then the electrode reactions look like this instead —
Negative electrode:
$H_2 \rightarrow 2H^+ + 2e^-$
Positive electrode:
$O_2 + 4H^+ + 4e^- \rightarrow 2H_2O$

Pros and cons of fuel cells

The major advantage of using fuel cells in cars, rather than the internal combustion engine, is that fuel cells are more efficient — they convert more of their available energy into kinetic energy to get the car moving. Internal combustion engines waste a lot of their energy producing heat.

There are other benefits too. For example, the only waste product is water, so there are no nasty toxic chemicals to dispose of and no CO_2 emissions from the cell itself. Fuel cells don't need to be recharged like batteries. As long as hydrogen and oxygen are supplied, the cell will continue to produce electricity.

The downside is that you need energy to produce a supply of hydrogen. This can be produced from the electrolysis of water — i.e. by reusing the waste product from the fuel cell, but this requires electricity — and this electricity is normally generated by burning fossil fuels. So the whole process isn't usually carbon neutral. Hydrogen is also highly flammable so it needs to be handled carefully when it is stored or transported. The infrastructure to provide hydrogen fuel for cars doesn't exist on a large scale yet, so refuelling stations are very rare at the moment.

Figure 3: *Electrolysis of water being used to make hydrogen and oxygen.*

Practice Questions — Application

Q1 Nickel/cadmium batteries are a common type of rechargeable battery. The two half-equations for the reactions happening in this type of battery are shown below:

$$Cd(OH)_{2(s)} + 2e^- \rightleftharpoons Cd_{(s)} + 2OH^-_{(aq)} \qquad E^\ominus = -0.88$$
$$NiO(OH)_{(s)} + H_2O_{(l)} + e^- \rightleftharpoons Ni(OH)_{2(s)} + OH^-_{(aq)} \qquad E^\ominus = +0.52$$

a) Calculate the EMF of this cell.

b) Write an equation for the overall reaction occurring in this cell.

Q2 An electric car is being powered by an alkaline hydrogen-oxygen fuel cell. The half-equations for the reactions occurring in this cell are:

$$H_{2(g)} + 2OH^-_{(aq)} \rightarrow 2H_2O_{(l)} + 2e^- \qquad E^\ominus = -0.83$$
$$O_{2(g)} + 2H_2O_{(l)} + 4e^- \rightarrow 4OH^-_{(aq)} \qquad E^\ominus = +0.40$$

a) Write an equation for the overall reaction occurring in this cell.

b) Draw the conventional representation of this cell.

Tip: See pages 81-83 for a recap on how to draw cell diagrams and calculate EMF.

Tip: Don't forget that platinum electrodes need to be included in cell diagrams too.

Practice Questions — Fact Recall

Q1 Why can you recharge a rechargeable battery?

Q2 Describe how an alkaline hydrogen-oxygen fuel cell works.

Q3 Explain why hydrogen-oxygen fuel cells are not necessarily carbon neutral.

Q4 Give an advantage and a disadvantage of using fuel cells.

Section Summary

Make sure you know...

- That electrochemical cells can be made by dipping two different metals in salt solutions of their own ions and connecting them by a wire and a salt bridge.
- That the direction of the reaction in each half-cell depends on their relative electrode potentials.
- That the reaction with the more negative electrode potential goes in the direction of oxidation and the reaction with the more positive electrode potential goes in the direction of reduction.
- The conventions for drawing conventional diagrams of electrochemical cells.
- That the half-cell on the left of a conventional cell diagram has the more negative electrode potential and undergoes oxidation — the one on the right is more positive and is reduced.
- How to write oxidation and reduction half-equations from cell diagrams.
- How to calculate standard cell potentials and related quantities using the equation
$$E^{\ominus}_{cell} = E^{\ominus}_{right\text{-}hand\ side} - E^{\ominus}_{left\text{-}hand\ side}.$$
- That temperature, pressure and concentration can all influence the cell potential.
- That standard electrode potentials are measured against the standard hydrogen electrode.
- That in the standard hydrogen electrode, hydrogen gas is bubbled into a solution of aqueous H^+ ions and platinum is used as the electrode.
- That standard conditions are 298 K (25 °C), 100 kPa and 1.00 mol dm^{-3}.
- What an electrochemical series is and how it can be used to predict the direction or feasibility of a reaction.
- That batteries are electrochemical cells.
- How to draw cell diagrams and calculate the EMF for the electrochemical cells in batteries.
- That non-rechargeable batteries use non-reversible reactions and rechargeable batteries use reversible reactions.
- How to write the electrode reactions in a lithium cell.
- How an alkaline hydrogen-oxygen fuel cell works.
- The advantages and disadvantages of using fuel cells instead of conventional batteries.

Exam-style Questions

1 The table below shows a short electrochemical series:

Half-reaction	$E^{\ominus}$ / V
$Mg^{2+}_{(aq)} + 2e^- \rightleftharpoons Mg_{(s)}$	−2.38
$V^{2+}_{(aq)} + 2e^- \rightleftharpoons V_{(s)}$	−1.18
$V^{3+}_{(aq)} + e^- \rightleftharpoons V^{2+}_{(aq)}$	−0.26
$Sn^{4+}_{(aq)} + 2e^- \rightleftharpoons Sn^{2+}_{(aq)}$	+0.15
$VO^{2+}_{(aq)} + 2H^+_{(aq)} + e^- \rightleftharpoons V^{3+}_{(aq)} + H_2O_{(l)}$	+0.34
$Fe^{3+}_{(aq)} + e^- \rightleftharpoons Fe^{2+}_{(aq)}$	+0.77
$VO_2^+{}_{(aq)} + 2H^+_{(aq)} + e^- \rightleftharpoons VO^{2+}_{(aq)} + H_2O_{(l)}$	+1.00

An electrochemical cell can be made by connecting an Mg^{2+}/Mg half-cell to an Fe^{2+}/Fe^{3+} half-cell with a platinum electrode.

1.1 Write half-equations for the oxidation and reduction reactions occurring in this cell.

(2 marks)

1.2 Draw a cell diagram for this cell using the conventional representation.

(2 marks)

1.3 Calculate the EMF of this cell under standard conditions.

(1 mark)

1.4 Using the information in the table, give the equations for any reactions which occur when aqueous Sn^{2+} ions are mixed with an acidified solution of VO_2^+ ions. Explain your answer.

(4 marks)

Standard electrode potentials are measured relative to the standard hydrogen electrode.

1.5 Explain what is meant by 'standard conditions'.

(1 mark)

1.6 The electrode potential of the standard hydrogen electrode is 0.00 V. Explain why.

(1 mark)

1.7 The standard hydrogen electrode is constructed using a platinum electrode. Suggest why platinum is a suitable metal to use for this purpose.

(1 mark)

When a standard hydrogen electrode was connected to an Ag^+/Ag half-cell, the reading on the voltmeter was +0.80 V.

1.8 What is the standard electrode potential for the reaction $Ag^+_{(aq)} + e^- \rightleftharpoons Ag_{(s)}$?

(1 mark)

1.9 What does this electrode potential tell you about the reactivity of $Ag_{(s)}$ compared to $V_{(s)}$? Explain your answer.

(2 mark)

2 Lithium-ion batteries are a type of rechargeable battery commonly used in mobile phones. The half-equations for the reactions that occur in a lithium-ion battery are shown below:

$$Li^+_{(aq)} + CoO_{2(s)} + e^- \rightleftharpoons Li^+[CoO_2]^-_{(s)}$$

$$Li_{(s)} \rightleftharpoons Li^+_{(aq)} + e^-$$

2.1 Combine the two half-equations to give the equation for the overall reaction occurring in this cell.

(1 mark)

2.2 Explain why rechargeable batteries can be recharged.

(1 mark)

Alkaline hydrogen-oxygen fuel cells can be used as an alternative source of commercially available electrical energy. They are commonly used to power electric vehicles.

2.3 Explain why the electrodes of a hydrogen-oxygen fuel cell are typically made by coating a porous ceramic material with a thin layer of platinum, rather than using solid platinum rods.

(2 marks)

2.4 Give two advantages of using hydrogen-oxygen fuel cells over the internal combustion engine.

(2 marks)

3   The table below shows a short electrochemical series:

Half-reaction	$E^{\ominus}$ / V
$Al^{3+}_{(aq)} + 3e^- \rightleftharpoons Al_{(s)}$	−1.66
$Zn^{2+}_{(aq)} + 2e^- \rightleftharpoons Zn_{(s)}$	−0.76
$Ni^{2+}_{(aq)} + 2e^- \rightleftharpoons Ni_{(s)}$	−0.25
$Cu^{2+}_{(aq)} + 2e^- \rightleftharpoons Cu_{(s)}$	+0.34
$Fe^{3+}_{(aq)} + e^- \rightleftharpoons Fe^{2+}_{(aq)}$	+0.77

Using the information in the table, determine which of the following reactions is not feasible.

A $Zn_{(s)} + 2Fe^{3+}_{(aq)} \rightarrow Zn^{2+}_{(aq)} + 2Fe^{2+}_{(aq)}$

B $3Zn_{(s)} + 2Al^{3+}_{(aq)} \rightarrow 3Zn^{2+}_{(aq)} + 2Al_{(s)}$

C $Ni_{(s)} + Cu^{2+}_{(aq)} \rightarrow Ni^{2+}_{(aq)} + Cu_{(s)}$

D $2Al_{(s)} + 3Ni^{2+}_{(aq)} \rightarrow 2Al^{3+}_{(aq)} + 3Ni_{(s)}$

(1 mark)

4   The conventional representation of an electrochemical cell is shown below.

$$Pt \mid Sn^{2+}_{(aq)}, Sn^{4+}_{(aq)} \parallel Tl^{3+}_{(aq)} \mid Tl_{(s)}$$

4.1   Write a half-equation for the reaction occurring at the positive electrode of this electrochemical cell.

(1 mark)

4.2   Calculate the electrode potential of the $Tl^{3+}_{(aq)}/Tl_{(s)}$ half-cell given that the overall cell potential is +0.57 V and the electrode potential of the $Sn^{4+}_{(aq)}/Sn^{2+}_{(aq)}$ half-cell is +0.15 V.

(1 mark)

4.3   Draw the conventional representation of an electrochemical cell that could be used to measure the standard electrode potential of the $Tl^{3+}_{(aq)}/Tl_{(s)}$ half-cell.

(1 mark)

1. Acids, Bases and K_w

There are a few different theories about what makes an acid and what makes a base. One of those theories is the Brønsted–Lowry theory. Here it is...

Brønsted–Lowry acids and bases

Brønsted–Lowry acids are proton donors — they release hydrogen ions (H^+) when they're mixed with water. You never get H^+ ions by themselves in water though — they're always combined with H_2O to form **hydroxonium ions**, H_3O^+. For example, for the general acid HA:

$$HA_{(aq)} + H_2O_{(l)} \rightarrow H_3O^+_{(aq)} + A^-_{(aq)}$$

Brønsted–Lowry bases do the opposite — they're proton acceptors. When they're in solution, they grab hydrogen ions from water molecules. For example, for the general base B:

$$B_{(aq)} + H_2O_{(l)} \rightarrow BH^+_{(aq)} + OH^-_{(aq)}$$

Dissociation in water

Acids and bases dissociate in water. This just means they break up into positively and negatively charged ions. The amount of dissociation depends on how weak or strong the acid or base is. **Strong acids** dissociate (or ionise) almost completely in water — nearly all the H^+ ions will be released. **Strong bases** (like sodium hydroxide) ionise almost completely in water too.

Examples ───────────

Hydrochloric acid is a strong acid: $HCl_{(g)} \rightarrow H^+_{(aq)} + Cl^-_{(aq)}$

Sodium hydroxide is a strong base: $NaOH_{(s)} \rightarrow Na^+_{(aq)} + OH^-_{(aq)}$

These reactions are actually reversible reactions but the equilibrium lies extremely far to the right, so only the forward reaction is shown in the equation.

Weak acids (e.g. ethanoic or citric) dissociate only very slightly in water — so only small numbers of H^+ ions are formed. An equilibrium is set up which lies well over to the left. **Weak bases** (such as ammonia) only slightly dissociate in water too. Just like with weak acids, the equilibrium lies well over to the left.

Examples ───────────

Ethanoic acid is a weak acid: $CH_3COOH_{(aq)} \rightleftharpoons CH_3COO^-_{(aq)} + H^+_{(aq)}$

Ammonia is a weak base: $NH_{3(aq)} + H_2O_{(l)} \rightleftharpoons NH_4^+_{(aq)} + OH^-_{(aq)}$

Acid and base reactions

Acids can't just throw away their protons — they can only get rid of them if there's a base to accept them. In this reaction the acid, HA, transfers a proton to the base, B:

$$HA_{(aq)} + B_{(aq)} \rightleftharpoons BH^+_{(aq)} + A^-_{(aq)}$$

Learning Objectives:

- Know that an acid is a proton donor.
- Know that a base is a proton acceptor.
- Know that acid–base equilibria involve the transfer of protons.
- Know that water is slightly dissociated.
- Know that $K_w = [H^+][OH^-]$ is derived from the equilibrium constant of the dissociation of water.
- Know that the value of K_w varies with temperature.
- Know that weak acids and weak bases dissociate only slightly in aqueous solution.

Specification Reference 3.1.12.1, 3.1.12.3, 3.1.12.4

Tip: The strength of an acid has nothing to do with its concentration. How strong an acid is depends on how much it dissociates in water. The concentration is just how diluted the acid is.

Tip: Whenever you see $H^+_{(aq)}$, it should really be $H_3O^+_{(aq)}$ but in practice it's usually okay to use just H^+, unless you need to show water acting as a base.

Tip: The equilibrium is far to the left for weak acids, and far to the right for strong acids.

Tip: Le Chatelier's principle was covered in Year 1, so check back if it's a little hazy in your mind.

Tip: You'll be using K_w to calculate pH on page 101, so make sure you understand what it means.

Tip: The units of K_w are <u>always</u> mol^2 dm^{-6} because mol $dm^{-3} \times mol$ $dm^{-3} = mol^2$ dm^{-6}.

Exam Tip
Remember — K_w only equals $[H^+]^2$ in <u>pure water</u>. If you're asked to write an expression for K_w, always give $K_w = [H^+][OH^-]$.

It's an equilibrium, so if you add more HA or B, the position of equilibrium moves to the right. But if you add more BH^+ or A^-, the equilibrium will move to the left, according to Le Chatelier's principle. When an acid is added to water, water acts as the base and accepts the proton:

$$HA_{(aq)} + H_2O_{(l)} \rightleftharpoons H_3O^+_{(aq)} + A^-_{(aq)}$$

The ionic product of water, K_w

Water dissociates into hydroxonium ions and hydroxide ions. So this equilibrium exists in water:

$$H_2O_{(l)} + H_2O_{(l)} \rightleftharpoons H_3O^+_{(aq)} + OH^-_{(aq)}$$

If you remove an H_2O from both sides, this simplifies to:

$$H_2O_{(l)} \rightleftharpoons H^+_{(aq)} + OH^-_{(aq)}$$

And, just like for any other equilibrium reaction, you can apply the equilibrium law and write an expression for the equilibrium constant:

$$K_c = \frac{[H^+][OH^-]}{[H_2O]}$$

Water only dissociates a tiny amount, so the equilibrium lies well over to the left. There's so much water compared to the amounts of H^+ and OH^- ions that the concentration of water is considered to have a constant value. So if you multiply the expression you wrote for K_c (which is a constant) by $[H_2O]$ (another constant), you get a constant. This new constant is called the **ionic product of water** and it is given the symbol K_w.

$$K_w = K_c \times [H_2O] = \frac{[H^+][OH^-]}{[\cancel{H_2O}]} \times \cancel{[H_2O]}$$

So... $\boxed{K_w = [H^+][OH^-]}$

K_w always has the same value for an aqueous solution at a given temperature. For example, at 298 K (25 °C), K_w has a value of 1.00×10^{-14} mol^2 dm^{-6}. The value of K_w changes as the temperature changes. In pure water, there is always one H^+ ion for each OH^- ion. So $[H^+] = [OH^-]$. That means if you are dealing with pure water, then you can say that:

$$\boxed{K_w = [H^+]^2}$$

Practice Questions — Fact Recall

Q1 What is the definition of:
   a) A Brønsted–Lowry acid? b) A Brønsted–Lowry base?

Q2 Write out the equations for:
   a) A general acid (HA) mixed with water.
   b) A general base (B) mixed with water.
   c) A general acid (HA) reacting with a general base (B)

Q3 Write out the equation for the dissociation of water.

Q4 a) What is K_w?
   b) Write out the equation for K_w.
   c) What are the units of K_w?
   d) Why can the equation be simplified to $K_w = [H^+]^2$ for water?

2. pH Calculations

There are lots of pH calculations that you'll need to be able to do in your exam. The next few pages tell you everything you need to know to do them.

The pH scale

The pH scale is a measure of the hydrogen ion concentration in a solution. The concentration of hydrogen ions in a solution can vary enormously, so those wise chemists of old decided to express the concentration on a logarithmic scale. pH can be calculated using the following equation:

$$pH = -\log_{10} [H^+]$$

$[H^+]$ is the concentration of hydrogen ions in a solution, measured in mol dm^{-3}. So, if you know the hydrogen ion concentration of a solution, you can calculate its pH by sticking the numbers into the formula.

┌─ **Example** ─ **Maths Skills** ────────────────────────────

A solution of hydrochloric acid has a hydrogen ion concentration of 0.010 mol dm^{-3}. What is the pH of the solution?

$$pH = -\log_{10} [H^+]$$
$$= -\log_{10} 0.010$$
$$= 2.00$$

Just substitute the [H$^+$] value into the pH formula and solve.

└───

The pH scale normally goes from 0 (very acidic) to 14 (very alkaline). pH 7 is regarded as being neutral. Solutions that have a very low pH include strong acids such as HCl and H_2SO_4. Strong bases such as NaOH and KOH have a very high pH. Pure water has a pH of 7 and is neutral.

Calculating [H⁺] from pH

If you've got the pH of a solution, and you want to know its hydrogen ion concentration, then you need the inverse of the pH formula:

$$[H^+] = 10^{-pH}$$

Now you can use this formula to find [H$^+$].

┌─ **Example** ─ **Maths Skills** ────────────────────────────

A solution of sulfuric acid has a pH of 1.52. What is the hydrogen ion concentration of this solution?

$$[H^+] = 10^{-pH}$$
$$= 10^{-1.52}$$
$$= 0.030 \text{ mol dm}^{-3}$$
$$= 3.0 \times 10^{-2} \text{ mol dm}^{-3}$$

Just substitute the pH value into the inverse pH formula and solve.

└───

Practice Questions — Application

Q1 A solution of sulfuric acid (H_2SO_4) has a hydrogen ion concentration of 0.050 mol dm^{-3}. Calculate the pH of this solution.

Q2 A solution of nitric acid (HNO_3) has a pH of 2.86. Calculate the concentration of hydrogen ions in this solution.

Q3 Calculate the pH of a solution of hydrochloric acid (HCl) with a hydrogen ion concentration of 0.020 mol dm^{-3}.

Learning Objectives:

- Know that the concentration of hydrogen ions in aqueous solution covers a very wide range. Therefore a logarithmic scale, the pH scale, is used as a measure of hydrogen ion concentration.
- Know that pH = –$\log_{10}$[H⁺].
- Be able to convert concentration of hydrogen ions into pH and vice versa.
- Be able to calculate the pH of a strong acid from its concentration.
- Be able to use K_w to calculate the pH of a strong base from its concentration.

Specification Reference 3.1.12.2, 3.1.12.3

Tip: Look at page 283 for more on how to use logs.

Tip: To calculate logarithms you need to use the 'log' button on your calculator. Different calculators work differently so make sure you know how to calculate logs on yours.

***Figure 1:** pH can be measured using a pH meter like this one.*

Tip: There are details on the different ways that you can measure pH in the Practical Skills section — see page 6.

pH of strong monoprotic acids

Monoprotic means that each molecule of an acid will release one proton when it dissociates. Hydrochloric acid (HCl) and nitric acid (HNO_3) are strong acids so they ionise fully:

$$HCl_{(aq)} \rightarrow H^+_{(aq)} + Cl^-_{(aq)}$$

HCl and HNO_3 are also monoprotic, so each mole of acid produces one mole of hydrogen ions. This means the H^+ concentration is the same as the acid concentration. So, if you know the concentration of the acid you know the H^+ concentration and you can calculate the pH.

Exam Tip
Calculating the pH of acids from their concentrations comes up in loads of calculations so you need to be really confident that you know how to do it.

Examples — Maths Skills

Calculate the pH of 0.10 mol dm^{-3} hydrochloric acid:

$$[HCl] = [H^+] = 0.10 \text{ mol dm}^{-3}.$$

So: $pH = -\log_{10} [H^+]$
$$= -\log_{10} 0.10$$
$$= 1.00$$

Calculate the pH of 0.050 mol dm^{-3} nitric acid:

$$[HNO_3] = [H^+] = 0.050 \text{ mol dm}^{-3}.$$

So: $pH = -\log_{10} 0.050$
$$= 1.30$$

If a solution of hydrochloric acid has a pH of 2.45, what is the concentration of the acid?

$$[HCl] = [H^+] = 10^{-pH}.$$

So: $[HCl] = 10^{-2.45}$
$$= 3.5 \times 10^{-3} \text{ mol dm}^{-3}$$

Figure 2: *Concentrated H_2SO_4 is a strong acid. It turns this universal indicator paper purple, which shows it has a pH between 0 and 1.*

pH of strong diprotic acids

Diprotic means that each molecule of an acid will release two protons when it dissociates. Sulfuric acid is an example of a strong diprotic acid:

$$H_2SO_{4(l)} \rightarrow 2H^+_{(aq)} + SO_4^{2-}_{(aq)}$$

So, diprotic acids produce two moles of hydrogen ions for each mole of acid, meaning that the H^+ concentration is twice the concentration of the acid.

Examples — Maths Skills

Calculate the pH of 0.100 mol dm^{-3} sulfuric acid:

$$[H^+] = 2 \times [H_2SO_4] = 0.200 \text{ mol dm}^{-3}.$$

So: $pH = -\log_{10} [H^+]$
$$= -\log_{10} 0.200$$
$$= 0.699$$

Calculate the pH of 0.25 mol dm^{-3} sulfuric acid:

$$[H^+] = 2 \times 0.25 = 0.50.$$

So: $pH = -\log_{10} [H^+]$
$$= -\log_{10} [0.50]$$
$$= 0.30$$

Tip: The rule that $[H^+] = 2 \times [HA]$ is only true for <u>strong</u> diprotic acids — you can't apply the same rule to weak diprotic acids because they don't fully ionise.

pH of strong bases

Sodium hydroxide (NaOH) and potassium hydroxide (KOH) are strong bases that fully ionise in water — they donate one mole of OH⁻ ions per mole of base. This means that the concentration of OH⁻ ions is the same as the concentration of the base. So for 0.02 mol dm⁻³ sodium hydroxide solution, [OH⁻] is also 0.02 mol dm⁻³. But to work out the pH you need to know [H⁺] — luckily this is linked to [OH⁻] through the ionic product of water, K_w:

$$K_w = [H^+][OH^-]$$

Tip: See page 98 for more information on K_w.

So if you know [OH⁻] for a strong aqueous base and K_w at a certain temperature, you can work out [H⁺] and then the pH. Just follow these steps:

Step 1: Find the values of K_w and [OH⁻]. You may be told these in the question or you may have to work them out.

Step 2: Rearrange the equation, substitute the values for K_w and [OH⁻] into the equation, and solve it to find [H⁺].

Step 3: Once you know [H⁺], substitute this into the pH equation ($pH = -\log_{10}[H^+]$) and solve it to find out the pH.

Example — Maths Skills

The value of K_w at 298 K is 1.0×10^{-14} mol² dm⁻⁶. Find the pH of 0.100 mol dm⁻³ NaOH at 298 K.

1. Find the values of K_w and [OH⁻]:

   - The value of K_w is given in the question as 1.0×10^{-14} mol² dm⁻⁶
   - NaOH is a strong base so will donate one mole of OH⁻ ions per mole of base. The concentration of NaOH is 0.100 mol dm⁻³ so [OH⁻] must be 0.100 mol dm⁻³.

2. Substitute the values of K_w and [OH⁻] into the K_w equation:

$$K_w = [H^+][OH^-]$$

$$\text{So } [H^+] = \frac{K_w}{[OH^-]} = \frac{1.0 \times 10^{-14}}{0.100} = 1.0 \times 10^{-13} \text{ mol dm}^{-3}$$

3. Substitute the value of [H⁺] into the pH equation:
$$pH = -\log_{10}(1.0 \times 10^{-13}) = 13.00$$

Figure 3: Sodium hydroxide turns this universal indicator paper dark blue, which shows it has a high pH.

Tip: You can use $K_w = [H^+]^2$ (p. 98) to calculate the pH of water. pH will vary with temperature, but if you know K_w at that temperature you can work out [H⁺] and then pH.

Practice Questions — Application

Q1 Hydrochloric acid (HCl) is a strong monoprotic acid. Calculate the pH of a 0.080 mol dm⁻³ solution of HCl.

Q2 Sulfuric acid (H_2SO_4) is a strong diprotic acid. Calculate the pH of a 0.025 mol dm⁻³ solution of H_2SO_4.

Q3 Potassium hydroxide (KOH) is a strong base. A 0.200 mol dm⁻³ solution of KOH was prepared at 50 °C. The value of K_w is 5.48×10^{-14} mol² dm⁻⁶ at this temperature. Calculate the pH of this solution.

Exam Tip
Before diving in to answer a question, you might find it useful to highlight the key bits of information in the question that you're likely to use.

Practice Questions — Fact Recall

Q1 Write out the equation that defines pH.

Q2 Explain what is meant by the terms monoprotic and diprotic.

- Be able to construct an expression for the dissociation constant K_a for a weak acid.
- Be able to perform calculations relating the pH of a weak acid to the dissociation constant K_a and the concentration.
- Know that $pK_a = -\log_{10}K_a$.
- Be able to convert K_a into pK_a, and vice versa.

Specification Reference 3.1.12.4

Tip: K_a is a type of equilibrium constant, so the formula for K_a is based on K_c.

Figure 1: Lemon juice contains citric acid. It turns this universal indicator paper orange, which shows that it's a weak acid.

Exam Tip
It's important to show all the steps of your working out when you're answering an exam question — that way, if your final answer is wrong, you can still pick up some marks.

3. The Acid Dissociation Constant

Calculating the pH of strong acids isn't too bad, but for weak acids things are a bit more complicated — you need to use the acid dissociation constant, K_a.

What is the acid dissociation constant?

Weak acids (like CH_3COOH) and weak bases dissociate only slightly in solution, so the $[H^+]$ isn't the same as the acid concentration. This makes it a bit trickier to find their pH. You have to use yet another equilibrium constant — the acid dissociation constant, K_a. The units of K_a are mol dm^{-3} and the equation for K_a is derived as follows:

For a weak aqueous acid, HA, you get the equilibrium $HA_{(aq)} \rightleftharpoons H^+_{(aq)} + A^-_{(aq)}$. As only a tiny amount of HA dissociates, you can assume that $[HA_{(aq)}] \gg [H^+_{(aq)}]$, so $[HA_{(aq)}]_{start} \approx [HA_{(aq)}]_{equilibrium}$.

So if you apply the equilibrium law, you get:

$$K_a = \frac{[H^+][A^-]}{[HA]}$$

When dealing with weak acids, you can assume that all the H$^+$ ions come from the acid, so $[H^+_{(aq)}] \approx [A^-_{(aq)}]$. So the formula for K_a can be simplified to:

$$K_a = \frac{[H^+]^2}{[HA]}$$

Finding the pH of weak acids

You can use K_a to find the pH of a weak acid. Just follow these steps.

Step 1: Write an expression for K_a for the weak acid.

Step 2: Rearrange the equation and substitute in the values you know to find $[H^+]^2$.

Step 3: Take the square root of the number to find $[H^+]$.

Step 4: Substitute $[H^+]$ into the pH equation to find the pH.

Example — **Maths Skills**

Find the pH of a 0.020 mol dm^{-3} solution of propanoic acid (CH_3CH_2COOH) at 298K. K_a for propanoic acid at this temperature is 1.30×10^{-5} mol dm^{-3}.

1. Write an expression for K_a for the weak acid:

$$K_a = \frac{[H^+][CH_3CH_2COO^-]}{[CH_3CH_2COOH]} = \frac{[H^+]^2}{[CH_3CH_2COOH]}$$

2. Rearrange it to find $[H^+]^2$:

$$[H^+]^2 = K_a[CH_3CH_2COOH]$$
$$= (1.30 \times 10^{-5}) \times 0.020$$
$$= 2.60 \times 10^{-7}$$

3. Take the square root of this number to find $[H^+]$:

$$[H^+] = \sqrt{2.60 \times 10^{-7}}$$
$$= 5.10 \times 10^{-4} \text{ mol dm}^{-3}$$

4. Use $[H^+]$ to find the pH of the acid:

$$pH = -\log_{10}[H^+]$$
$$= -\log_{10} 5.10 \times 10^{-4}$$
$$= 3.292$$

Finding the concentration of weak acids

If you already know the pH you can use K_a to find the concentration of the acid. You don't need to know anything new for this type of calculation — you use the same formulas you used to find the pH.

Step 1: Substitute the pH into the inverse pH equation to calculate $[H^+]$.

Step 2: Write an expression for K_a.

Step 3: Rearrange the equation to give the concentration of the acid.

Step 4: Substitute the values for K_a and $[H^+]$ into the equation and solve it.

Figure 2: *Ethanoic acid is a weak acid.*

┌─ **Example** — **Maths Skills** ──────────────

The pH of an ethanoic acid (CH_3COOH) solution is 3.02 at 298 K. Calculate the molar concentration of this solution. The K_a of ethanoic acid is 1.75×10^{-5} mol dm^{-3} at 298 K.

1. Use the pH of the acid to find $[H^+]$:
$$[H^+] = 10^{-pH}$$
$$= 10^{-3.02}$$
$$= 9.5 \times 10^{-4} \text{ mol dm}^{-3}$$

2. Write an expression for K_a:
$$K_a = \frac{[H^+][CH_3COO^-]}{[CH_3COOH]} = \frac{[H^+]^2}{[CH_3COOH]}$$

3. Rearrange it to give $[CH_3COOH]$:
$$[CH_3COOH] = \frac{[H^+]^2}{K_a}$$

4. Substitute in K_a and $[H^+]$ and solve the equation to find $[CH_3COOH]$:
$$[CH_3COOH] = \frac{(9.5 \times 10^{-4})^2}{1.75 \times 10^{-5}} = 0.052 \text{ mol dm}^{-3}$$

Exam Tip
In the exam you might not be given the chemical formula of the acid you're looking at — you may have to work it out for yourself. See your Year 1 notes if you need a recap on nomenclature.

Finding the K_a of weak acids

If you know both the concentration and the pH, you can use them to find the K_a of the weak acid. Just find $[H^+]$ (as shown in the example above), substitute the values you know into the expression for K_a and solve.

┌─ **Example** — **Maths Skills** ──────────────

A solution of 0.162 mol dm^{-3} HCN has a pH of 5.050 at 298 K. What is the value of K_a for HCN at 298 K?

1. Use the pH of the acid to find $[H^+]$:
$$[H^+] = 10^{-pH}$$
$$= 10^{-5.050}$$
$$= 8.91 \times 10^{-6} \text{ mol dm}^{-3}$$

2. Write an expression for K_a:
$$K_a = \frac{[H^+][CN^-]}{[HCN]} = \frac{[H^+]^2}{[HCN]}$$

3. Substitute in the values for $[H^+]$ and $[HCN]$:
$$K_a = \frac{[H^+]^2}{[HCN]} = \frac{(8.91 \times 10^{-6})^2}{0.162} = 4.90 \times 10^{-10} \text{ mol dm}^{-3}$$

Exam Tip
If you can't work out the chemical formula of an acid, just use HA instead and you might still get the marks.

Exam Tip
You need to be able to do all three types of calculation in the exam — any one of them could crop up so make sure you understand these examples.

The logarithmic constant pK_a

The value of K_a varies massively from one acid to the next. This can sometimes make the numbers difficult to manage so to make life easier, scientists often use the pK_a instead. pK_a is calculated from K_a in exactly the same way as pH is calculated from $[H^+]$ — and vice versa:

$$p K_a = -\log_{10}(K_a) \qquad\qquad K_a = 10^{-pK_a}$$

Tip: Notice how pK_a values aren't annoyingly tiny like K_a values.

So if an acid has a K_a value of 1.50×10^{-7} mol dm^{-3}, then:

$$pK_a = -\log_{10}(K_a)$$
$$= -\log_{10}(1.50 \times 10^{-7})$$
$$= 6.824$$

Tip: The larger the pK_a, the weaker the acid. Strong acids have very small pK_a values.

And if an acid has a pK_a value of 4.320, then:

$$K_a = 10^{-pK_a}$$
$$= 10^{-4.320}$$
$$= 4.79 \times 10^{-5} \text{ mol dm}^{-3}$$

Just to make things that bit more complicated, there might be a pK_a value in a 'find the pH' type of question. If so, you need to convert it to K_a so that you can use the K_a expression.

Tip: These are the same steps as you followed on page 102 but with an extra step (converting the pK_a into K_a) at the beginning.

Example — Maths Skills

Calculate the pH of 0.050 mol dm^{-3} methanoic acid (HCOOH). Methanoic acid has a pK_a of 3.750 at 298 K.

1. Convert the pK_a value to a K_a value:
$$K_a = 10^{-pK_a}$$
$$= 10^{-3.750}$$
$$= 1.78 \times 10^{-4} \text{ mol dm}^{-3}$$

2. Write out an expression for K_a:
$$K_a = \frac{[H^+][HCOO^-]}{[HCOOH]} = \frac{[H^+]^2}{[HCOOH]}$$

Tip: '$\log_{10}$' is often written as just 'log'.

3. Rearrange it to give $[H^+]^2$:
$$[H^+]^2 = K_a[HCOOH]$$
$$= 1.78 \times 10^{-4} \times 0.050$$
$$= 8.9 \times 10^{-6}$$

4. Take the square root to get $[H^+]$:
$$[H^+] = \sqrt{8.9 \times 10^{-6}}$$
$$= 2.98 \times 10^{-3} \text{ mol dm}^{-3}$$

5. Substitute $[H^+]$ into the pH equation and solve:
$$pH = -\log(2.98 \times 10^{-3})$$
$$= 2.526$$

Exam Tip
pH values for weak acids are usually between 2 and 5. If you get an answer much bigger or smaller than this in your exam, double-check your calculation — you may have gone wrong somewhere.

It works the other way around too. Sometimes you are asked to calculate K_a but have to give your answer as a pK_a value. In this case, you just work out the K_a value as usual and then convert it to pK_a — and Bob's your pet hamster.

Q1 A solution of the weak acid hydrocyanic acid (HCN) has a concentration of 2.0 mol dm^{-3}. The K_a of this acid at 25 °C is 4.9×10^{-10} mol dm^{-3}.

  a) Write down an expression for the K_a of this acid.

  b) Calculate the pH of this solution at 25 °C

Q2 A solution of the weak acid nitrous acid (HNO$_2$) has a pH of 3.80 at 25 °C. The K_a of this acid at 25 °C is 4.0×10^{-4} mol dm^{-3}. Determine the concentration of this solution at 25 °C.

Q3 The K_a of lactic acid (a weak acid) at 25 °C is 1.38×10^{-4} mol dm^{-3}. Calculate the pH of a 0.48 mol dm^{-3} solution of lactic acid at 25 °C.

Q4 A 0.28 mol dm^{-3} solution of a weak acid (HA) has a pH of 4.11 at 25 °C. Calculate the K_a of this acid at 25 °C.

Q5 Methanoic acid (HCOOH) is a weak acid. It has a K_a of 1.8×10^{-4} mol dm^{-3} at 298 K. The pH of a solution of methanoic acid was measured to be 3.67 at 298 K. Determine the concentration of this solution of methanoic acid.

Q6 The weak acid ethanoic acid has a pK_a of 4.78 at 298 K. A 0.25 mol dm^{-3} solution of ethanoic acid was prepared.

  a) Determine the K_a of ethanoic acid at 298 K.

  b) Calculate the pH of this solution at 298 K.

Q7 A 0.154 mol dm^{-3} weak acid solution has a pH of 4.50 at 45 °C. Calculate the pK_a of this acid at 45 °C.

Q8 The pK_a of hydrofluoric acid, HF (a weak acid), is 3.14 at a certain temperature. Calculate the concentration of a solution of hydrofluoric acid that has a pH of 3.20 at this temperature.

Q9 A weak acid (HX) has a pK_a of 4.50 at 25 °C. Calculate the pH of a 0.6 mol dm^{-3} solution of this acid at 25 °C.

Exam Tip
You'll almost certainly have to use expressions for terms like pH and pK_a in the exam so you really, really need to make sure that you know the formulas. Have a look at pages 278-279 for a summary of all the formulas in this section.

Q1 What are the units for K_a?

Q2 a) Write the general equation for the acid dissociation constant K_a for a general acid HA.

  b) How can you simplify this formula for weak acid?

  c) Rearrange your answer to b) to give an expression for calculating [HA].

Q3 Give two things that K_a can be used for.

Q4 a) Write out the expression that defines pK_a.

  b) Rearrange this equation to give an expression for K_a.

- Be able to carry out titrations of acids with bases.

- Understand the typical shape of pH curves for acid–base titrations in all combinations of weak and strong monoprotic acids and bases.

- Be able to sketch and explain the shapes of typical pH curves.

- Be able to use pH curves to select an appropriate indicator.

- Be able to make up a volumetric solution and carry out a simple acid-base titration (Required Practical 1).

- Be able to investigate how pH changes when a weak acid reacts with a strong base and when a strong acid reacts with a weak base (Required Practical 9).

Specification Reference 3.1.12.5

Tip: Sometimes you'll hear about alkalis being used in titrations, sometimes bases. Don't get yourself in a muddle over it — an alkali is just a type of base, it's a base that's <u>soluble in water</u>.

Tip: Before you carry out any experiment, make sure you have considered all safety precautions that you need to take.

Tip: You need to repeat titrations to make sure your results are reliable.

4. Titrations and pH Curves

When acids and bases are mixed together a neutralisation reaction occurs — H^+ ions from the acid join with OH^- ions from the base to create water. If there are equal numbers of H^+ and OH^- ions the mixture will be neutral (pH 7). What do titrations and pH curves have to do with this? Read on...

Titrations

Titrations allow you to find out exactly how much alkali is needed to neutralise a quantity of acid. Here's how you do one...

REQUIRED PRACTICAL **1**

Step 1: You measure out some acid of known concentration using a pipette and put it in a flask, along with some appropriate **indicator** (indicators change colour at a certain pH — see page 108 for more).

Step 2: Do a rough titration — add the alkali to the acid using a burette fairly quickly to get an approximate idea where the solution changes colour. This is the **end point** — the point at which all of the acid is just neutralised. Give the flask a regular swirl to make sure the acid and alkali are mixed properly.

Step 3: Repeat step one and then do an accurate titration. Run the alkali in to within 2 cm³ of the end point, then add it drop by drop. If you don't notice exactly when the solution changes colour you've overshot and your result won't be accurate.

Step 4: Record the amount of alkali needed to neutralise the acid.

It's best to repeat this process a few times, making sure you get very similar answers each time (within about 0.1 cm³ of each other).

You can also find out how much acid is needed to neutralise a quantity of alkali. It's exactly the same process as above, but you add acid to alkali instead. The equipment you'll need to do a titration is illustrated in Figure 1.

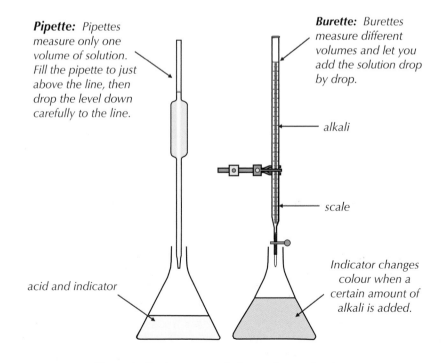

Pipette: *Pipettes measure only one volume of solution. Fill the pipette to just above the line, then drop the level down carefully to the line.*

Burette: *Burettes measure different volumes and let you add the solution drop by drop.*

alkali

scale

acid and indicator

Indicator changes colour when a certain amount of alkali is added.

Figure 1: *Equipment needed to perform a titration.*

pH curves

REQUIRED PRACTICAL **9**

pH curves show the results of titration experiments. They can be made by plotting the pH of the titration mixture against the amount of base added as the titration goes on. The pH of the mixture can be measured using a pH meter and the scale on the burette can be used to see how much base has been added.

The shape of the curve looks a bit different depending on the strengths of the acid and base that were used. The graphs below show the pH curves for the different combinations of strong and weak monoprotic acids and bases:

Figure 2: *A student using a pH meter to measure pH during an acid–base titration.*

Strong acid/strong base

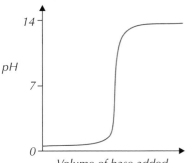

The pH starts around 1, as there's an excess of strong acid.
It finishes up around pH 13, when you have an excess of strong base.

Strong acid/weak base

The pH starts around 1, as there's an excess of strong acid.
It finishes up around pH 9, when you have an excess of weak base.

Tip: If you titrate a base with an acid instead, the shapes of the curves stay the same, but they're reversed. For example:
Strong base/strong acid

Strong base/weak acid

Weak base/strong acid

Weak base/weak acid

Weak acid/strong base

The pH starts around 5, as there's an excess of weak acid.
It finishes up around pH 13, when you have an excess of strong base.

Weak acid/weak base

The pH starts around 5, as there's an excess of weak acid.
It finishes up around pH 9, when you have an excess of weak base.

All the graphs apart from the weak acid/weak base graph have a bit that's almost vertical — the mid-point of this vertical section is the equivalence point or end point. At this point, a tiny amount of base causes a sudden, big change in pH — it's here that all the acid is just neutralised.

You don't get such a sharp change in a weak acid/weak base titration. If you used an indicator for this type of titration, its colour would change very gradually, and it would be very tricky to see the exact end point. So you're usually better using a pH meter to find the end point for this type of titration.

Indicators

When you use an indicator, you need it to change colour exactly at the end point of your titration. So you need to pick one that changes colour over a narrow pH range that lies entirely on the vertical part of the pH curve. So for the titration shown in Figure 3 (below) you'd want an indicator that changed colour somewhere between pH 8 and pH 11:

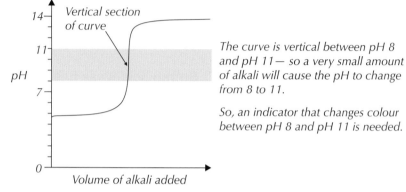

The curve is vertical between pH 8 and pH 11— so a very small amount of alkali will cause the pH to change from 8 to 11.

So, an indicator that changes colour between pH 8 and pH 11 is needed.

Figure 3: *Graph showing how to select an indicator.*

Figure 4: *The red to yellow colour change of methyl orange.*

Methyl orange and **phenolphthalein** are indicators that are often used for acid–base titrations. They each change colour over a different pH range:

Name of indicator	Colour at low pH	Approx. pH of colour change	Colour at high pH
Methyl orange	red	3.1 – 4.4	yellow
Phenolphthalein	colourless	8.3 – 10	pink

- For a strong acid/strong base titration, you can use either of these indicators — there's a rapid pH change over the range for both indicators.
- For a strong acid/weak base only methyl orange will do. The pH changes rapidly across the range for methyl orange, but not for phenolphthalein.
- For a weak acid/strong base, phenolphthalein is the stuff to use. The pH changes rapidly over phenolphthalein's range, but not over methyl orange's.
- For weak acid/weak base titrations there's no sharp pH change, so no indicator will work — you should just use a pH meter.

Figure 5: *The colourless to pink colour change of phenolphthalein*

You need to be able to use a pH curve to select an appropriate indicator:

Exam Tip
In your exam, you'll usually be given a table of indicators to choose from, like in this example — so don't worry, you don't have to learn all these indicators and their pH ranges.

┌─ **Example** ───────────────────────

The graph to the right shows the pH curve produced when a strong acid is added to a weak base. From the table below, select an indicator that you could use for this titration.

Volume of acid added

Indicator	pH range
Bromophenol blue	3.0 – 4.6
Litmus	5.0 – 8.0
Cresol purple	7.6 – 9.2

The graph shows that the vertical part of the pH curve is between about pH 2 and pH 6. So you need an indicator with a pH range between 2 and 6. The only indicator that changes colour within this range is bromophenol blue. So in this example, bromophenol blue is the right indicator to choose.

Practice Questions — Application

Q1 The graphs below show the pH curves for four different acid–base titrations. For each reaction state what type of acid and base (i.e. strong/weak) were used and select an appropriate indicator from the table below.

Indicator	pH range
Orange IV	1.4 – 2.6
Methyl orange	3.1 – 4.4
Litmus	5.0 – 8.0
Cresol purple	7.6 – 9.2
Phenolphthalein	8.3 – 10

a)

b)

c)

d)

Q2 Neutral red is an indicator which changes colour from red to yellow between pH 6.8 and pH 8.0. Sketch the pH curve for a titration reaction that this indicator could be used for.

Practice Questions — Fact Recall

Q1 Sketch the pH curve produced when:
   a) A strong acid neutralises a weak base.
   b) A strong base neutralises a strong acid.
   c) A weak acid neutralises a strong base.

Q2 a) What happens at the end point of a titration reaction?
   b) How can you see that the end point has been reached when you're carrying out a titration?
   c) How can you tell the end point has been reached using a pH curve?

Q3 How would you know if an indicator is suitable for a particular titration reaction?

Learning Objective:

- Be able to perform calculations for the titrations of acids with bases, based on experimental results.

Specification Reference 3.1.12.5

5. Titration Calculations

Now that you've learnt all about titrations it's time to find out what you can do with the results. There are a few calculations you'll need to be able to do — the next few pages tell you how.

Titration results

When you've done a titration you can use your results to calculate the concentration of your acid or base. There are a few things you can do to make sure your titration results are as accurate as possible:

- Measure the neutralisation volume as precisely as you possibly can. This will usually be to the nearest 0.05 cm^3.

- It's a good idea to repeat the titration at least three times and take a mean titre value. That'll help you to make sure your answer is reliable.

- Don't use any anomalous (unusual) results — as a rough guide, all your results should be within ± 0.1 cm^3 of each other.

If you use a pH meter rather than an indicator, you can draw a pH curve of the titration and use it to work out how much acid or base is needed for neutralisation. You do this by finding the equivalence point (the mid–point of the line of rapid pH change) and drawing a vertical line downwards until it meets the x-axis. The value at this point on the x-axis is the volume of acid or base needed — see Figure 1.

Figure 1: *Finding how much base is needed for neutralisation.*

Figure 2: *A pH meter being used to monitor the pH during a titration.*

Tip: You came across the formula:

moles = conc. × vol. / **1000**

in Year 1, but you need to know it for Year 2 as well. The dividing by 1000 bit is to get the volume from cm^3 to dm^3 — if your volume is already in dm^3 then it's just:

moles = conc. × vol.

Calculating concentrations

Monoprotic acids

Once you know the neutralisation volume you can use it to calculate the concentration of the acid or base. To do this:

Step 1: Write out a balanced equation for the titration reaction.

Step 2: Decide what you know already and what you need to know — usually you'll be given the two volumes and a concentration and you'll have to work out the other concentration.

Step 3: For one reagent you'll know both the concentration and the volume. Calculate the number of moles of this reagent using the equation:

$$\text{moles} = \frac{\text{concentration (mol dm}^{-3}) \times \text{volume (cm}^3)}{1000}$$

Step 4: Use the molar ratios in the balanced equation to find out how many moles of the other reagent reacted.

Step 5: Calculate the unknown concentration using the equation:

$$\text{concentration} = \frac{\text{moles} \times 1000}{\text{volume}}$$

in mol dm⁻³   *in cm³*

── Maths Skills ─────────────────

The graph on the right shows the results when 0.500 mol dm⁻³ HCl was titrated against 35.0 cm³ of NaOH. Calculate the concentration of the NaOH solution.

From the graph you can see that 25 cm³ of HCl was required to neutralise the NaOH. You can use this information to work out the concentration of the NaOH solution by following the steps on the previous page.

Exam Tip
You won't always have to read the volume of acid off a pH curve in the exam — you might just be told the neutralisation volume, in which case you'll have one less job to do.

1. The balanced equation for this titration reaction is:

$$HCl + NaOH \rightarrow NaCl + H_2O$$

2. You know the concentration of HCl (0.500 mol dm⁻³), the volume of HCl (25.0 cm³) and the volume of NaOH (35.0 cm³). You need to know the concentration of NaOH.

3. Calculate the moles of HCl:

$$\text{moles HCl} = \frac{\text{concentration} \times \text{volume}}{1000} = \frac{0.500 \times 25.0}{1000} = 0.0125 \text{ moles}$$

4. From the equation, you know 1 mole of HCl neutralises 1 mole of NaOH. So 0.0125 moles of HCl must neutralise 0.0125 moles of NaOH.

5. Calculate the concentration of NaOH:

$$\text{Conc. NaOH} = \frac{\text{moles} \times 1000}{\text{volume}} = \frac{0.0125 \times 1000}{35.0} = 0.357 \text{ mol dm}^{-3}$$

Tip: In these calculations the units of concentration should always be mol dm⁻³.

Diprotic acids

A diprotic acid is one that can release two protons when it's in solution. Ethanedioic acid (HOOC–COOH) is diprotic. When ethanedioic acid reacts with a base like sodium hydroxide, it's neutralised. But the reaction happens in two stages, because the two protons are removed from the acid separately. This means that when you titrate ethanedioic acid with a strong base you get a pH curve with two equivalence points:

Tip: pH curves for diprotic acids look a bit different to those for monoprotic acids. For more on pH curves, see page 107.

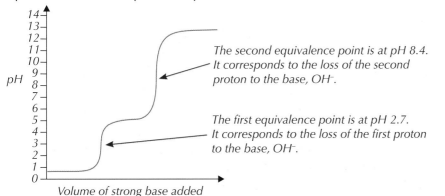

The second equivalence point is at pH 8.4. It corresponds to the loss of the second proton to the base, OH⁻.

The first equivalence point is at pH 2.7. It corresponds to the loss of the first proton to the base, OH⁻.

Tip: The curve won't always look exactly like this. The pH at the start, end and equivalence points will vary depending on the concentrations of the acid and the base used.

First equivalence point: $HOOC-COOH_{(aq)} + OH^-_{(aq)} \rightarrow HOOC-COO^-_{(aq)} + H_2O_{(l)}$

Second equivalence point: $HOOC-COO^-_{(aq)} + OH^-_{(aq)} \rightarrow {}^-OOC-COO^-_{(aq)} + H_2O_{(l)}$

You can calculate the concentration of a diprotic acid from titration data in the same way as you did for a monoprotic acid. Just remember that the acid is diprotic so you'll need twice as many moles of base as moles of acid.

┌─ **Example** ── Maths Skills ─────────────────

25.0 cm³ of ethanedioic acid, $C_2H_2O_4$, was completely neutralised by 20.0 cm³ of 0.100 mol dm⁻³ KOH solution. Calculate the concentration of the ethanedioic acid solution.

1. The balanced equation for this titration reaction is:

$$C_2H_2O_4 + 2KOH \rightarrow K_2C_2O_4 + 2H_2O$$

2. You know the volume of $C_2H_2O_4$ (25.0 cm³), the volume of KOH (20.0 cm³) and the concentration of KOH (0.100 mol dm⁻³). You need to know the concentration of $C_2H_2O_4$.

3. Calculate the moles of KOH:

$$\text{moles KOH} = \frac{\text{concentration} \times \text{volume}}{1000} = \frac{0.100 \times 20.0}{1000} = 0.002 \text{ moles}$$

4. You know from the equation that you need 2 moles of KOH to neutralise 1 mole of $C_2H_2O_4$. So 0.002 moles of KOH must neutralise $(0.002 \div 2) = 0.001$ moles of $C_2H_2O_4$.

5. Calculate the concentration of $C_2H_2O_4$:

$$\text{Conc. } C_2H_2O_4 = \frac{\text{moles} \times 1000}{\text{volume}} = \frac{0.001 \times 1000}{25} = 0.0400 \text{ mol dm}^{-3}$$

Exam Tip
You need to be able to do calculations for both monoprotic and diprotic acids so make sure you understand these two examples.

Tip: Because it's a diprotic acid, you need twice as many moles of base as moles of acid.

Practice Questions — Application

Q1 In a titration, the equivalence point was reached after 13.8 cm³ of a 1.50 mol dm⁻³ solution of HCl had been added to 20.0 cm³ of NaOH. Calculate the concentration of the NaOH solution.

Q2 Nitric acid (HNO_3) was added to 30.0 cm³ of a 0.250 mol dm⁻³ solution of NaOH in the presence of methyl orange. A colour change was observed after 17.8 cm³ of the acid had been added. Calculate the concentration of the nitric acid solution.

Q3 A 0.250 mol dm⁻³ KOH solution was titrated against 24.0 cm³ of HCl. The experiment was repeated three times and the amount of KOH required to neutralise the HCl each time is given in the table below.

	Titration 1	Titration 2	Titration 3
Titre volume (cm³ KOH)	22.40	22.50	22.40

a) Calculate the average titre volume for this titration.
b) Calculate the concentration of the HCl solution.

Q4 The graph below shows the pH curve produced when 0.850 mol dm^{-3}
    HCl was titrated against 30.0 cm^3 of an NaOH solution of unknown
    concentration.

Volume of HCl added (cm³)

Tip: When you're
writing the equations
for a titration remember
that it's a neutralisation
reaction so the products
will be a salt and water.

    Calculate the concentration of the NaOH solution.

Q5 32.0 cm^3 of a KOH solution is fully neutralised when 18.0 cm^3 of
    a 0.400 mol dm^{-3} solution of H_2SO_4 is added to it. Calculate the
    concentration of the KOH solution.

Q6 When a 1.20 mol dm^{-3} solution of KOH was titrated against
    20.0 cm^3 of carbonic acid (H_2CO_3), 26.2 cm^3 of KOH was
    required to fully neutralise the acid. Calculate the concentration
    of the carbonic acid solution.

Practice Questions — Fact Recall

Q1 Write out the equation that links the number of moles, the volume
    and the concentration of a solution.

Q2 Sketch the pH curve produced when a strong base is added to a
    strong diprotic acid in a titration.

Q3 Explain why the pH curve for the titration of a diprotic acid is
    different to a pH curve for the titration of a monoprotic acid.

Q4 How many moles of a diprotic acid does it take to neutralise 1 mole
    of NaOH?

Learning Objectives:

- Know that a buffer solution maintains an approximately constant pH, despite dilution or addition of small amounts of acid or base.
- Know that acidic buffer solutions contain a weak acid and the salt of that weak acid.
- Know that basic buffer solutions contain a weak base and the salt of that weak base.
- Be able to explain qualitatively the action of acidic and basic buffers.
- Know some applications of buffer solutions.

Specification Reference 3.1.12.6

Tip: The acid has to be a weak acid — you can't make an acidic buffer with a strong acid.

Tip: Acidic buffers work slightly differently to basic buffers, which are covered on the next page — but the principle of how buffers work is the same for both types.

Figure 1: *An acidic buffer solution.*

6. Buffer Action

Sometimes, it's useful to have a solution that doesn't change pH when small amounts of acid or alkali are added to it. That's where buffers come in handy.

What is a buffer?

A **buffer** is a solution that resists changes in pH when small amounts of acid or alkali are added. A buffer doesn't stop the pH from changing completely — it does make the changes very slight though. Buffers only work for small amounts of acid or base — put too much in and they won't be able to cope. You get acidic buffers and basic buffers.

Acidic buffers

Acidic buffers have a pH of less than 7 — they contain a mixture of a weak acid with one of its salts. They can resist a change in pH when either an acid or a base is added to the solution.

--- **Example** ---

A mixture of ethanoic acid and sodium ethanoate ($CH_3COO^-Na^+$) is an acidic buffer. The ethanoic acid is a weak acid, so it only slightly dissociates:

$$CH_3COOH_{(aq)} \rightleftharpoons H^+_{(aq)} + CH_3COO^-_{(aq)}$$

But the salt fully dissociates into its ions when it dissolves:

$$CH_3COONa_{(s)} \xrightarrow{water} CH_3COO^-_{(aq)} + Na^+_{(aq)}$$

So in the solution you've got heaps of undissociated ethanoic acid molecules ($CH_3COOH_{(aq)}$), and heaps of ethanoate ions ($CH_3COO^-_{(aq)}$) from the salt.

When you alter the concentration of H^+ or OH^- ions in the buffer solution the equilibrium position moves to counteract the change (this is down to Le Chatelier's principle). Here's how it all works:

Resisting an acid

The large number of CH_3COO^- ions make sure that the buffer can cope with the addition of acid. If you add a small amount of acid the H^+ concentration increases. Most of the extra H^+ ions combine with CH_3COO^- ions to form CH_3COOH. This shifts the equilibrium to the left, reducing the H^+ concentration to close to its original value. So the pH doesn't change much.

$$\text{Addition of } H^+ \text{ (acid)}$$
$$\xleftarrow{}$$
$$CH_3COOH_{(aq)} \rightleftharpoons H^+_{(aq)} + CH_3COO^-_{(aq)}$$

Resisting a base

If a small amount of base (e.g. NaOH) is added, the OH^- concentration increases. Most of the extra OH^- ions react with H^+ ions to form water — removing H^+ ions from the solution. This causes more CH_3COOH to dissociate to form H^+ ions — shifting the equilibrium to the right. There's no problem doing this as there's loads of spare CH_3COOH molecules. The H^+ concentration increases until it's close to its original value, so the pH doesn't change much.

$$\text{Addition of } OH^- \text{ (base)}$$
$$\xrightarrow{}$$
$$CH_3COOH_{(aq)} \rightleftharpoons H^+_{(aq)} + CH_3COO^-_{(aq)}$$

Basic buffers

Basic buffers have a pH greater than 7 — and they contain a mixture of a weak base with one of its salts. They can resist changes in pH when acid or base is added, just like acidic buffers can.

Tip: You can't make basic buffers with strong bases — they have to be weak bases.

Example

A solution of ammonia (NH_3, a weak base) and ammonium chloride (NH_4Cl, a salt of ammonia) acts as a basic buffer.

The salt fully dissociates in solution:

$$NH_4Cl_{(aq)} \xrightarrow{water} NH_4^+{}_{(aq)} + Cl^-{}_{(aq)}$$

Some of the NH_3 molecules will also react with water molecules:

$$NH_3{}_{(aq)} + H_2O_{(l)} \rightleftharpoons NH_4^+{}_{(aq)} + OH^-{}_{(aq)}$$

So the solution will contain loads of ammonium ions (NH_4^+), and lots of ammonia molecules too. The equilibrium position of this reaction can move to counteract changes in pH:

Figure 2: *This basic buffer will maintain a pH of 10.00 when small amounts of acid or alkali are added.*

Resisting an acid

If a small amount of acid is added, the H^+ concentration increases, making the solution more acidic. Some of the H^+ ions react with OH^- ions to make H_2O. When this happens the equilibrium position moves to the right to replace the OH^- ions that have been used up. This reaction will remove most of the extra H^+ ions that were added — so the pH won't change much.

Addition of H⁺ (acid)
→

$$NH_3{}_{(aq)} + H_2O_{(l)} \rightleftharpoons NH_4^+{}_{(aq)} + OH^-{}_{(aq)}$$

Exam Tip
You don't need to memorise these specific examples but you do need to be able to explain how both acidic and basic buffers work.

Resisting a base

If a small amount of base is added, the OH^- concentration increases, making the solution more alkaline. Most of the extra OH^- ions will react with the NH_4^+ ions, to form NH_3 and H_2O. So the equilibrium will shift to the left, removing OH^- ions from the solution, and stopping the pH from changing much.

Addition of OH⁻ (base)
←

$$NH_3{}_{(aq)} + H_2O_{(l)} \rightleftharpoons NH_4^+{}_{(aq)} + OH^-{}_{(aq)}$$

Figure 3: *A lovely blue buffer solution being prepared by a lovely blue-gloved scientist.*

Dilution

Acidic and basic buffers can also resist changes in pH when diluted by water. If a small amount of water is added to a buffer, the water slightly dissociates. So the extra H^+ and OH^- ions push the equilibrium the same amount in both directions, leaving it unchanged.

Acidic and basic buffers — summary

How buffers work can be a bit tricky to get your head round, so here's a nice summary diagram to help you out:

Tip: pH is determined by [H⁺], but because OH⁻ will combine with H⁺ and remove it from solution, [OH⁻] affects [H⁺] and so affects pH. A rise in [OH⁻] will increase the pH, a fall in [OH⁻] will decrease the pH. Unless there's a buffer present, that is.

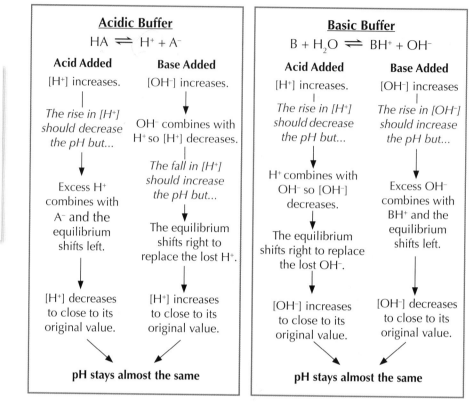

Acidic Buffer

$$HA \rightleftharpoons H^+ + A^-$$

Acid Added	Base Added
[H⁺] increases.	[OH⁻] increases.
The rise in [H⁺] should decrease the pH but...	OH⁻ combines with H⁺ so [H⁺] decreases.
	The fall in [H⁺] should increase the pH but...
Excess H⁺ combines with A⁻ and the equilibrium shifts left.	The equilibrium shifts right to replace the lost H⁺.
[H⁺] decreases to close to its original value.	[H⁺] increases to close to its original value.

pH stays almost the same

Basic Buffer

$$B + H_2O \rightleftharpoons BH^+ + OH^-$$

Acid Added	Base Added
[H⁺] increases.	[OH⁻] increases
The rise in [H⁺] should decrease the pH but...	*The rise in [OH⁻] should increase the pH but...*
H⁺ combines with OH⁻ so [OH⁻] decreases.	
The equilibrium shifts right to replace the lost OH⁻.	Excess OH⁻ combines with BH⁺ and the equilibrium shifts left.
[OH⁻] increases to close to its original value.	[OH⁻] decreases to close to its original value.

pH stays almost the same

Applications of buffers

Alkaline conditions make the surface of individual hairs rougher, so most shampoos have a pH of around 5.5, which keeps hair smooth and shiny. Buffers are added to shampoo to maintain this pH while you wash your hair. Biological washing powders contain buffers too. They keep the pH at the right level for the enzymes to work best. There are also lots of biological buffer systems in our bodies, making sure all our tissues are kept at the right pH. For example, it's vital that blood stays at a pH very near to 7.4, so it contains a buffer system.

Figure 4: *Shampoos contain buffers to stop the pH of your hair from changing too much.*

Practice Questions — Fact Recall

Q1 What is a buffer?

Q2 What do acidic buffers contain?

Q3 Explain how an acidic buffer resists changes in pH when:
  a) a small amount of acid is added.
  b) a small amount of base is added.

Q4 What do basic buffers contain?

Q5 Explain how a basic buffer resists changes in pH when:
  a) a small amount of acid is added.
  b) a small amount of base is added.

Q6 Give two real-life applications of buffers.

7. Calculating the pH of Buffers

Learning Objective:

- Be able to calculate the pH of acidic buffer solutions.

Specification Reference 3.1.12.6

You need to be able to calculate the pH of buffer solutions. These calculations look scary, but don't worry — they're not nearly as bad as they look.

Calculations using known concentrations

If you know the K_a of the weak acid and the concentrations of the weak acid and its salt, calculating the pH of an acidic buffer isn't too tricky. Here's how to go about it:

Step 1: Write out the expression for the K_a of the weak acid.

Step 2: Rearrange the equation to give an expression for $[H^+]$.

Step 3: Substitute the value for K_a and the concentrations of the acid and salt into the equation.

Step 4: Solve the equation to find a value for $[H^+]$.

Step 5: Substitute your value for $[H^+]$ into the pH equation ($pH = -\log[H^+]$) and solve it to calculate the pH.

Tip: Writing expressions for K_a was covered on page 102. Have a look back if you need a recap.

Tip: See page 99 for a reminder on how to calculate pH.

Example ── Maths Skills

A buffer solution contains 0.400 mol dm⁻³ methanoic acid, HCOOH, and 0.600 mol dm⁻³ sodium methanoate, HCOO⁻Na⁺. For methanoic acid, $K_a = 1.6 \times 10^{-4}$ mol dm⁻³. What is the pH of this buffer?

1. Write the expression for K_a of the weak acid:

$$\text{HCOOH}_{(aq)} \rightleftharpoons \text{H}^+_{(aq)} + \text{HCOO}^-_{(aq)} \quad \text{so} \quad K_a = \frac{[\text{H}^+][\text{HCOO}^-]}{[\text{HCOOH}]}$$

2. Rearrange the equation to get $[H^+]$:

$$[\text{H}^+] = \frac{K_a \times [\text{HCOOH}]}{[\text{HCOO}^-]}$$

3. Substitute in the value of K_a and the concentrations given in the question. You have to make a few assumptions here:

   - HCOO⁻Na⁺ is fully dissociated, so assume that the equilibrium concentration of HCOO⁻ is the same as the initial concentration of HCOO⁻Na⁺.
   - HCOOH is only slightly dissociated, so assume that its equilibrium concentration is the same as its initial concentration.

$$[\text{H}^+] = \frac{K_a \times [\text{HCOOH}]}{[\text{HCOO}^-]} = \frac{(1.6 \times 10^{-4}) \times 0.400}{0.600}$$

Tip: Remember — the concentrations in the expression for K_a all have to be equilibrium concentrations.

4. Solve to find $[H^+]$:

$$[\text{H}^+] = \frac{(1.6 \times 10^{-4}) \times 0.400}{0.600} = 1.07 \times 10^{-4} \text{ mol dm}^{-3}$$

5. Use your value of $[H^+]$ to calculate the pH:

$$pH = -\log[\text{H}^+]$$
$$= -\log(1.07 \times 10^{-4})$$
$$= \mathbf{3.97}$$

Another way to make acidic buffers

Mixing a weak acid with its salt is not the only way to make an acidic buffer. You could also take a weak acid and add a small amount of alkali, so that some of the acid is neutralised to make a salt, but some is left un-neutralised. The reaction mixture would then contain a weak acid and its salt, so would act as an acidic buffer. You can calculate the pH of an acidic buffer that has been made this way by following the steps below:

Step 1: Write out the equation for the neutralisation reaction — remember acid + base → salt + water.

Step 2: Calculate the number of moles of acid and base at the start of the reaction using the volumes and concentrations given in the question.

Step 3: Use the molar ratios in the equation to work out the moles of acid and salt left at the end of the reaction.

Step 4: Calculate the concentration of the acid and salt in the buffer solution by dividing by the volume of the solution — this is the volume of the acid and the base added together.

Step 5: Then you're ready to calculate the pH.

Tip: The <u>molar ratios</u> tell you how many moles of acid will react with a certain number of moles of base, and how many moles of salt are produced. These numbers will <u>always</u> be in the same ratio for a given reaction.

Tip: It's really important that you know equations like:

$$moles = \frac{conc. \times vol.}{1000}$$

You won't be able to do the harder calculations if you haven't got your head around the basics. Check out pages 277-279 for a summary of the equations that you need to know.

Example — Maths Skills

A buffer is formed by mixing 15 cm³ of 0.1 mol dm⁻³ sodium hydroxide (NaOH) and 30 cm³ of 0.6 mol dm⁻³ propanoic acid (CH_3CH_2COOH). Calculate the pH of this buffer solution ($K_a = 1.35 \times 10^{-5}$ mol dm⁻³).

1. Write out the equation for the reaction:

    $$CH_3CH_2COOH + NaOH \rightarrow CH_3CH_2COO^-Na^+ + H_2O$$

2. Calculate the number of moles of acid and base:

    $$Moles\ CH_3CH_2COOH = \frac{Conc. \times Vol.}{1000} = \frac{0.6 \times 30}{1000} = 0.018\ moles$$

    $$Moles\ NaOH = \frac{Conc. \times Vol.}{1000} = \frac{0.1 \times 15}{1000} = 0.0015\ moles$$

3. The acid is in excess, so all the base reacts. There's 0.0015 moles of NaOH at the start of the reaction. If it all reacts there will be 0.0015 moles of salt at the end of the reaction.

    The equation shows us that 1 mole of base will react with 1 mole of acid to give 1 mole of salt. So if there are 0.0015 moles of salt, 0.0015 moles of acid must have been used up.
    This leaves 0.018 – 0.0015 = 0.0165 moles of acid.

    So, the buffer solution contains 0.0015 moles of $CH_3CH_2COO^-Na^+$ and 0.0165 moles of CH_3CH_2COOH.

4. Calculate the concentration of acid and salt in the buffer solution:

    The total volume of the solution is 15 + 30 = 45 cm³

    $$Conc.\ CH_3CH_2COOH = \frac{moles \times 1000}{volume} = \frac{0.0165 \times 1000}{45}$$

    $$= 0.366...\ mol\ dm^{-3}$$

$$\text{Conc. } CH_3CH_2COO^-Na^+ = \frac{moles \times 1000}{volume} = \frac{0.0015 \times 1000}{45}$$

$$= 0.0333... \text{ mol dm}^{-3}$$

5. Work out the pH as before:

$$CH_3CH_2COOH \rightleftharpoons H^+ + CH_3CH_2COO^- \quad \text{so} \quad K_a = \frac{[H^+][CH_3CH_2COO^-]}{[CH_3CH_2COOH]}$$

$$[H^+] = \frac{K_a \times [CH_3CH_2COOH]}{[CH_3CH_2COO^-]} = \frac{(1.35 \times 10^{-5}) \times 0.366...}{0.0333...}$$

$$= 1.485 \times 10^{-4} \text{ mol dm}^{-3}$$

$$pH = -\log[H^+] = -\log(1.485 \times 10^{-4}) = 3.828$$

Tip: This step was covered in more detail on page 102 — have a look back if you need a quick reminder of what's going on.

Practice Questions — Application

Q1 An acidic buffer solution contains 0.200 mol dm⁻³ propanoic acid (CH_3CH_2COOH) and 0.350 mol dm⁻³ potassium propanoate. For propanoic acid, $K_a = 1.35 \times 10^{-5}$ mol dm⁻³.

a) Write an expression for the K_a of propanoic acid.

b) Calculate the concentration of H⁺ ions in this buffer solution.

c) Calculate the pH of this buffer solution.

Q2 A buffer solution contains 0.150 mol dm⁻³ ethanoic acid and 0.250 mol dm⁻³ potassium ethanoate. For ethanoic acid $K_a = 1.74 \times 10^{-5}$ mol dm⁻³. Calculate the pH of this buffer.

Q3 A buffer is made by mixing 30.0 cm³ of 0.500 mol dm⁻³ propanoic acid (CH_3CH_2COOH) with 20.0 cm³ of 0.250 mol dm⁻³ potassium hydroxide (KOH). For propanoic acid, $K_a = 1.35 \times 10^{-5}$ mol dm⁻³.

a) Write an equation to show the reaction of propanoic acid with potassium hydroxide.

b) Calculate the number of moles of propanoic acid and potassium hydroxide at the beginning of the reaction.

c) Calculate the concentration of propanoic acid and potassium propanoate in the buffer solution.

d) Calculate the concentration of H⁺ ions in this buffer solution.

e) Calculate the pH of the buffer solution.

Q4 A buffer is formed by mixing together 25.0 cm³ of 0.200 mol dm⁻³ methanoic acid (HCOOH) and 15.0 cm³ of 0.100 mol dm⁻³ sodium hydroxide (NaOH). For methanoic acid, $K_a = 1.6 \times 10^{-4}$ mol dm⁻³. Calculate the pH of this buffer.

Section Summary

Make sure you know...

- That a Brønsted–Lowry acid is a proton donor and a Brønsted–Lowry base is a proton acceptor.
- That strong acids/bases dissociate fully in water while weak acids/bases only partially dissociate.
- That acid–base reactions involve the transfer of protons — $HA + B \rightleftharpoons BH^+ + A^-$.
- That water is weakly dissociated and the ionic product of water is $K_w = [H^+][OH^-]$ which is equivalent to $[H^+]^2$ for pure water.
- That the value of K_w varies with temperature.
- That $pH = -\log[H^+]$ where $[H^+]$ is the concentration of H^+ ions in mol dm^{-3}.
- How to convert pH into $[H^+]$ and vice versa.
- How to calculate the pH of a strong acid from its concentration.
- How to calculate the pH of a strong base from its concentration, using K_w.
- That K_a is the dissociation constant for a weak acid, and how to write expressions for K_a.
- How to calculate the pH of a weak acid from its concentration and K_a.
- How to calculate the concentration of a weak acid from its pH and K_a.
- How to calculate K_a for a weak acid from its pH and concentration.
- That $pK_a = -\log(K_a)$ and how to convert K_a to pK_a and vice versa.
- What the pH curves for all the different combinations of weak and strong acids and bases look like.
- How to use pH curves to select an appropriate pH indicator to use in a titration.
- How to calculate the concentration of monoprotic and diprotic acids using the results of a titration.
- What a buffer is and how both acidic and basic buffers can resist changes in pH and dilution.
- That buffer solutions contain a weak acid/base and its salt.
- That buffers are used in shampoos, biological washing powders and biological systems.
- How to calculate the pH of an acidic buffer.

Exam-style Questions

1   A scientist has a 0.20 mol dm^{-3} solution of aqueous potassium hydroxide, KOH.
    She knows that K_w has a value of 1.00×10^{-14} mol^2 dm^{-6} at 298 K.
    What is the pH of this solution, to 2 decimal places?

    A   13.30

    B   12.50

    C   0.69

    D   28.78

2   Ammonia, a weak base, is titrated with nitric acid, a strong acid.
    The change in pH is recorded in a graph. Which of the following
    graphs would you expect to represent the titration?

3   Thymol blue is an indicator that has a colour change at two different pH ranges.

Indicator	pH range	colour change
Thymol blue	1.2 – 2.8	red to yellow
	8.0 – 9.6	yellow to red

When titrating certain acids, it is useful to have an indicator with two colour changes. The titration of which of the following acids would benefit from using thymol blue, rather than an indicator with just one colour change?

A   Nitric acid

B   Methanoic acid

C   Ethanedioic acid

D   Hydrochloric acid

4   The concentrations of strong acids and strong bases can be found by carrying out titrations. Titrations are usually done at room temperature (25 °C). The value of K_w at 25 °C is 1.0×10^{-14} mol^2 dm^{-6}.

4.1   Give the expression for K_w.

(1 mark)

4.2   Give the expression for pH.

(1 mark)

4.3   Calculate the pH of a 0.15 mol dm^{-3} solution of NaOH at 25 °C.

(3 marks)

In a titration reaction at 25 °C, 25 cm^3 of this 0.15 mol dm^{-3} solution of NaOH was neutralised by 18.5 cm^3 of a HCl solution of unknown concentration.

4.4   Which of the graphs below (A, B and C) shows the pH curve for this reaction?

(1 mark)

4.5   Calculate the concentration of the unknown HCl solution.

(3 marks)

4.6   Calculate the pH of the HCl solution.

(2 marks)

The pH curve for another titration is shown below.

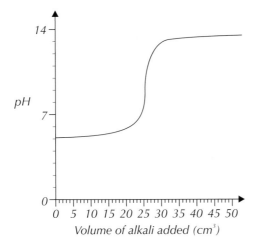

Indicator	pH range
Orange IV	1.4 – 2.6
Bromophenol blue	3.0 – 4.6
Litmus	5.0 – 8.0
Phenolphthalein	8.3 – 10

4.7 Suggest an acid and a base that could have been used in this titration.

(2 marks)

4.8 From the table above, suggest an indicator that would be suitable for this titration.

(1 mark)

5 Methanoic acid (HCOOH) is a weak acid. A 0.24 mol dm^{-3} solution of HCOOH has a pH of 2.2 at 25 °C.

5.1 Write out the equation for the dissociation of HCOOH.

(1 mark)

5.2 Write out an expression for K_a for this acid.

(1 mark)

5.3 Calculate the pK_a of methanoic acid at 25 °C.

(3 marks)

A buffer solution can be formed by mixing 30 cm^3 of this 0.24 mol dm^{-3} methanoic acid with 20 cm^3 of 0.15 mol dm^{-3} sodium hydroxide (NaOH).

5.4 Calculate the pH of this buffer.

(6 marks)

5.5 Explain how this buffer resists changes in pH when an acid is added.

(3 marks)

5.6 Suggest three substances where you could find a pH buffer.

(3 marks)

1. Period 3 Elements

Learning Objectives:

- Know the reactions of Na and Mg with water.
- Be able to describe the trends in the reactions of the elements Na, Mg, Al, Si, P and S with oxygen, limited to the formation of Na_2O, MgO, Al_2O_3, SiO_2, P_4O_{10}, SO_2 and SO_3.

Specification Reference 3.2.4

Periodicity means the trends that occur across a period of the periodic table. You did a little bit about periodicity in Year 1, but in Year 2 you need to know a bit more about the trends which occur across Period 3.

Period 3

Period 3 is the third row in the periodic table. The elements of Period 3 are sodium (Na), magnesium (Mg), aluminium (Al), silicon (Si), phosphorus (P), sulfur (S), chlorine (Cl) and argon (Ar) — see Figure 1.

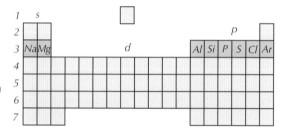

Figure 1: Period 3 of the periodic table.

Reactions with water

You need to know how two of the Period 3 elements — sodium and magnesium — react with water. Sodium and magnesium are the first two elements in Period 3. Sodium is in Group 1, and magnesium is in Group 2. When they react, sodium loses one electron to form an Na^+ ion, while magnesium loses two electrons to form Mg^{2+}. Sodium is more reactive than magnesium because it takes less energy to lose one electron than it does to lose two. So more energy (usually heat) is needed for magnesium to react. This is shown in their reactions with water.

Sodium

Sodium reacts vigorously with cold water, forming a molten ball on the surface, fizzing and producing H_2 gas:

$$2Na_{(s)} + 2H_2O_{(l)} \rightarrow 2NaOH_{(aq)} + H_{2(g)}$$

The reaction produces sodium hydroxide, so forms a strongly alkaline solution (pH 12 – 14).

Figure 2: The reaction of sodium with water.

Magnesium

Magnesium reacts very slowly with cold water. You can't see any reaction, but it forms a weakly alkaline solution (pH 9 – 10), which shows that a reaction has occurred:

$$Mg_{(s)} + 2H_2O_{(l)} \rightarrow Mg(OH)_{2(aq)} + H_{2(g)}$$

The solution is only weakly alkaline because magnesium hydroxide is not very soluble in water, so relatively few hydroxide ions are produced. Magnesium reacts much faster with steam (i.e. when there is more energy), to form magnesium oxide.

$$Mg_{(s)} + H_2O_{(g)} \rightarrow MgO_{(s)} + H_{2(g)}$$

Tip: Don't worry about the reactions of the other Period 3 elements with water. You only need to know about sodium and magnesium.

Reactions with oxygen

Period 3 elements form oxides when they react with oxygen. They're usually oxidised to their highest oxidation states — the same as their group numbers. So, sodium, which is in Group 1, has an oxidation state of +1 in sodium oxide. Magnesium (Group 2) has an oxidation state of +2 in magnesium oxide. Sulfur is the exception to this — it forms SO_2, in which it's only got a +4 oxidation state (a high temperature and a catalyst are needed to make SO_3, where sulfur has an oxidation state of +6).

The equations are all really similar — element + oxygen → oxide:

$$2Na_{(s)} + \tfrac{1}{2}O_{2(g)} \rightarrow Na_2O_{(s)} \qquad \text{sodium oxide}$$
$$Mg_{(s)} + \tfrac{1}{2}O_{2(g)} \rightarrow MgO_{(s)} \qquad \text{magnesium oxide}$$
$$2Al_{(s)} + 1\tfrac{1}{2}O_{2(g)} \rightarrow Al_2O_{3(s)} \qquad \text{aluminium oxide}$$
$$Si_{(s)} + O_{2(g)} \rightarrow SiO_{2(s)} \qquad \text{silicon dioxide}$$
$$P_{4(s)} + 5O_{2(g)} \rightarrow P_4O_{10(s)} \qquad \text{phosphorus(V) oxide}$$
$$S_{(s)} + O_{2(g)} \rightarrow SO_{2(g)} \qquad \text{sulfur dioxide}$$

The more reactive metals (Na, Mg) and the non-metals (P, S) react readily in air, while Al and Si react slowly — see the table below:

Element	Oxide	Reaction in air	Flame
Na	Na_2O	Vigorous	Yellow
Mg	MgO	Vigorous	Brilliant white
Al	Al_2O_3	Slow	N/A
Si	SiO_2	Slow	N/A
P	P_4O_{10}	Spontaneously combusts	Brilliant white
S	SO_2	Burns steadily	Blue

You can use the colours of the flames produced when the Period 3 elements react with air to identify them (e.g. if you burn a Period 3 element and it produces a blue flame, you know it's sulfur). This is known as a flame test.

Practice Question — Application

Q1 The table shows the reactions of three Period 3 elements with oxygen:

Element	Reaction in air	Flame
A	Vigorous	Yellow
B	Vigorous	Brilliant white
C	Burns steadily	Blue

   a) Identify the three elements A, B and C.

   b) Write an equation for each of these reactions.

Practice Questions — Fact Recall

Q1 a) Write an equation to show the reaction of water with:

     (i) sodium   (ii) magnesium

   b) Which of these elements reacts more vigorously with water? Why?

Q2 Write an equation to show the reaction of:

   a) aluminium with oxygen.   b) phosphorus with oxygen.

Tip: Have a peek back at your Year 1 notes for more on oxidation states.

Tip: SO_2 reacts with excess oxygen and a vanadium catalyst to form SO_3 (see p.155):
$$SO_{2\,(g)} + \tfrac{1}{2}O_{2(g)} \underset{}{\overset{V_2O_5 \text{(cat.)}}{\rightleftharpoons}} SO_{3(g)}$$

Tip: All of these oxides are white solids except for sulfur dioxide, which is a colourless gas.

Figure 3: The yellow flame produced when sodium burns.

Figure 4: The blue flame produced when sulfur burns.

- Be able to explain the trend in the melting point of the highest oxides of the elements Na-S in terms of their structure and bonding.

- Be able to describe the reactions of the oxides of the elements Na–S with water, limited to Na_2O, MgO, Al_2O_3, SiO_2, P_4O_{10}, SO_2 and SO_3, and know the pH of the solutions formed.

- Be able to explain the trends in the reactions of the oxides with water in terms of the type of bonding present in each oxide.

- Know the structures of the acids and anions formed when P_4O_{10}, SO_2 and SO_3 react with water.

- Be able to write equations for the reactions that occur between the oxides of the elements Na-S and given acids and bases.

Specification Reference 3.2.4

2. Period 3 Oxides

Knowing the trends in the Period 3 elements isn't enough for A Level. You also need to know about the trends in the properties of the Period 3 oxides.

Melting points

The differences in the melting points of the Period 3 oxides are all down to differences in their structure and bonding. The trend in melting points across Period 3 is shown in Figure 1.

Figure 1: The trend in melting points of the Period 3 oxides as you move across Period 3.

Na_2O, MgO and Al_2O_3 — the metal oxides — all have high melting points because they form **giant ionic lattices**. The strong forces of attraction between each ion mean it takes a lot of heat energy to break the bonds and melt them. MgO has a higher melting point than Na_2O because magnesium forms 2+ ions, which attract O^{2-} ions more strongly than the 1+ sodium ions in Na_2O. Al_2O_3 has a lower melting point than you might expect because the 3+ ions distort the oxygen's electron cloud making the bonds partially covalent.

SiO_2 has a higher melting point than the other non-metal oxides because it has a giant **macromolecular** structure. Strong covalent bonds hold the structure together so lots of energy is needed to break the bonds and the melting temperature is high.

P_4O_{10} and SO_3 are covalent molecules. They have relatively low melting points because they form simple molecular structures. The molecules are attracted to each other by weak intermolecular forces (dipole-dipole and van der Waals), which take little energy to overcome.

Exam Tip

If you're asked to explain the trend in melting points of the Period 3 oxides, make sure you mention their structure <u>and</u> the type of bonding.

Reactions with water

The ionic oxides of the metals Na and Mg both contain oxide ions (O^{2-}). When they dissolve in water, the O^{2-} ions accept protons from the water molecules to form hydroxide ions. The solutions are both alkaline, but NaOH is more soluble in water, so it forms a more alkaline solution than $Mg(OH)_2$:

$$Na_2O_{(s)} + H_2O_{(l)} \rightarrow 2NaOH_{(aq)} \qquad \text{pH 12 - 14}$$
$$MgO_{(s)} + H_2O_{(l)} \rightarrow Mg(OH)_{2(aq)} \qquad \text{pH 9 - 10}$$

The simple covalent oxides of the non-metals phosphorus and sulfur form acidic solutions. All of the acids are strong and so the pH of their solutions is about 0-1 (for solutions with a concentration of at least 1 mol dm⁻³). They will dissociate in solution to form a conjugate base.

The reactions of some of the Period 3 oxides with water are shown in Figure 3.

Reaction of non-metal Period 3 oxide with water	Acid formed	Dissociation of Period 3 acid in water
$P_4O_{10(s)} + 6H_2O_{(l)} \rightarrow 4H_3PO_{4(aq)}$	phosphoric(V) acid	$H_3PO_{4(aq)} \rightarrow 3H^+_{(aq)} + PO_4^{3-}_{(aq)}$
$SO_{2(g)} + H_2O_{(l)} \rightarrow H_2SO_{3(aq)}$	sulfurous acid (or sulfuric(IV) acid)	$H_2SO_{3(aq)} \rightarrow 2H^+_{(aq)} + SO_3^{2-}_{(aq)}$
$SO_{3(g)} + H_2O_{(l)} \rightarrow H_2SO_{4(aq)}$	sulfuric(VI) acid	$H_2SO_{4(aq)} \rightarrow 2H^+_{(aq)} + SO_4^{2-}_{(aq)}$

Figure 3: The acids and their conjugate bases that form when some of the Period 3 oxides react with water.

Figure 2: NaOH and H_2SO_4 can both be made by reacting Period 3 oxides with water.

The giant covalent structure of silicon dioxide means that it is insoluble in water. However, it will react with bases to form salts so it's classed as acidic.

Aluminium oxide, which is partially ionic and partially covalently bonded, is also insoluble in water. But, it will react with acids and bases to form salts — i.e. it can act as an acid or a base, so it is classed as **amphoteric**.

Tip: If you're struggling to remember this, just think — SiO_2 is the main component of sand and sand definitely doesn't dissolve in water.

Tip: Amphoteric means it has the properties of an acid and a base.

Reactions with acids and bases

The equation for neutralising an acid with a base is a classic:

$$\text{Acid} + \text{Base} \rightarrow \text{Salt} + \text{Water}$$

And it's no different for reactions of the Period 3 oxides. You may be asked to write equations for these reactions. Here are some examples:

Sodium and magnesium oxides are basic so will neutralise acids:

Examples
$$Na_2O_{(s)} + 2HCl_{(aq)} \rightarrow 2NaCl_{(aq)} + H_2O_{(l)}$$
$$MgO_{(s)} + H_2SO_{4(aq)} \rightarrow MgSO_{4(aq)} + H_2O_{(l)}$$

Silicon, phosphorus and sulfur oxides are acidic so will neutralise bases:

Examples
$$SiO_{2(s)} + 2NaOH_{(aq)} \rightarrow Na_2SiO_{3(aq)} + H_2O_{(l)}$$
$$P_4O_{10(s)} + 12NaOH_{(aq)} \rightarrow 4Na_3PO_{4(aq)} + 6H_2O_{(l)}$$
$$SO_{2(g)} + 2NaOH_{(aq)} \rightarrow Na_2SO_{3(aq)} + H_2O_{(l)}$$
$$SO_{3(g)} + 2NaOH_{(aq)} \rightarrow Na_2SO_{4(aq)} + H_2O_{(l)}$$

Exam Tip
In your exam you could be asked to write an equation for any Period 3 oxide with any simple acid or base, so make sure you understand these reactions — just learning the examples won't be enough.

Aluminium oxides are amphoteric so can neutralise acids or bases:

Examples
$$Al_2O_{3(s)} + 3H_2SO_{4(aq)} \rightarrow Al_2(SO_4)_{3(aq)} + 3H_2O_{(l)}$$
$$Al_2O_{3(s)} + 2NaOH_{(aq)} + 3H_2O_{(l)} \rightarrow 2NaAl(OH)_{4(aq)}$$

Practice Question — Application

Q1 The properties of three Period 3 oxides are shown in the table below:

Oxide	Structure	Melting point (°C)	Acidic/basic
A	Giant ionic lattice	2852	Basic
B	Giant ionic lattice	2045	Amphoteric
C	Macromolecular	1710	Acidic

    a) Suggest the identities of the three oxides A, B and C.

    b) Explain why A has a higher melting point than B.

Practice Questions — Fact Recall

Q1 a) Describe the structure and bonding of:

       (i) MgO (ii) Al_2O_3 (iii) SiO_2 (iv) P_4O_{10}

    b) Write equations for the reactions of oxides (i) and (iv) with water.

    c) State whether the oxides (i) – (iv) are acidic, basic or amphoteric.

Q2 a) Write an equation to show the neutralisation of HCl by MgO.

    b) Write an equation to show the neutralisation of NaOH by SO_2.

Section Summary

Make sure you know...

- That sodium is more reactive than magnesium because it takes less energy for sodium to lose one electron than it does for magnesium to lose two.
- How sodium and magnesium react with water (including equations and pH of the resulting solutions).
- How each of the elements in Period 3 reacts with oxygen to produce an oxide.
- The trend in melting points of the highest oxides of the Period 3 elements and that the differences in the melting points are due to differences in their structure and bonding.
- That the ionic Period 3 oxides (Na_2O/MgO) react with water to form basic hydroxides.
- That the simple covalent oxides (P_4O_{10}/SO_2/SO_3) react with water to form strong acids.
- The structures of the acids and anions formed when P_4O_{10}, SO_2 and SO_3 react with water.
- That SiO_2 is macromolecular and so is insoluble in water, but that it will react with bases — so is classified as acidic.
- That Al_2O_3 has ionic and covalent character so is insoluble in water, but that it will react with acids and bases — so is classified as amphoteric.
- How to write equations for the reactions between Period 3 oxides and simple acids and bases.

Exam-style Questions

1   Sodium and magnesium are both elements in Period 3 of the periodic table.

        Sodium reacts vigorously with water but the reaction of magnesium with water is very slow.

1.1   Write an equation to show the reaction of magnesium with water.

(1 mark)

1.2   Explain why magnesium reacts less vigorously with water than sodium.

(2 marks)

        Sodium and magnesium both react vigorously with oxygen to produce oxides. These oxides are structurally similar but they have very different melting temperatures.

1.3   Write an equation to show the reaction of sodium with oxygen.

(1 mark)

1.4   What colour is the flame that is produced when sodium is burnt in air?

(1 mark)

1.5   Describe the structure of sodium oxide and magnesium oxide.

(2 marks)

1.6   State which oxide has the higher melting point and explain why their melting temperatures are different.

(2 marks)

        Non-metal Period 3 elements such as silicon, phosphorus and sulfur also react with oxygen to produce oxides.

1.7   Explain why sulfur dioxide has a relatively low melting point.

(2 marks)

1.8   Explain why the melting point of silicon dioxide is unusually high.

(2 marks)

2   The Period 3 oxides react differently with water.

2.1   Write equations showing the reactions of magnesium oxide and sulfur dioxide with water. Give the approximate pHs of the solutions formed when the concentration of the product of each reaction is greater than 1 mol dm^3.

(4 marks)

2.2   Name one Period 3 oxide that is insoluble in water.

(1 mark)

2.3   State which Period 3 oxide is amphoteric.

(1 mark)

2.4   Write two equations showing the reaction of this amphoteric oxide with an acid and a base.

(2 marks)

1. Transition Metals — The Basics

Some of the most precious materials in the world are transition metals. They're also responsible for some pretty interesting and important chemistry.

The d block

The **d block** is the block of elements in the middle of the periodic table. Most of the elements in the d block are **transition metals** (or transition elements). You only need to know about the transition elements in the first row of the d block (Period 4). These are the elements from titanium to copper — see Figure 1.

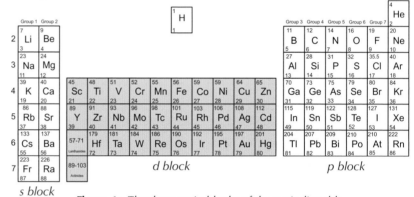

Figure 1: The three main blocks of the periodic table. The transition elements are in the d block.

Figure 2: A variety of transition metals.

What is a transition metal?

Here's the definition of a transition metal:

> A transition metal is a metal that can form one or more stable ions with an incomplete d sub-level.

A **d sub-level** can contain up to 10 electrons. So transition metals must form at least one ion that has between 1 and 9 electrons in the d sub-level. All the Period 4 d block elements are transition metals apart from scandium and zinc (p. 131).

Electron configurations

The electron configurations of elements can be figured out by following a few simple rules:

- Electrons fill up the lowest energy **sub-levels** first.
- Electrons fill **orbitals** singly before they start sharing.

The transition metals generally follow the same rules — see Figure 3. The 4s sub-level usually fills up first because it has lower energy than the 3d sub-level. Once the 4s sub-level is full, the 3d sub-level starts to fill up. The 3d orbitals are occupied singly at first. They only double up when they have to. But, there are a couple of exceptions...

- Chromium prefers to have one electron in each orbital of the 3d sub-level and just one in the 4s sub-level — this gives it more stability.
- Copper prefers to have a full 3d sub-level and just one electron in the 4s sub-level — it's more stable that way.

		3d					4s		
Ti	[Ar]	↑	↑				↑↓	[Ar] $3d^2 4s^2$
V	[Ar]	↑	↑	↑			↑↓	[Ar] $3d^3 4s^2$
Cr	[Ar]	↑	↑	↑	↑	↑	↑	[Ar] $3d^5 4s^1$
Mn	[Ar]	↑	↑	↑	↑	↑	↑↓	[Ar] $3d^5 4s^2$
Fe	[Ar]	↑↓	↑	↑	↑	↑	↑↓	[Ar] $3d^6 4s^2$
Co	[Ar]	↑↓	↑↓	↑	↑	↑	↑↓	[Ar] $3d^7 4s^2$
Ni	[Ar]	↑↓	↑↓	↑↓	↑	↑	↑↓	[Ar] $3d^8 4s^2$
Cu	[Ar]	↑↓	↑↓	↑↓	↑↓	↑↓	↑	[Ar] $3d^{10} 4s^1$

Figure 3: The electron configurations of the Period 4 d block transition metals.

Transition metal ions

Transition metal atoms form positive ions. When this happens, the 4s electrons are removed first, then the 3d electrons.

Example

Iron forms Fe^{2+} ions and Fe^{3+} ions.

When it forms 2+ ions, it loses both its 4s electrons:

$$Fe = [Ar]3d^6 4s^2 \rightarrow Fe^{2+} = [Ar]3d^6$$

Only once the 4s electrons are removed can a 3d electron be removed.

E.g. $Fe^{2+} = [Ar]3d^6 \rightarrow Fe^{3+} = [Ar]3d^5$

You might be asked to write the electron configuration of a transition metal ion in the exam. To do this, just follow these steps:

- Write down the electron configuration of the atom.
- Work out how many electrons have been removed to make the ion by looking at the charge on the ion.
- Remove that number of electrons from the electron configuration, taking them out of the 4s orbital first and then the 3d orbitals.

Example

Write out the electron configuration of Mn^{2+} ions.

- The electron configuration of Mn atoms is $[Ar]3d^5 4s^2$.
- Two electrons are removed to convert Mn atoms into Mn^{2+} ions.
- Removing the electrons starting from the 4s orbital gives $[Ar]3d^5 4s^0$.
- So the electron configuration of Mn^{2+} ions is $[Ar]3d^5$.

Scandium and zinc

Sc and Zn aren't transition metals as their stable ions don't have incomplete d sub-levels. Scandium only forms one ion, Sc^{3+}, which has an empty d sub-level. Scandium has the electron configuration $[Ar]3d^1 4s^2$, so when it loses three electrons to form Sc^{3+}, it ends up with the electron configuration [Ar]. Zinc only forms one stable ion, Zn^{2+}, which has a full d sub-level. Zinc has the electron configuration $[Ar]3d^{10} 4s^2$. When it forms Zn^{2+} it loses two electrons, both from the 4s sub-level. This means it keeps its full 3d sub-level.

Tip: Sub-levels are made of orbitals — for example, s sub-levels contain one orbital, p sub-levels contain three orbitals and d sub-levels contain five orbitals. Each orbital can hold two electrons.

Tip: The electron configurations of all the transition metals start in the same way — $1s^2 2s^2 2p^6 3s^2 3p^6$. This is the same as the electron configuration of the element argon, so [Ar] is used as a short way of writing it.

Exam Tip
The atomic number in the periodic table tells you how many electrons each atom has — you should be able to work the electron configuration out from there.

Tip: You can work out how many electrons have been lost using oxidation states — see page 132.

Figure 4: A lump of zinc.

Properties of the transition metals

Physical properties

The properties of the transition elements don't gradually change across the periodic table like you might expect. They're all typical metals and have similar physical properties.

Tip: Look back at your Year 1 notes for more on periodicity.

- They all have a high density.
- They all have high melting and high boiling points.

Chemical properties

The chemical properties of the transition metals are much more interesting. They have a few special chemical properties that you need to know about:

Tip: All of the chemical properties of the transition elements are covered in more detail later in the section.

- They can form **complex ions** — see pages 134-136.
  E.g. iron forms a complex ion with water — $[Fe(H_2O)_6]^{2+}$.
- They form coloured ions — see pages 140-141.
  E.g. Fe^{2+} ions are pale green and Fe^{3+} ions are yellow.
- They're good **catalysts** — see pages 155-158.
  E.g. iron is the catalyst used in the Haber process.
- They can exist in variable **oxidation states** — see page 149.
  E.g. iron can exist in the +2 oxidation state as Fe^{2+} ions and in the +3 oxidation state as Fe^{3+} ions.

Some common coloured ions and oxidation states are shown below. The colours refer to the aqueous ions.

Figure 5: *The different colours of the aqueous transition metal ions.*

Element	Ion	Oxidation state	Colour
Ti	Ti^{2+}	+2	violet
	Ti^{3+}	+3	purple
V	V^{2+}	+2	violet
	V^{3+}	+3	green
	VO^{2+}	+4	blue
	VO_2^{+}	+5	yellow
Cr	Cr^{3+}	+3	green
	$Cr_2O_7^{2-}$	+6	orange
Mn	Mn^{2+}	+2	very pale pink/ colourless
	MnO_4^{2-}	+6	green
	MnO_4^{-}	+7	purple
Fe	Fe^{2+}	+2	pale green
	Fe^{3+}	+3	yellow
Co	Co^{2+}	+2	pink
Ni	Ni^{2+}	+2	green
Cu	Cu^{2+}	+2	pale blue

Figure 6: *A table showing some common stable ions of the Period 4 transition metals, their oxidation states and their colours.*

These elements show variable oxidation states because the energies of the 4s and the 3d sub-levels are very similar. So different numbers of electrons can be gained or lost using fairly similar amounts of energy.

Tip: Look back at your Year 1 notes for more on oxidation states and how to find them.

The incomplete d sub-level

It's the incomplete d sub-level that causes the special chemical properties of transition metals. d block elements without an incomplete d sub-level don't have these properties.

┌─ Example ───────────────────────────────

Scandium and zinc don't form ions with incomplete d sub-levels. As a result, they don't have the same chemical properties as transition metals.

For example, they can't form complex ions, they don't form coloured ions and they can't exist in variable oxidation states.

Practice Questions — Application

Q1 Write out the electron configurations for the following transition metal elements:

a) V   b) Co   c) Mn   d) Ni

Q2 Write out the electron configurations for the following transition metal ions:

a) V^{3+} b) Co^{2+} c) Mn^{2+} d) Ni^{2+}

Q3 Using electron configurations, explain why zinc is not a transition metal, despite being in the d block of the periodic table.

Exam Tip
If you're asked for a full electron configuration, you need to write it all out starting from $1s^2$ — don't use [Ar].

Practice Questions — Fact Recall

Q1 Where in the periodic table are transition elements found?

Q2 What is the definition of a transition metal?

Q3 How many electrons can a d sub-level hold?

Q4 Give two rules that are usually followed when working out electron configurations.

Q5 a) Explain why chromium has the electron configuration $[Ar]3d^54s^1$ and not $[Ar]3d^44s^2$ as you would expect.

b) Explain why copper has the electron configuration $[Ar]3d^{10}4s^1$ and not $[Ar]3d^94s^2$ as you would expect.

Q6 Give four chemical properties that all of the transition metals have in common.

Q7 What feature of transition metals causes their chemical properties?

Learning Objectives:

- Know that a complex is a central metal ion surrounded by ligands.

- Know that a ligand is a molecule or ion that forms a co-ordinate bond with a transition metal by donating a pair of electrons.

- Understand that ligands can be monodentate (e.g. H_2O, NH_3 and Cl^-), bidentate (e.g. $NH_2CH_2CH_2NH_2$ and $C_2O_4{}^{2-}$) or multidentate (e.g. $EDTA^{4-}$).

- Know that co-ordination number is the number of co-ordinate bonds to the central metal atom or ion.

- Know that transition metal ions commonly form octahedral complexes with small ligands (e.g. H_2O and NH_3).

- Know that transition metal ions commonly form tetrahedral complexes with larger ligands (e.g. Cl^-).

- Know that square planar complexes are also formed.

- Know that Ag^+ forms the linear complex $[Ag(NH_3)_2]^+$ as used in Tollens' reagent.

Specification Reference
3.2.5.1, 3.2.5.2, 3.2.5.3

2. Complex Ions

The ability to form complex ions is an important property of transition metals. You probably haven't come across complex ions before but the next few pages should tell you everything you need to know.

What are complex ions?

A **complex ion** is a metal ion surrounded by co-ordinately bonded ligands. A **co-ordinate bond** (or dative covalent bond) is a covalent bond in which both electrons in the shared pair come from the same atom. In a complex, they come from the ligands. So, a **ligand** is an atom, ion or molecule that donates a pair of electrons to a central metal ion.

> **Example**
>
> $[Cu(H_2O)_6]^{2+}$
>
> The central metal ion is a Cu^{2+} ion and water molecules are acting as ligands. There are six water molecules that each form a co-ordinate bond with the Cu^{2+} ion:
>
>
>
> *Arrows represent a co-ordinate bond.*
>
> *Water molecules act as ligands.*
>
> *Central transition metal ion.*

The different types of ligand

A ligand must have at least one lone pair of electrons, or it won't have anything to use to form a co-ordinate bond. But different ligands can have different numbers of lone pairs and can form different numbers of co-ordinate bonds. Ligands that can only form one co-ordinate bond are called **monodentate**.

> **Examples**
>
> Here are some examples of monodentate ligands:
>
>
>
> *Ammonia*   *Chloride ions*   *Water*
>
> Ammonia and chloride ions only have one lone pair of electrons to donate to form a co-ordinate bond. Water has two lone pairs of electrons but because they are so close together, it can only form one co-ordinate bond at a time.

Ligands that can form more than one co-ordinate bond are called **multidentate**.

> **Example**
>
> $EDTA^{4-}$ is a multidentate ligand:
>
>

Tip: EDTA stands for ethylenediaminetetra-acetic acid.

EDTA^{4-} has six lone pairs (two on nitrogen atoms and four on oxygen atoms) so it can form six co-ordinate bonds with a metal ion.

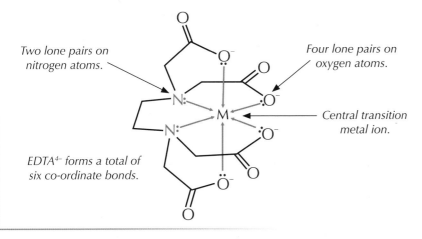

Two lone pairs on nitrogen atoms.

Four lone pairs on oxygen atoms.

Central transition metal ion.

EDTA^{4-} forms a total of six co-ordinate bonds.

Tip: EDTA^{4-} is hexadentate — hexa meaning six.

Figure 1: *Molecular model of EDTA.*

Multidentate ligands that can form two co-ordinate bonds are called **bidentate**.

┌─ **Example** ─────────────────────────

Ethane-1,2-diamine ($\overset{\cdot\cdot}{N}H_2CH_2CH_2\overset{\cdot\cdot}{N}H_2$) is a bidentate ligand. It has two amine groups, each of which has a lone pair of electrons that it can donate to form a co-ordinate bond. In complex ions, each ethane-1,2-diamine molecule forms two co-ordinate bonds with the metal ion. In the complex ion below, there are three ethane-1,2-diamine molecules forming six co-ordinate bonds:

Each ethane-1,2-diamine molecule forms two co-ordinate bonds with the central metal ion.

Exam Tip
Don't worry, you'll never be expected to draw the shape of EDTA or complex ions containing EDTA in the exam.

Tip: Ethane-1,2-diamine ligands can be abbreviated to 'en'. For example, $[Cu(en)_3]^{2+}$.

Oxidation states of metals in complex ions

The overall charge on a complex ion is put outside the square brackets. For example, $[Cu(H_2O)_6]^{2+}$ has a total charge of +2. You can work out the oxidation state of the metal ion within a complex using this equation:

| The oxidation state of the metal ion | = | The total charge of the complex | − | The sum of the charges of the ligands |

Tip: You should be familiar with oxidation states by now — but if not, have a look back at your Year 1 notes.

┌─ **Example** ─────────────────────────

What is the oxidation state of Co in $[CoCl_4]^{2-}_{(aq)}$?

The total charge of $[CoCl_4]^{2-}_{(aq)}$ is –2 and each Cl$^-$ ligand has an charge of –1. So in this complex:

cobalt's oxidation state = total charge – sum of Cl$^-$ charges

= (–2) – (4 × –1)

= **+2**

Exam Tip
You might have to work out the oxidation state of a transition metal in a complex ion in the exam, so make sure you know this equation.

Shapes of complex ions

The shape of a complex ion depends on its **co-ordination number**. This is the number of co-ordinate bonds that are formed with the central metal ion. The usual co-ordination numbers are 6 and 4. If the ligands are small, like H_2O or NH_3, 6 can fit around the central metal ion. But if the ligands are larger, like Cl^-, only 4 can fit around the central metal ion.

Six co-ordinate bonds

Complex ions that contain six co-ordinate bonds have an octahedral shape.

Examples — Maths Skills

$$[Fe(H_2O)_6]^{2+}_{(aq)} \qquad [Co(NH_3)_6]^{2+}_{(aq)} \qquad [Cu(NH_3)_4(H_2O)_2]^{2+}_{(aq)}$$

Many octahedral complex ions are hexaaqua complexes. This means there are six water ligands around the central ion.

The different types of bond arrow show that the complex is 3-D. The wedge-shaped arrows represent bonds coming towards you and the dashed arrows represent bonds sticking out behind the molecule.

Four co-ordinate bonds

Complex ions with four co-ordinate bonds usually have a tetrahedral shape.

Examples — Maths Skills

$$[CuCl_4]^{2-} \qquad [CoCl_4]^{2-}$$

Figure 2: *The flask on the left shows the pink colour of hexaaqua cobalt(II) ions. The flask on the right shows the blue colour of cobalt(II) ions complexed as $[CoCl_4]^{2-}$.*

But in a few complexes four co-ordinate bonds form a square planar shape.

Example — Maths Skills

Cisplatin ($PtCl_2(NH_3)_2$) has a square planar shape:

Two co-ordinate bonds

Some silver complexes have 2 co-ordinate bonds and form a linear shape.

Example — Maths Skills

$[Ag(NH_3)_2]^+$ forms a linear shape, as shown: $\left[H_3N\text{:}\!\longrightarrow\!Ag\!\longleftarrow\!\text{:}NH_3 \right]^+$

Practice Questions — Application

Q1 What is the co-ordination number of the transition metal in each of the following complex ions:

a) $[CuF_6]^{4-}$ b) $[Ag(S_2O_3)_2]^{3-}$ c) $[CuCl_4]^{2-}$

Q2 Deduce the oxidation state of the transition metal in each of the complex ions in Q1.

Q3 Describe and draw the shape of each complex ion in Q1.

Q4 $C_2O_4^{2-}$ is a bidentate ligand. Its structure is shown below:

a) Copy the diagram and circle the atoms that could form a co-ordinate bond with a metal ion.

b) How many $C_2O_4^{2-}$ ligands would you expect to bind to a single Cu^{2+} ion?

Q5 $[Ni(CN)_4]^{2-}$ is a complex ion. It does not have a tetrahedral shape. What shape could it have instead? Draw the structure of $[Ni(CN)_4]^{2-}$.

Practice Questions — Fact Recall

Q1 Define the following terms:

a) Complex ion b) Co-ordinate bond c) Ligand

Q2 a) Explain what is meant by the terms monodentate, bidentate and multidentate.

b) Give an example of each type of ligand mentioned in a).

Q3 What is meant by the term co-ordination number?

Learning Objectives:
- Know that octahedral complexes can display optical isomerism with bidentate ligands.
- Know that octahedral and square planar complexes can display *cis-trans* isomerism (a special case of *E-Z* isomerism) with monodentate ligands.
- Know that cisplatin is a *cis* isomer.

Specification Reference 3.2.5.3

3. Isomerism in Complex Ions

Complex ions can show optical and cis-trans isomerism because the ligands can be arranged in various different ways around the central metal ion.

Optical isomerism in complex ions

Optical isomerism is a type of **stereoisomerism**. Stereoisomers have the same molecular formula but a different orientation of their bonds in space. For complex ions, optical isomers form when an ion can exist as two non-superimposable mirror images. This happens in octahedral complexes when three bidentate ligands are attached to the central ion. Optical isomers are also known as **enantiomers**.

Example — **Maths Skills**

When three ethane-1,2-diamine molecules ($H_2NCH_2CH_2NH_2$) use the lone pairs on both nitrogen atoms to co-ordinately bond with nickel, two optical isomers are formed.

mirror line

Tip: If you're finding it difficult to see that the complexes in the example are non-superimposable mirror images of each other try building their 3-D structures using a molecular model kit (or matchsticks and modelling clay).

Cis-trans isomerism in complex ions

Cis-trans isomerism is another type of stereoisomerism.

Cis-trans isomerism in square planar complex ions

Square planar complex ions that have two pairs of ligands show *cis-trans* isomerism. When two paired ligands are directly opposite each other it's the *trans* isomer and when they're next to each other it's the *cis* isomer.

Example — **Maths Skills**

$NiCl_2(NH_3)_2$ has *cis* and *trans* isomers.

cis-$NiCl_2(NH_3)_2$ *trans*-$NiCl_2(NH_3)_2$

Exam Tip
If you're asked to draw a complex ion in the exam, make sure you use dashed bonds and wedged bonds to show that the structure is 3-D — you'll lose marks if you don't.

Cisplatin

Cisplatin is a complex of platinum(II) with two chloride ions and two ammonia molecules in a square planar shape (see Figure 1).

Figure 1: The structure of cisplatin.

Cisplatin can be used to treat some types of cancer. Cancer is caused by cells in the body dividing uncontrollably and forming tumours. Cisplatin is active against a variety of cancers, including lung and bladder cancer, because it prevents cancer cells from reproducing.

Cis-trans isomerism in octahedral complex ions

Octahedral complexes with four ligands of one type and two ligands of another type can also exhibit *cis-trans* isomerism. If the two odd ligands are opposite each other you've got the *trans* isomer, if they're next to each other then you've got the *cis* isomer.

> **Example** — **Maths Skills**
>
> $NiCl_2(H_2O)_4$ has a *trans* and a *cis* isomer.
>
>
>
> *trans-NiCl$_2$(H$_2$O)$_4$*   *cis-NiCl$_2$(H$_2$O)$_4$*

Tip: If the two chloride ions were on opposite sides of the complex to each other the molecule would be transplatin. Transplatin has different biological effects to cisplatin.

Tip: The downside is that cisplatin also prevents normal cells from reproducing — including blood and hair cells. This can cause hair loss and suppress the immune system, increasing the risk of infection. Cisplatin may also cause damage to the kidneys.

Tip: If a complex has an overall charge of zero, you don't need to put the formula in square brackets.

Practice Questions — Application

Q1 State what type of stereoisomerism the following complex ions will exhibit:
   a) $PtCl_2(H_2O)_2$
   b) $[Co(en)_3]^{2+}$
   c) $Cu(OH)_2(H_2O)_4$

Q2 Draw the *cis* and *trans* isomers of $NiCl_2(H_2O)_2$.

Tip: If you're asked about the isomerism shown in a complex ion, sometimes it helps to draw out the structure of the ion first — then you'll get a better idea of the possible isomers.

Practice Questions — Fact Recall

Q1 Name two types of stereoisomerism that complex ions can exhibit.

Q2 Draw the structure of cisplatin.

4. Formation of Coloured Ions

This section explains why different complex ions are different colours and how this can be used to identify them.

Energy levels

Normally the 3d orbitals of transition metal ions have the same energy. But when ligands bond to the ions, some orbitals are given more energy than others. This splits the 3d orbitals into different energy levels — see Figure 1.

Figure 1: *The different orbital energy levels in complex ions.*

Electrons tend to occupy the lower orbitals (the ground state). To jump up to the higher orbitals (excited states) they need energy equal to the **energy gap**, ΔE. They get this energy from visible light — see Figure 2.

Figure 2: *The transition of an electron from the ground state to the excited state.*

The energy absorbed when electrons jump up can be worked out using this equation:

$$\Delta E = h\nu = hc/\lambda$$

Where ΔE is the energy absorbed (J),
h = Planck's constant (6.63×10^{-34} Js),
ν = frequency of light absorbed (hertz/Hz),
c = the speed of light (3.00×10^{8} m s^{-1})
and λ = wavelength of light absorbed (m)

The amount of energy needed to make electrons jump depends upon the central metal ion and its oxidation state, the ligands, and the co-ordination number, as these affect the size of the energy gap.

The colours of compounds

When visible light hits a transition metal ion, some frequencies are absorbed as electrons jump up to the higher orbitals. The frequencies absorbed depend on the size of the energy gap (ΔE). The rest of the frequencies are reflected. These reflected frequencies combine to make the complement of the colour of the absorbed frequencies — this is the colour you see.

┌ **Example** ─────────────────────────────

$[Cu(H_2O)_6]^{2+}$ ions absorb yellow light. The remaining frequencies combine to produce the complementary colour — in this case that's blue.
So $[Cu(H_2O)_6]^{2+}$ solution appears blue.

└──────────────────────────────────

If there are no 3d electrons or the 3d sub-level is full, then no electrons will jump, so no energy will be absorbed. If there's no energy absorbed, the compound will look white or colourless because all the light will be reflected.

Learning Objectives:

- Know that d electrons move from the ground state to an excited state when light is absorbed and that the energy difference between the ground state and the excited state is given by:
  $\Delta E = h\nu = hc/\lambda$.

- Know that transition metal ions can be identified by their colour.

- Know that colour arises when some of the wavelengths of visible light are absorbed and the remaining wavelengths are transmitted or reflected.

- Know that changes in oxidation state, co-ordination number and ligand alter ΔE and this leads to a change in colour.

- Know that absorption of visible light is used in spectroscopy.

- Know that a simple colorimeter can be used to determine the concentration of coloured ions in a solution.

Specification Reference 3.2.5.4

Tip: It's the incomplete d sub-level that means transition metals can absorb light. If it were empty/full there would be no electrons to jump between energy levels.

Identifying transition metal ions

It'd be nice if each transition metal formed ions or complexes with just one colour, but sadly it's not that simple. The colour of a complex can be altered by any of the factors that can affect the size of the energy gap (ΔE).

Changes in oxidation state

If the oxidation state of a transition metal in a complex ion changes, then the colour of the complex ion may also change.

Tip: See page 132 for more examples of transition metals with multiple oxidation states.

Examples

Complex ions containing iron change colour when the oxidation state of iron increases from +2 to +3.

Complex:	$[Fe(H_2O)_6]^{2+}$	$\rightarrow$	$[Fe(H_2O)_6]^{3+}$
Oxidation state:	+2	$\rightarrow$	+3
Colour:	pale green	$\rightarrow$	yellow

Complex ions containing vanadium change colour when the oxidation state of vanadium increases from +2 to +3.

Complex:	$[V(H_2O)_6]^{2+}$	$\rightarrow$	$[V(H_2O)_6]^{3+}$
Oxidation state:	+2	$\rightarrow$	+3
Colour:	violet	$\rightarrow$	green

Figure 3: *The test tube on the left shows the violet colour of a V(II) solution. The test tube on the right shows the green colour of a V(III) solution.*

Changes in co-ordination number

Changes in co-ordination number may also result in a colour change. This always involves a change of ligand too.

Example

Complex ions containing Cu change colour when the co-ordination number of Cu decreases from 6 to 4.

Complex:	$[Cu(H_2O)_6]^{2+} + 4Cl^-$	$\rightarrow$	$[CuCl_4]^{2-} + 6H_2O$
Co-ordination number:	6	$\rightarrow$	4
Colour:	blue	$\rightarrow$	yellow

Tip: All the colours on this page refer to aqueous solutions.

Changes in ligand

Changing the ligand can cause a colour change, even if the oxidation state and co-ordination number remain the same.

Example

If $[Co(H_2O)_6]^{2+}$ is converted to $[Co(NH_3)_6]^{2+}$ the colour will change from pink to straw coloured.

Complex:	$[Co(H_2O)_6]^{2+} + 6NH_3$	$\rightarrow$	$[Co(NH_3)_6]^{2+} + 6H_2O$
Oxidation state:	+2	$\rightarrow$	+2
Colour:	pink	$\rightarrow$	straw coloured

Spectroscopy

Spectroscopy can be used to determine the concentration of a solution by measuring how much light it absorbs. White light is shone through a filter, which is chosen to only let the colour of light through that is absorbed by the sample. The light then passes through the sample to a **colorimeter**, which shows how much light was absorbed by the sample. The more concentrated a coloured solution is, the more light it will absorb.

Tip: Spectroscopy is the study of what happens when radiation interacts with matter. There are loads of different types — NMR spectroscopy is covered on pages 254-264.

So you can use this measurement to work out the concentration of a solution of transition metal ions — see Figure 5.

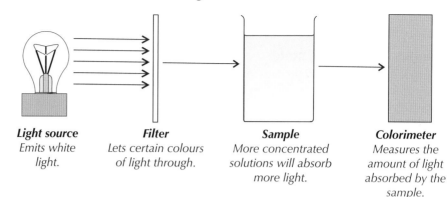

Light source
Emits white light.

Filter
Lets certain colours of light through.

Sample
More concentrated solutions will absorb more light.

Colorimeter
Measures the amount of light absorbed by the sample.

Figure 5: Measuring the concentration of a solution using spectrometry.

Figure 4: A student using a colorimeter to measure the absorbance of a solution of Cu^{2+} ions.

Before you can find the unknown concentration of a sample, you have to produce a **calibration graph** (or calibration curve) — like the lovely one below.

Relative absorbance

Absorbance of sample measured in colorimeter

Concentration of sample is read here

Concentration of ion

Tip: Calibration graphs like this one are usually a straight line because, at low concentrations, the amount of light absorbed is directly proportional to the number of complex ions in the solution.

This involves measuring the absorbencies of known concentrations of solutions and plotting the results on a graph. Once you've done this, you can measure the absorbance of your sample and read its concentration off the graph.

Example — **Maths Skills**

Say you want to find the concentration of a solution of $[Cu(H_2O)_6]^{2+}$ ions. These ions absorb yellow light so you'll need a filter that only lets yellow light through. You then need to measure the absorbance of some $[Cu(H_2O)_6]^{2+}$ ion solutions that you know the concentration of. Your results will look something like this:

Tip: Different complex ions absorb different wavelengths of light so you'll need a different filter to measure the absorbance of each one.

Concentration (mol dm^{-3})	Relative Absorbance
0.2	0.050
0.3	0.055
0.4	0.100
0.6	0.150
1.0	0.250
1.6	0.400

Plotting these results on a graph gives you a calibration graph. Once you have your calibration graph, you measure the absorbance of the unknown solution, then read its concentration off the graph.

For example, if its relative absorbance is 0.225, its concentration is around 0.9 mol dm^{-3}.

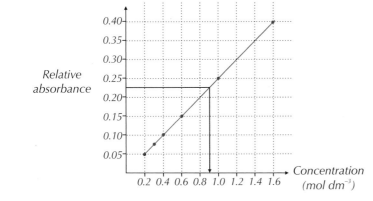

Tip: When you plot a calibration curve, concentration goes on the *x*-axis and absorbance goes on the *y*-axis.

Spectroscopy is a useful method for measuring the concentration of coloured ions because it's easy to get loads of readings and you can work out the concentration quite quickly. Plus, you can measure very low concentrations and it doesn't use up any of the substance or interfere with any reactions.

Exam Tip
For the exam you'll need to know how concentrations are determined using spectroscopy and why spectroscopy is a good method to use, so read these pages carefully.

Practice Questions — Application

Q1 When the following reaction occurs, the colour of the solution changes from violet to green.

$$[Cr(H_2O)_6]^{3+} + 6NH_3 \rightarrow [Cr(NH_3)_6]^{3+} + 6H_2O$$

What causes the change in colour of the solution?

Q2 This reaction is accompanied by a green to yellow colour change:

$$[Fe(H_2O)_6]^{2+} \rightarrow [Fe(H_2O)_6]^{3+} + e^-$$

What has caused the change in colour of the solution?

Q3 $[Cu(H_2O)_6]^{2+}$ ions absorb light with a wavelength of 580 nm (580×10^{-9} m). What is the energy gap (ΔE) between the split 3d orbitals of the Cu^{2+} ion?

Practice Questions — Fact Recall

Q1 What happens to the 3d orbitals of a transition metal when a ligand binds to it?

Q2 a) What type of energy is needed for an electron to jump from a lower energy orbital to a higher energy orbital?

b) Write the equation for calculating the energy absorbed (ΔE) when an electron jumps between orbitals.

Q3 Explain why transition metal ions have colour.

Q4 List three things that could cause the colour of a complex ion to change.

Q5 a) Describe how spectroscopy can be used to measure the amount of light absorbed by a solution of complex ions.

b) Explain how you would produce a calibration graph to measure the concentration of a solution of complex ions.

5. Ligand Substitution Reactions

Ligands around a central metal ion can switch places with other ligands in ligand substitution reactions.

Ligand substitution reactions

One ligand can be swapped for another ligand — this is **ligand substitution** (or ligand exchange). It pretty much always causes a colour change.

Substitution of similarly sized ligands

If the ligands are of similar size (e.g. H_2O and NH_3) then the co-ordination number of the complex ion doesn't change, and neither does the shape.

⌐ **Example** ───────────────────────────

H_2O and NH_3 ligands are similarly sized and are both uncharged. This means that H_2O ligands can be exchanged with NH_3 ligands without any change in co-ordination number or shape. There will still be a colour change due to the change of ligand.

$$[Co(H_2O)_6]^{2+}_{(aq)} + 6NH_{3(aq)} \rightarrow 6H_2O_{(l)} + [Co(NH_3)_6]^{2+}_{(aq)}$$

Co-ordination number: 6
octahedral,
pink

Co-ordination number: 6
octahedral,
straw coloured

Substitution of different sized ligands

If the ligands are different sizes (e.g. Cl^- is larger than H_2O and NH_3) there's a change of co-ordination number and a change of shape.

⌐ **Example** ───────────────────────────

In a copper-aqua complex, the H_2O ligands can be exchanged with Cl^- ligands. The shape of the complex changes from octahedral to tetrahedral because fewer of the larger Cl^- ligands can fit around the central metal ion. There is also a colour change during this reaction.

$$[Cu(H_2O)_6]^{2+}_{(aq)} + 4Cl^-_{(aq)} \rightarrow 6H_2O_{(l)} + [CuCl_4]^{2-}_{(aq)}$$

Co-ordination number: 6
octahedral,
pale blue

Co-ordination number: 4
tetrahedral,
yellow-green

Partial substitution of ligands

Sometimes the substitution is only partial — not all of the six H_2O ligands are substituted.

> **Example**
>
> In a copper-aqua complex, some of the H_2O ligands can be exchanged with NH_3 ligands whilst some H_2O ligands remain where they are.
>
> In this example, four of the H_2O ligands are substituted with NH_3 ligands. The shape of the complex changes from octahedral to elongated octahedral and there is also a colour change.
>
> $$[Cu(H_2O)_6]^{2+}_{(aq)} + 4NH_{3(aq)} \rightarrow [Cu(NH_3)_4(H_2O)_2]^{2+}_{(aq)} + 4H_2O_{(l)}$$
>
>   *octahedral*   *elongated octahedral*
>   *pale blue*   *deep blue*

Tip: In the example on the left you only get *trans*-$[Cu(NH_3)_4(H_2O)_2]^{2+}$ when an <u>excess</u> of NH_3 is added. Otherwise you get $[Cu(H_2O)_4(OH)_2]$ (a blue precipitate) instead.

Haem and haemoglobin

Haemoglobin is a protein found in blood that helps to transport oxygen around the body. It contains Fe^{2+} ions, which are hexa-co-ordinated — six lone pairs are donated to them to form six co-ordinate bonds. Four of the lone pairs come from nitrogen atoms, which form a circle around the Fe^{2+}. This part of the molecule is called **haem**. The molecule that the four nitrogen atoms are part of is a multidentate ligand called a **porphyrin**. A protein called a **globin** and either an oxygen or a water molecule also bind to the Fe^{2+} ion to form an octahedral structure — see Figure 2.

Porphyrin ring

Central Fe^{2+} ion

Figure 2: The structure of haemoglobin when it is bound to oxygen or water.

Figure 1: Red blood cells are packed full of haemoglobin.

In the body, both water and oxygen will bind to the Fe^{2+} ions as ligands, so the complex can transport oxygen to where it's needed, and then swap it for a water molecule. In the lungs, where the oxygen concentration is high, water ligands are substituted for oxygen molecules to form oxyhaemoglobin, which is carried around the body in the blood. When the oxyhaemoglobin gets to a place where oxygen is needed, the oxygen molecules are exchanged for water molecules. The haemoglobin then returns to the lungs and the whole process starts again. The process of oxygen transport is summarised in Figure 4 (on the next page).

Tip: When the Fe^{2+} ion is bound to water the complex is called deoxyhaemoglobin and when it's bound to oxygen it's called oxyhaemoglobin.

Carbon monoxide poisoning

When carbon monoxide is inhaled, the haemoglobin can substitute its water ligands for carbon monoxide ligands, forming carboxyhaemoglobin (Figure 3). This is bad news because carbon monoxide forms a very strong bond with the Fe^{2+} ion and doesn't readily exchange with oxygen or water ligands, meaning the haemoglobin can't transport oxygen any more. Carbon monoxide poisoning starves the organs of oxygen — it can cause headaches, dizziness, unconsciousness and even death if it's not treated.

Figure 3:
Carboxyhaemoglobin.

Summary of the oxygen transport process

Here's an overview of how haemoglobin transports oxygen round the body:

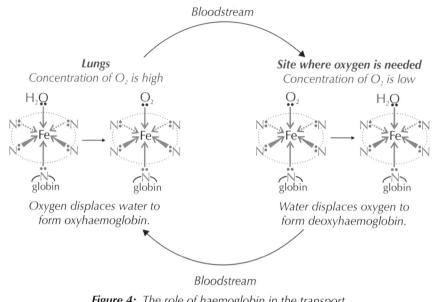

Figure 4: *The role of haemoglobin in the transport of oxygen around the body.*

Complex ion stability

Ligand exchange reactions can be easily reversed, unless the new complex ion is much more stable than the old one. If the new ligands form stronger bonds with the central metal ion than the old ligands did, the change is less easy to reverse.

> **Example**
>
> CN⁻ ions form stronger co-ordinate bonds than H_2O molecules with Fe^{3+} ions. So, the complex formed with CN⁻ ions will be more stable than the complex formed with H_2O molecules. This means that the substitution of water molecules by CN⁻ ions in an iron(III) complex is hard to reverse.
>
> $$[Fe(H_2O)_6]^{3+}_{(aq)} + 6CN^-_{(aq)} \rightarrow [Fe(CN)_6]^{3-}_{(aq)} + 6H_2O_{(l)}$$

Multidentate ligands, such as $EDTA^{4-}$, form more stable complexes than monodentate ligands, so ligand exchange reactions involving bidentate and multidentate ligands are hard to reverse.

Figure 5: *EDTA⁴⁻ bonding to a central metal ion. EDTA⁴⁻ can bind with six bonds to the metal ion via nitrogen and oxygen atoms.*

> **Example**
>
> Complexes that contain the bidentate ligand ethane-1,2-diamine are more stable than those that contain water molecule ligands. So, reactions where water molecules are substituted by ethane-1,2-diamine are hard to reverse.
>
> $$[Cu(H_2O)_6]^{2+}_{(aq)} + 3NH_2CH_2CH_2NH_{2(aq)} \rightarrow [Cu(NH_2CH_2CH_2NH_2)_3]^{2+}_{(aq)} + 6H_2O_{(l)}$$

Enthalpy change

When a ligand exchange reaction occurs, bonds are broken and formed. The strength of the bonds being broken is often very similar to the strength of the new bonds being made. So the enthalpy change for a ligand exchange reaction is usually very small.

--- Example ---

Substituting ammonia with ethane-1,2-diamine in a nickel complex

In this reaction, six co-ordinate bonds break between Ni and N in $[Ni(NH_3)_6]^{2+}$ and six co-ordinate bonds are formed between Ni and N in $[Ni(NH_2CH_2CH_2NH_2)_3]^{2+}$. This means the enthalpy change for the reaction is very small (only -13 kJ mol^{-1}).

$$[Ni(NH_3)_6]^{2+} + 3NH_2CH_2CH_2NH_2 \rightarrow [Ni(NH_2CH_2CH_2NH_2)_3]^{2+} + 6NH_3$$

$$\Delta H = -13 \text{ kJ mol}^{-1}$$

Break 6 co-ordinate bonds between Ni and N   *Form 6 co-ordinate bonds between Ni and N*

This is actually a reversible reaction, but the equilibrium lies so far to the right that it is thought of as being irreversible.

Entropy change

When monodentate ligands are substituted with bidentate or multidentate ligands, the number of particles increases — the more particles, the greater the entropy. Reactions that result in an increase in entropy are more likely to occur. So that's why multidentate ligands always form much more stable complexes than monodentate ligands. This is known as the **chelate effect**.

--- Example ---

In the example above, $[Ni(NH_2CH_2CH_2NH_2)_3]^{2+}$ is much more stable than $[Ni(NH_3)_6]^{2+}$. This isn't accounted for by an enthalpy change, but an increase in entropy can explain it.

The number of particles in the reaction increases from 4 to 7. This means that there is a large increase in entropy for the reaction and therefore the $[Ni(NH_2CH_2CH_2NH_2)_3]^{2+}$ formed in the reaction is more stable than the $[Ni(NH_3)_6]^{2+}$ complex.

$$[Ni(NH_3)_6]^{2+} + 3NH_2CH_2CH_2NH_2 \rightarrow [Ni(NH_2CH_2CH_2NH_2)_3]^{2+} + 6NH_3$$

4 particles   *7 particles*

When the hexadentate ligand EDTA^{4-} replaces monodentate or bidentate ligands, the complex formed is loads more stable. It's difficult to reverse these reactions, because reversing them would cause a decrease in the system's entropy.

--- Example ---

In the reaction below, the EDTA^{4-} ligand is replacing six NH_3 ligands. This increases the number of particles in the reaction from 2 to 7.

$$[Cr(NH_3)_6]^{3+} + EDTA^{4-} \rightarrow [Cr(EDTA)]^- + 6NH_3$$

This means that the entropy of the system has greatly increased and so the $[Cr(EDTA)]^-$ complex formed will be more stable than the $[Cr(NH_3)_6]^{3+}$ complex.

Exam Tip
When you're asked about the chelate effect in an exam make sure you talk about enthalpy and entropy otherwise you could lose out on valuable marks.

Tip: Entropy is covered in more detail on pages 30-31.

Tip: There's more information on the EDTA^{4-} ligand on pages 134 and 135.

Tip: The enthalpy change for this reaction is almost zero, and the entropy change is large and positive. This makes the free energy change negative ($\Delta G = \Delta H - T\Delta S$), so the reaction is feasible (see page 33).

Practice Questions — Application

Q1 The H_2O ligands in $[Fe(H_2O)_6]^{3+}$ can be exchanged for other ligands. Predict the shape of the complex ions formed after the following substitutions:

    a) All the H_2O ligands exchanged for OH^- ligands.

    b) The six H_2O ligands exchanged for four Cl^- ligands.

Q2 Write an equation for the formation of $[MnCl_4]^{2-}$ from a hexaaqua manganese(II) ion and chloride ions.

Q3 The metal-aqua ion $[Cu(H_2O)_6]^{2+}$ will undergo a ligand substitution reaction with excess ammonia to form $[Cu(NH_3)_4(H_2O)_2]^{2+}$.

    a) Write an equation for this reaction.

    b) State the shape of $[Cu(NH_3)_4(H_2O)_2]^{2+}$.

Q4 Ethane-1,2-diamine is a bidentate ligand.

    a) Write an equation for the substitution of all the ammonia ligands in $[Cr(NH_3)_6]^{3+}$ with ethane-1,2-diamine $(NH_2CH_2CH_2NH_2)$ ligands.

    b) Explain why the new complex formed is more stable than $[Cr(NH_3)_6]^{3+}$.

Figure 6: *The reaction between $Cu^{2+}_{(aq)}$ ions and excess ammonia. A $[Cu(NH_3)_4(H_2O)_2]^{2+}$ complex ion is formed which has a deep blue colour.*

Practice Questions — Fact Recall

Q1 State whether the colour, co-ordination number and/or the shape of the complex ion changes in the following situations.

    a) Ligand exchange of similarly sized ligands.

    b) Ligand exchange of differently sized ligands.

Q2 a) What is the role of haemoglobin in the body?

    b) Where do the six co-ordinate bonds come from in haemoglobin?

Q3 Haemoglobin is found in red blood cells.

    a) Explain what happens to haemoglobin in the lungs.

    b) Explain what happens to haemoglobin at sites where oxygen is needed.

Q4 Explain why carbon monoxide is toxic.

Q5 What is the chelate effect?

6. Variable Oxidation States

Transition metals can usually form more than one type of ion and, in different ions, transition metals can have different oxidation states. These variable oxidation states are another important feature of the transition metals.

Oxidation states of vanadium

You learnt on page 132 that one of the properties of transition metals is that they can exist in variable oxidation states. When you switch between oxidation states, it's a redox reaction — the metal ions are either oxidised or reduced. For example, vanadium can exist in four oxidation states in solution — the +2, +3, +4 and +5 states.

You can tell them apart by their different colours:

Oxidation state of vanadium	Formula of ion	Colour of ion
+5	$VO_2^+{}_{(aq)}$	Yellow
+4	$VO^{2+}{}_{(aq)}$	Blue
+3	$V^{3+}{}_{(aq)}$	Green
+2	$V^{2+}{}_{(aq)}$	Violet

Vanadium(V) can be reduced by adding it to zinc metal in an acidic solution.

Example

To begin with, the solution turns from yellow to blue as vanadium(V) is reduced to vanadium(IV).

$$2VO_2^+{}_{(aq)} + Zn_{(s)} + 4H^+{}_{(aq)} \rightarrow 2VO^{2+}{}_{(aq)} + Zn^{2+}{}_{(aq)} + 2H_2O_{(l)}$$

The solution then changes colour from blue to green as vanadium(IV) is reduced to vanadium(III).

$$2VO^{2+}{}_{(aq)} + Zn_{(s)} + 4H^+{}_{(aq)} \rightarrow 2V^{3+}{}_{(aq)} + Zn^{2+}{}_{(aq)} + 2H_2O_{(l)}$$

Finally, vanadium(III) is reduced to vanadium(II), and so the solution changes from green to violet.

$$2V^{3+}{}_{(aq)} + Zn_{(s)} \rightarrow 2V^{2+}{}_{(aq)} + Zn^{2+}{}_{(aq)}$$

Redox potentials

The **redox potential** of an ion or atom tells you how easily it is reduced to a lower oxidation state. They're the same as **electrode potentials** (see page 80). The more positive the redox potential, the less stable the ion will be and so the more likely it is to be reduced. For example, in the table below, copper(II) has a redox potential of +0.15 V, so is less stable and more likely to be reduced than chromium(III) which has a redox potential of −0.74 V.

Half equation	Standard electrode potential (V)
$Cr^{3+}{}_{(aq)} + e^- \rightleftharpoons Cr^{2+}{}_{(aq)}$	−0.74
$Cu^{2+}{}_{(aq)} + e^- \rightleftharpoons Cu^+{}_{(aq)}$	+0.15

Figure 1: From left to right — $VO_2^+{}_{(aq)}$, $VO^{2+}{}_{(aq)}$, $V^{3+}{}_{(aq)}$, and $V^{2+}{}_{(aq)}$.

Tip: VO_2^+ is sometimes referred to as a 'vanadate(V) ion'.

The redox potentials in the table are standard electrode potentials — they've been measured with the reactants at a concentration of 1 mol dm³ against a standard hydrogen electrode, under standard conditions (see page 84). The redox potential of an ion won't always be the same as its standard electrode potential. It can vary depending on the environment that the ion is in.

Ligands affect redox potential

Standard electrode potentials are measured in aqueous solution, so any ions will be surrounded by water ligands. Different ligands may make the redox potential larger or smaller, depending on how well they bind to the metal ion in a particular oxidation state.

pH affects redox potential

Some ions need H⁺ ions to be present in order to be reduced.

> **Example**
>
> $$2VO_2^+{}_{(aq)} + 4H^+{}_{(aq)} + 2e^- \rightleftharpoons 2VO^{2+}{}_{(aq)} + 2H_2O_{(l)}$$

Others release OH⁻ ions into solution when they are reduced.

> **Example**
>
> $$CrO_4^{2-}{}_{(aq)} + 4H_2O_{(l)} + 3e^- \rightleftharpoons Cr(OH)_{3(s)} + 5OH^-{}_{(aq)}$$

For reactions such as these, the pH of the solution affects the size of the redox potential. In general, redox potentials will be more positive in more acidic solutions, because the ion is more easily reduced.

Tollens' reagent

Silver is a transition metal that is most commonly found in the +1 oxidation state (Ag^+). It is easily reduced to silver metal.

$$Ag^+{}_{(aq)} + e^- \rightarrow Ag_{(s)} \qquad \text{Standard electrode potential} = +0.80 \text{ V}$$

Figure 2: *Tollens' reagent forms a 'silver mirror' when added to aldehydes.*

Tollens' reagent uses this reduction reaction to distinguish between aldehydes and ketones. It's prepared by adding just enough ammonia solution to silver nitrate solution to form a colourless solution containing the complex ion $[Ag(NH_3)_2]^+$.

When added to aldehydes, Tollens' reagent reacts to give a silver mirror on the inside of the test tube. The aldehyde is oxidised to a carboxylate anion, and the Ag^+ ions are reduced to silver metal.

$$RCHO_{(aq)} + 2[Ag(NH_3)_2]^+{}_{(aq)} + 3OH^-{}_{(aq)} \rightarrow$$
$$RCOO^-{}_{(aq)} + 2Ag_{(s)} + 4NH_{3(aq)} + 2H_2O_{(l)}$$

Tollens' reagent can't oxidise ketones, so it won't react with them, and no silver mirror will form.

Practice Question — Application

Q1 The table below shows the redox potentials of iron(II) and manganate(VII).

Half equation	Standard electrode potential (V)
$Fe^{3+}_{(aq)} + e^- \rightleftharpoons Fe^{2+}_{(aq)}$	+0.77
$MnO_4^-{}_{(aq)} + 5e^- \rightleftharpoons Mn^{2+}_{(aq)}$	+1.55

Which ion is more easily reduced? Explain your answer.

Practice Questions — Fact Recall

Q1 Write an equation for the reaction in which vanadium(III) is reduced to vanadium(II) by zinc.

Q2 Name two things that can influence the size of the redox potential for a transition metal ion.

Q3 What would you observe if you were to react Tollens' reagent with
  a) an aldehyde,
  b) a ketone?

Q4 What is the formula of the complex ion found in Tollens' reagent?

Learning Objectives:

- Know the redox titrations of Fe^{2+} and $C_2O_4^{2-}$ with MnO_4^-.
- Be able to perform calculations for these titrations and similar redox reactions.

Specification Reference 3.2.5.5

Tip: Titrations usually involve hazardous substances, so make sure you carry out a risk assessment first.

Tip: Titrations are covered in loads more detail on page 106.

Tip: You can also do titrations the other way round — adding the reducing agent to the oxidising agent.

Figure 1: *A student reading a burette during a titration experiment.*

7. Transition Metal Titrations

You might remember covering titrations in Unit 1. Well... you can do titrations with transition metals too. And the best bit is, you don't even need an indicator because the transition metal ions change colour all on their own.

Performing titrations

You can use titrations to find out how much oxidising agent is needed to exactly react with a quantity of reducing agent. If you know the concentration of either the oxidising agent or the reducing agent, you can use the titration results to work out the concentration of the other.

Transition metals have variable oxidation states which means they are often present in either the oxidising or reducing agent. Their colour changes also make them useful in titrations as it's easy to spot the end point.

- First you measure out a quantity of reducing agent (e.g. aqueous Fe^{2+} ions or aqueous $C_2O_4^{2-}$ ions) using a pipette, and put it in a conical flask.
- Using a measuring cylinder, you add about 20 cm^3 of dilute sulfuric acid to the flask — this is in excess, so you don't have to be too exact. The acid is added to make sure there are plenty of H^+ ions to allow the oxidising agent to be reduced.
- Now you add the oxidising agent, e.g. aqueous potassium manganate(VII), to the reducing agent using a burette, swirling the conical flask as you go.
- The oxidising agent that you add reacts with the reducing agent. This reaction will continue until all of the reducing agent is used up.
- The very next drop you add to the flask will give the mixture the colour of the oxidising agent. (You could use a coloured reducing agent and a colourless oxidising agent instead — then you'd be watching for the moment that the colour in the flask disappears.)
- Stop when the mixture in the flask just becomes tainted with the colour of the oxidising agent (the end point) and record the volume of the oxidising agent added. This is the rough titration.
- Now you do some accurate titrations. You need to do a few until you get two or more readings that are within 0.10 cm^3 of each other.

The equipment you'll need to do a titration is shown in Figure 2.

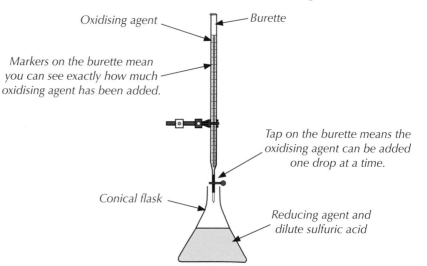

Figure 2: *The equipment needed to perform a titration.*

Titration reactions

You need to know the titration reactions of the reducing agents Fe^{2+} and $C_2O_4^{2-}$ ions with the oxidising agent manganate(VII), MnO_4^-, in aqueous potassium manganate(VII):

- Titration of Fe^{2+} with MnO_4^-:

$$MnO_4^-{}_{(aq)} + 8H^+{}_{(aq)} + 5Fe^{2+}{}_{(aq)} \rightarrow Mn^{2+}{}_{(aq)} + 4H_2O_{(l)} + 5Fe^{3+}{}_{(aq)}$$

- Titration of $C_2O_4^{2-}$ with MnO_4^-:

$$2MnO_4^-{}_{(aq)} + 16H^+{}_{(aq)} + 5C_2O_4^{2-}{}_{(aq)} \rightarrow 2Mn^{2+}{}_{(aq)} + 8H_2O_{(l)} + 10CO_{2(g)}$$

The solution turns purple at the end point of these reactions (see Figure 3).

Calculating the concentration of a reagent

Once you've done a titration you can use your results to calculate the concentration of either the oxidising agent or the reducing agent. To do this:

Figure 3: *$KMnO_4$ being added to Fe^{2+} ions. The solution turns purple at the end point.*

Step 1: Write out a balanced equation for the redox reaction that's happening in the conical flask.

Step 2: Decide what you know already and what you need to know — usually you'll know the two volumes and the concentration of one of the reagents and want to find the concentration of the other reagent.

Step 3: For the reagent you know both the concentration and the volume for, calculate the number of moles of this reagent using the equation:

$$\text{moles} = \frac{\text{concentration} \, (\text{mol dm}^{-3}) \times \text{volume} \, (\text{cm}^3)}{1000}$$

Step 4: Use the molar ratios in the balanced equation to find out how many moles of the other reagent were present in the solution.

Step 5: Calculate the unknown concentration using the equation:

$$\text{concentration} \, (\text{mol dm}^{-3}) = \frac{\text{moles} \times 1000}{\text{volume} \, (\text{cm}^3)}$$

┌─ **Example** ── **Maths Skills** ─────────────────────

27.5 cm³ of 0.0200 mol dm⁻³ aqueous potassium manganate(VII) reacted with 12.5 cm³ of acidified sodium ethanedioate solution.
Calculate the concentration of $C_2O_4^{2-}$ ions in the solution.

1. The balanced equation for this titration reaction is:

$$2MnO_4^-{}_{(aq)} + 16H^+{}_{(aq)} + 5C_2O_4^{2-}{}_{(aq)} \rightarrow 2Mn^{2+}{}_{(aq)} + 8H_2O_{(l)} + 10CO_{2(g)}$$

2. Work out the number of moles of MnO_4^- ions.

$$\text{moles } MnO_4^- = \frac{\text{conc.} \times \text{volume}}{1000} = \frac{0.0200 \times 27.5}{1000} = 5.50 \times 10^{-4} \text{ moles}$$

3. From the molar ratios in the equation, you know 2 moles of MnO_4^- reacts with 5 moles of $C_2O_4^{2-}$. So 5.50×10^{-4} moles of MnO_4^- must react with $(5.50 \times 10^{-4} \times 5) \div 2 = 1.375 \times 10^{-3}$ moles of $C_2O_4^{2-}$.

4. Calculate the concentration of $C_2O_4^{2-}$:

$$\text{conc. } C_2O_4^{2-} = \frac{\text{moles} \times 1000}{\text{volume}}$$

$$= \frac{(1.375 \times 10^{-3}) \times 1000}{12.5} = \textbf{0.110 mol dm}^{-3}$$

Tip: $C_2O_4^{2-}$ is called ethanedioate.

Tip: These calculations are the same as those for acid-base titrations covered on page 110.

Tip: In these calculations the units of concentration should always be mol dm⁻³.

Calculating the volume of a reagent

If you know the concentration of both the solutions, you can calculate unknown volumes. You follow the same steps as if you were trying to find the concentration — but at the end, you rearrange the equation to find the volume instead.

Example ── **Maths Skills** ─────────────────────────────

Aqueous potassium manganate(VII) with a concentration of 8.00×10^{-3} mol dm^{-3} was used to completely oxidise 25.0 cm^3 of 0.0600 mol dm^{-3} acidified iron(II) sulfate solution. Calculate the volume of potassium manganate(VII) solution that was used in the reaction.

1. The balanced equation for this titration reaction is:

$$MnO_4{}^{2-}{}_{(aq)} + 8H^+{}_{(aq)} + 5Fe^{2+}{}_{(aq)} \rightarrow Mn^{2+}{}_{(aq)} + 4H_2O_{(l)} + 5Fe^{3+}{}_{(aq)}$$

2. Work out the number of moles of Fe^{2+} ions.

$$\text{moles Fe}^{2+} = \frac{\text{conc.} \times \text{volume}}{1000} = \frac{0.0600 \times 25.0}{1000} = 1.50 \times 10^{-3} \text{ moles}$$

3. From molar ratios in the equation, you know that 5 moles of Fe^{2+} react with 1 mole of MnO$_4{}^{2-}$. So 1.50×10^{-3} moles of Fe^{2+} must react with $1.50 \times 10^{-3} \div 5 = 3.00 \times 10^{-4}$ moles.

4. Calculate the volume of the MnO$_4{}^{2-}$ ion solution :

$$\text{volume of MnO}_4{}^{2-} = \frac{\text{moles} \times 1000}{\text{conc.}} = \frac{(3.00 \times 10^{-4}) \times 1000}{0.00800} = \mathbf{37.5 \text{ cm}^3}$$

Practice Questions — Application

Q1 28.3 cm^3 of a 0.0500 mol dm^{-3} acidified iron(II) sulfate solution reacted exactly with 30.0 cm^3 of aqueous potassium manganate(VII). Calculate the concentration of the potassium manganate(VII) solution.

Q2 Aqueous potassium manganate(VII) with a concentration of 0.0750 mol dm^{-3} was used to completely react with 28.0 cm^3 of a 0.600 mol dm^{-3} solution of acidified sodium ethanedioate. Calculate the volume of potassium manganate(VII) solution used.

Q3 A 0.450 mol dm^{-3} solution of acidified iron(II) sulfate completely reacted with 24.0 cm^3 of a 0.0550 mol dm^{-3} solution of aqueous potassium manganate(VII). Calculate the volume of iron(II) sulfate solution used.

Exam Tip
These questions are quite wordy. You might find it helpful to highlight the key bits of information in the question that you're going to use.

Practice Questions — Fact Recall

Q1 Why is acid added to the reducing agent in redox titrations?

Q2 a) Name an oxidising agent used in redox titrations.

  b) What colour change would be observed if the oxidising agent from your answer to part a) was added to a colourless reducing agent?

8. Transition Metal Catalysts

A catalyst is something that speeds up the rate of a reaction by providing an alternative reaction pathway with a lower activation energy and doesn't get used up — you learnt all about them in Year 1. Transition metals make really good catalysts.

Why transition metals make good catalysts

Transition metals and their compounds make good **catalysts** because they can change oxidation states by gaining or losing electrons within their d orbitals. This means they can transfer electrons to speed up reactions.

--- Example ---

The **Contact Process** is used industrially to make sulfuric acid. One of the key steps in this process is:

$$SO_{2(g)} + \tfrac{1}{2}O_{2(g)} \xrightarrow{\text{V}_2\text{O}_{5(s)} \text{ catalyst}} SO_{3(g)}$$

Vanadium(V) oxide (V_2O_5) catalyses this reaction in two steps.
First, vanadium(V) oxide oxidises SO_2 to SO_3 and is itself reduced to vanadium(IV) oxide:

$$V_2O_5 + SO_2 \rightarrow V_2O_4 + SO_3$$

The reduced catalyst is then oxidised by oxygen gas back to its original state:

$$V_2O_4 + \tfrac{1}{2}O_2 \rightarrow V_2O_5$$

Vanadium(V) oxide is able to oxidise SO_2 to SO_3 because it can be reduced to vanadium(IV) oxide. It's then oxidised back to vanadium(V) oxide by oxygen ready to start all over again. If vanadium didn't have a variable oxidation state, it wouldn't be able to catalyse this reaction.

Elements in the other blocks of the periodic table (e.g. the s block) generally aren't used to catalyse redox reactions because they don't have an incomplete 3d sub-level and don't have variable oxidation states.

Heterogeneous catalysts

A **heterogeneous catalyst** is one that is in a different phase from the reactants — i.e. in a different physical state.

--- Examples ---

There are two examples of heterogenous catalysts that you need to know about.

1. Iron, which is used in the **Haber Process** for making ammonia:

$$N_{2(g)} + 3H_{2(g)} \xrightarrow{\text{Fe}_{(s)} \text{ catalyst}} 2NH_{3(g)}$$

2. Vanadium(V) oxide that's used in the Contact Process (see above):

$$SO_{2(g)} + \tfrac{1}{2}O_{2(g)} \xrightarrow{\text{V}_2\text{O}_{5(s)} \text{ catalyst}} SO_{3(g)}$$

In all of these reactions, the catalyst is a solid and the reactants are gases. The gases are passed over the solid catalyst.

Learning Objectives:

- Know that transition metals and their compounds can act as catalysts.
- Understand the importance of variable oxidation states in catalysis.
- Explain, with equations, how V_2O_5 acts as a heterogeneous catalyst in the Contact Process.
- Know that a heterogeneous catalyst is in a different phase from the reactants and that the reaction occurs on the surface.
- Know that Fe is used as a heterogeneous catalyst in the Haber Process.
- Understand the use of a support medium to maximise the surface area of a catalyst and minimise the cost.
- Know that catalysts can become poisoned by impurities and consequently have reduced efficiency, and that this has a cost implication.
- Know that a homogeneous catalyst is in the same phase as the reactants.
- Know that in homogeneous catalysis, the reaction proceeds through an intermediate species.
- Explain, with equations, how Fe^{2+} ions catalyse the reaction between I^- and $S_2O_8^{2-}$, and how Mn^{2+} ions autocatalyse the reaction between $C_2O_4^{2-}$ and MnO_4^-.

Specification Reference 3.2.5.6

Use of a support medium

When a heterogenous catalyst is used, the reaction happens on the surface of the catalyst. So increasing the surface area of the catalyst increases the number of molecules that can react at the same time, increasing the rate of the reaction. A support medium is often used to make the area of a catalyst as large as possible.

Example

Catalytic converters (which 'clean up' emissions from car engines) contain a ceramic lattice coated with a thin layer of rhodium. The rhodium acts as a catalyst helping to convert the really nasty waste gases to less harmful products. Here's one of the reactions that occurs in a catalytic converter:

$$2CO_{(g)} + 2NO_{(g)} \xrightarrow{\text{Rh}_{(s)} \text{ catalyst}} 2CO_{2(g)} + N_{2(g)}$$

The lattice structure maximises the surface area of the catalyst, making it more effective. And it minimises the cost of the catalyst because only a thin coating is needed.

Figure 1: A catalytic converter fitted to a car.

Tip: Adsorbed means stuck to the surface.

Tip: Catalytic poisoning is only a problem for heterogenous catalysts — homogenous catalysts aren't affected because the reaction doesn't occur on their surface.

Tip: A lead compound called TEL used to be added to petrol to help engines run smoothly. It was phased out in the 80s and 90s so catalytic converters could be used (and also because lead is really poisonous).

Tip: Don't get confused between homogenous and heterogenous catalysts. Just remember — homo- means 'same' and homogeneous catalysts are in the same phase as the reactants.

Catalyst poisoning

During a reaction, reactants are adsorbed onto active sites on the surfaces of heterogeneous catalysts. Impurities in the reaction mixture may also bind to the catalyst's surface and block reactants from being adsorbed. This process is called **catalyst poisoning**. Catalyst poisoning reduces the surface area of the catalyst available to the reactants, slowing down the reaction. It also increases the cost of a chemical process because less product can be made in a certain time or with a certain amount of energy. The catalyst may even need replacing or regenerating, which also costs money.

Examples

Lead poisons the catalyst in catalytic converters:
Catalytic converters reduce harmful emissions from car engines. Lead can coat the surface of the catalyst in a catalytic converter, so vehicles that have them fitted must only be run on unleaded petrol.

Sulfur poisons the iron catalyst in the Haber process:
The hydrogen in the Haber process is produced from methane. The methane is obtained from natural gas, which contains impurities, including sulfur compounds. Any sulfur that is not removed is adsorbed onto the iron, forming iron sulfide, and stopping the iron from catalysing the reaction efficiently.

Catalyst poisoning can be reduced by purifying the reactants. This removes many of the impurities which would otherwise poison the catalyst.

Homogeneous catalysts

Homogeneous catalysts are in the same physical state as the reactants. Usually a homogeneous catalyst is an aqueous catalyst for a reaction between two aqueous solutions.

A homogeneous catalyst works by forming an intermediate species. The reactants combine with the catalyst to make an intermediate species, which then reacts to form the products and reform the catalyst. This causes the enthalpy profile for a homogeneously catalysed reaction to have two humps in it, corresponding to the two reactions. The activation energy needed to form the intermediates (and to form the products from the intermediates) is lower than that needed to make the products directly from the reactants (see Figure 2).

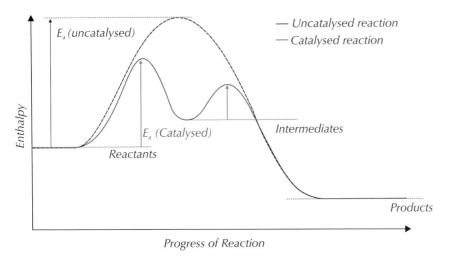

Figure 2: Enthalpy profile for a reaction with a homogenous catalyst. E_a represents the activation energy.

Tip: You met enthalpy profile diagrams in Year 1 so if you need a quick reminder about what it all means — get your old Year 1 notes out.

The catalyst is always reformed so it can carry on catalysing the reaction. There are two reactions catalysed by homogenous catalysts that you need to know about:

Fe²⁺ catalysing the reaction between $S_2O_8^{2-}$ and I^-

The redox reaction between iodide ions and peroxodisulfate ($S_2O_8^{2-}$) ions is shown below:

$$S_2O_8^{2-}{}_{(aq)} + 2I^-{}_{(aq)} \rightarrow I_{2(aq)} + 2SO_4^{2-}{}_{(aq)}$$

Tip: Fe^{2+}, $S_2O_8^{2-}$ and I^- are all in the aqueous phase so Fe^{2+} is a homogenous catalyst.

This reaction takes place annoyingly slowly because both ions are negatively charged. The ions repel each other, so it's unlikely they'll collide and react. But if Fe^{2+} ions are added, things are really speeded up because each stage of the reaction involves a positive and a negative ion, so there's no repulsion. First, the Fe^{2+} ions are oxidised to Fe^{3+} ions by the $S_2O_8^{2-}$ ions:

$$S_2O_8^{2-}{}_{(aq)} + 2Fe^{2+}{}_{(aq)} \rightarrow 2Fe^{3+}{}_{(aq)} + 2SO_4^{2-}{}_{(aq)}$$

Tip: The negative charges of the two ions is one reason why this reaction has high activation energy.

The newly formed intermediate Fe^{3+} ions now easily oxidise the I^- ions to iodine, and the catalyst is regenerated:

$$2Fe^{3+}{}_{(aq)} + 2I^-{}_{(aq)} \rightarrow I_{2(aq)} + 2Fe^{2+}{}_{(aq)}$$

You can test for iodine by adding starch solution — it'll turn blue-black if iodine is present — see Figure 3.

Mn²⁺ autocatalysing the reaction between MnO_4^- and $C_2O_4^{2-}$

Another example of a homogeneous catalyst is Mn^{2+} in the reaction between $C_2O_4^{2-}$ and MnO_4^-. It's an **autocatalysis** reaction because Mn^{2+} is a product of the reaction and acts as a catalyst for the reaction. This means that as the reaction progresses and the amount of the product increases, the reaction speeds up. The equation for this reaction is shown below:

$$2MnO_4^-{}_{(aq)} + 16H^+{}_{(aq)} + 5C_2O_4^{2-}{}_{(aq)} \rightarrow 2Mn^{2+}{}_{(aq)} + 8H_2O_{(l)} + 10CO_{2(g)}$$

Figure 3: A starch test for iodine. Starch solution is added and the solution turns black if iodine is present.

There isn't any Mn^{2+} present at the beginning of the reaction to catalyse it, so at first the rate of reaction is very slow. During this uncatalysed part of the reaction, the activation energy is very high. This is because the reaction proceeds via the collision of negative ions, which requires a lot of energy to achieve. But once a little bit of the Mn^{2+} catalyst has been made it reacts with the MnO_4^- ions to make Mn^{3+} ions:

$$4Mn^{2+}_{(aq)} + MnO_4^-{}_{(aq)} + 8H^+_{(aq)} \rightarrow 5Mn^{3+}_{(aq)} + 4H_2O_{(l)}$$

The Mn^{3+} ions are the intermediate. They then react with the $C_2O_4^{2-}$ ions to make CO_2 and reform the Mn^{2+} catalyst:

$$2Mn^{3+}_{(aq)} + C_2O_4^{2-}{}_{(aq)} \rightarrow 2Mn^{2+}_{(aq)} + 2CO_{2(g)}$$

Because Mn^{2+} autocatalyses the reaction, the rate of reaction increases with time as more catalyst is made. This means a concentration-time graph for this reaction looks a bit unusual — see Figure 4.

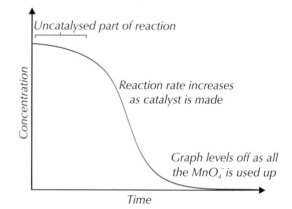

Figure 4: *Concentration-time graph for a reaction where autocatalysis is taking place.*

Practice Question — Application

Q1 Manganese dioxide ($MnO_{2(s)}$) is used as a catalyst for the following reaction: $2H_2O_{2(l)} \rightarrow 2H_2O_{(l)} + O_{2(g)}$

  a) What type of catalyst is MnO_2 in this reaction?
  b) Explain why MnO_2 can act as a catalyst.

Practice Questions — Fact Recall

Q1 What are heterogenous catalysts and homogenous catalysts?
Q2 Give two examples of industrial processes which use a heterogenous catalyst. For each example, name the catalyst and write an equation for the reaction it catalyses.
Q3 Why is a heterogenous catalyst often spread over a support medium?
Q4 What is catalytic poisoning and how can it be reduced?
Q5 Explain how Fe^{2+} speeds up the rate of reaction between $S_2O_8^{2-}$ and I^-.
Q6 What is autocatalysis? Give an example of a reaction where it occurs.

9. Metal-Aqua Ions

This topic's all about complex ions and their reactions. If you've forgotten what complex ions are have a quick look back at pages 134-136.

Hydration of metal ions

Co-ordinate bonds always involve one substance donating an electron pair to another. When metal compounds dissolve in water, the water molecules form co-ordinate bonds with the metal ions. This forms **metal-aqua complex ions**. In general, six water molecules form co-ordinate bonds with each metal ion. The water molecules do this by donating a non-bonding pair of electrons from their oxygen.

--- Examples ---

Copper can form the metal-aqua ion $[Cu(H_2O)_6]^{2+}$.
Each H_2O ligand donates a lone pair of electrons to the copper ion, forming a co-ordinate bond.

co-ordinate bond

$[Cu(H_2O)_6]^{2+}$

The diagrams show the metal-aqua ions formed by iron(II) — $[Fe(H_2O)_6]^{2+}$ and by aluminium — $[Al(H_2O)_6]^{3+}$.

$[Fe(H_2O)_6]^{2+}$ $[Al(H_2O)_6]^{3+}$

Water molecules are neutral, so the charge on the complex ion must also be the charge on the metal ion.

The acidity of metal-aqua ion solutions

In a solution containing metal-aqua 2+ ions, there's a reaction between the metal-aqua ion and the water — this is a hydrolysis or acidity reaction. The metal-aqua 2+ ions release H^+ ions, so an acidic solution is formed. There's only slight dissociation though, so the solution is only weakly acidic.

Learning Objectives:

- Know that metal-aqua ions are formed in aqueous solution: $[M(H_2O)_6]^{2+}$, limited to M = Fe and Cu, $[M(H_2O)_6]^{3+}$, limited to M = Al and Fe.

- Understand that the acidity of $[M(H_2O)_6]^{3+}$ is greater than that of $[M(H_2O)_6]^{2+}$.

- Be able to explain, in terms of the charge/size ratio of the metal ion, why the acidity of $[M(H_2O)_6]^{3+}$ is greater than that of $[M(H_2O)_6]^{2+}$.

- Know that some metal hydroxides show amphoteric character by dissolving in both acids and bases (e.g. hydroxides of Al^{3+}).

- Be able to describe and explain the simple test tube reactions of $M^{2+}_{(aq)}$ ions, limited to M = Fe and Cu, and of $M^{3+}_{(aq)}$ ions, limited to M = Al and Fe, with the bases OH^-, NH_3 and CO_3^{2-}.

- Know how to carry out simple test tube reactions to identify transition metal ions in aqueous solution. (Required Practical 11).

Specification Reference 3.2.6

Tip: Iron can form metal-aqua complexes in the oxidation states +2 and +3, so it can form the complexes $[Fe(H_2O)_6]^{2+}$ and $[Fe(H_2O)_6]^{3+}$.

Example

$[Fe(H_2O)_6]^{2+}$ will dissociate in water to form $[Fe(OH)(H_2O)_5]^+$:

$$[Fe(H_2O)_6]^{2+}_{(aq)} + H_2O_{(l)} \rightleftharpoons [Fe(OH)(H_2O)_5]^+_{(aq)} + H_3O^+_{(aq)}$$

Metal-aqua 3+ ions react in the same way. They form more acidic solutions though.

Example

$[Al(H_2O)_6]^{3+}$ will dissociate in water to form $[Al(OH)(H_2O)_5]^{2+}$:

$$[Al(H_2O)_6]^{3+}_{(aq)} + H_2O_{(l)} \rightleftharpoons [Al(OH)(H_2O)_5]^{2+}_{(aq)} + H_3O^+_{(aq)}$$

Relative acidity of 2+ and 3+ metal-aqua ion solutions

Metal 3+ ions are pretty small but have a big charge — so they've got a high charge density (otherwise known as charge/size ratio). The metal 2+ ions have a much lower charge density. This makes the 3+ ions much more polarising than the 2+ ions. More polarising power means that they attract electrons from the oxygen atoms of the co-ordinated water molecules more strongly, weakening the O–H bond. So it's more likely that a hydrogen ion will be released. And more hydrogen ions means a more acidic solution — so metal 3+ ions are more acidic than metal 2+ ions.

Further hydrolysis of metal-aqua ions

Adding OH⁻ ions to solutions of metal-aqua 3+ ions produces insoluble precipitates of metal hydroxides. Here's why:

- In water, metal-aqua 3+ ions form the equilibrium:

$$[M(H_2O)_6]^{3+}_{(aq)} + H_2O_{(l)} \rightleftharpoons [M(OH)(H_2O)_5]^{2+}_{(aq)} + H_3O^+_{(aq)}$$

If you add OH⁻ ions to the equilibrium H_3O^+ ions are removed — this shifts the equilibrium to the right.

- Now another equilibrium is set up in the solution:

$$[M(OH)(H_2O)_5]^{2+}_{(aq)} + H_2O_{(l)} \rightleftharpoons [M(OH)_2(H_2O)_4]^+_{(aq)} + H_3O^+_{(aq)}$$

Again the OH⁻ ions remove H_3O^+ ions from the solution, pulling the equilibrium to the right.

- This happens one last time — now you're left with an insoluble uncharged metal hydroxide:

$$[M(OH)_2(H_2O)_4]^+_{(aq)} + H_2O_{(l)} \rightleftharpoons M(OH)_3(H_2O)_{3(s)} + H_3O^+_{(aq)}$$

- The overall equation for this reaction is:

$$[M(H_2O)_6]^{3+}_{(aq)} + 3H_2O_{(l)} \rightleftharpoons M(OH)_3(H_2O)_{3(s)} + 3H_3O^+_{(aq)}$$

Figure 1: Metal-aqua ion precipitates. From left to right — copper(II) hydroxide, iron(II) hydroxide iron(III) hydroxide, and aluminium(III) hydroxide.

The same thing happens with metal-aqua 2+ ions (e.g. Fe or Cu), except this time there are only two steps:

Step 1: $[M(H_2O)_6]^{2+}_{(aq)} + H_2O_{(l)} \rightleftharpoons [M(OH)(H_2O)_5]^+_{(aq)} + H_3O^+_{(aq)}$

Step 2: $[M(OH)(H_2O)_5]^+_{(aq)} + H_2O_{(l)} \rightleftharpoons M(OH)_2(H_2O)_{4(s)} + H_3O^+_{(aq)}$

Example

Adding NaOH to a solution of iron 3+ ions will produce a brown precipitate.

$$[Fe(H_2O)_6]^{3+}_{(aq)} + H_2O_{(l)} \rightleftharpoons [Fe(OH)(H_2O)_5]^{2+}_{(aq)} + H_3O^+_{(aq)}$$

$$[Fe(OH)(H_2O)_5]^{2+}_{(aq)} + H_2O_{(l)} \rightleftharpoons [Fe(OH)_2(H_2O)_4]^+_{(aq)} + H_3O^+_{(aq)}$$

$$[Fe(OH)_2(H_2O)_4]^+_{(aq)} + H_2O_{(l)} \rightleftharpoons Fe(OH)_3(H_2O)_{3(s)} + H_3O^+_{(aq)}$$

brown precipitate

All the metal hydroxide precipitates will dissolve in acid. They act as Brønsted-Lowry bases and accept H+ ions. This reverses the hydrolysis reactions above.

Example

Adding an acid to iron(III) hydroxide will reform the soluble metal-aqua ion.

$$Fe(OH)_3(H_2O)_{3(s)} + H^+_{(aq)} \rightleftharpoons [Fe(OH)_2(H_2O)_4]^+_{(aq)}$$

$$[Fe(OH)_2(H_2O)_4]^+_{(aq)} + H^+_{(aq)} \rightleftharpoons [Fe(OH)(H_2O)_5]^{2+}_{(aq)}$$

$$[Fe(OH)(H_2O)_5]^{2+}_{(aq)} + H^+_{(aq)} \rightleftharpoons [Fe(H_2O)_6]^{3+}_{(aq)}$$

Some metal hydroxides are **amphoteric** — they can act as both acids and bases. This means they'll dissolve in an excess of base as well as in acids.

Example

Aluminium hydroxide is amphoteric. It acts as a Brønsted-Lowry acid and donates H+ ions to the OH- ions:

$$Al(OH)_3(H_2O)_{3(s)} + OH^-_{(aq)} \rightleftharpoons [Al(OH)_4(H_2O)_2]^-_{(aq)} + H_2O_{(l)}$$

It can also act as a Brønsted-Lowry base and accept H+ ions:

$$Al(OH)_3(H_2O)_{3(s)} + 3H^+_{(aq)} \rightleftharpoons [Al(H_2O)_6]^{3+}_{(aq)}$$

Figure 2: Brown precipitate of iron(III) hydroxide.

Figure 3: Limonitic rocks. The rocks contain a large amount of hydrated iron(III) hydroxide, which gives them their distinctive reddish brown colour.

Hydrolysis of metal-aqua ions using NH₃

The obvious way of adding hydroxide ions is to use a strong alkali, like sodium hydroxide solution — but you can use ammonia solution too. When ammonia dissolves in water it can accept protons from the water molecules to form NH_4^+ ions and OH- ligands. This gives the same results as adding NaOH.

Example

$[Fe(H_2O)_6]^{3+}_{(aq)}$ will react with ammonia to form a $Fe(OH)_3(H_2O)_3$ complex.

$$[Fe(H_2O)_6]^{3+}_{(aq)} + 3NH_{3(aq)} \rightleftharpoons Fe(OH)_3(H_2O)_{3(s)} + 3NH_4^+_{(aq)}$$

yellow solution   *brown precipitate*

In some cases, a further reaction happens if you add an excess of ammonia solution — the H_2O and OH- ligands are displaced by NH_3 ligands. This will happen with Cu^{2+} complexes.

Example

Copper(II) hydroxide will react with excess ammonia to form a $[Cu(NH_3)_4(H_2O)_2]^{2+}$ complex.

$$[Cu(OH)_6]^{4-}_{(aq)} + 4NH_{3(aq)} \rightleftharpoons [Cu(NH_3)_4(H_2O)_2]^{2+}_{(aq)} + 6OH^-_{(aq)}$$

pale blue solution   *dark blue solution*

Exam Tip
Make sure you remember that it's Cu(II) ions that will react with excess ammonia — Fe(II), Fe(III), and Al(III) ions won't.

Hydrolysis of metal-aqua ions using Na_2CO_3

Metal 2+ ions react with sodium carbonate to form insoluble metal carbonates, like this:

$$[M(H_2O)_6]^{2+}_{(aq)} + CO_3^{2-}_{(aq)} \rightleftharpoons MCO_{3(s)} + 6H_2O_{(l)}$$

But, metal 3+ ions don't form $M_2(CO_3)_3$ species when you react them with sodium carbonate. They are stronger acids (see page 160) so they always form hydroxide precipitates instead. The carbonate ions react with the H_3O^+ ions, removing them from the solution and forming bubbles of carbon dioxide gas.

$$2[M(H_2O)_6]^{3+}_{(aq)} + 3CO_3^{2-}_{(aq)} \rightleftharpoons 2M(OH)_3(H_2O)_{3(s)} + 3CO_{2(g)} + 3H_2O_{(l)}$$

Figure 4: *Copper(II) carbonate. A green-blue precipitate is formed when carbonate ions react with aqueous copper(II) ions.*

Tests to identify metal ions

REQUIRED PRACTICAL **11**

Test tube reactions provide a qualitative way of working out the identity of unknown metal ions in solution. Adding different reagents, such as sodium hydroxide, ammonia and sodium carbonate, to separate samples of a metal ion solution and recording what you see should help you identify what metal ion is present. Here's what you should do:

- Measure out samples of the unknown metal ion solution into three separate test tubes.
- To the first test tube, add sodium hydroxide solution dropwise using a dropping pipette and record any changes you see. Then add more NaOH dropwise so that it is in excess. Record any changes.
- To the second test tube, add ammonia solution dropwise using a dropping pipette and record any changes you see. Keep adding ammonia so that it's in excess. Record any changes.
- To the third test tube, add sodium carbonate solution dropwise. Record your observations.

Tip: If you're carrying out this practical, don't forget to do a risk assessment. Some of the solutions may irritate your skin and eyes, so make sure you wear gloves, a lab coat and goggles. Ammonia is poisonous if you breathe it in, so it's best to use it in a fume cupboard.

Dropping pipette containing test reagent (sodium hydroxide, ammonia or sodium carbonate).

Solutions containing unknown metal ion.

Figure 5: *The equipment needed to perform metal ion tests.*

On pages 159-162, you learnt about some of the reactions of copper(II), iron(II), iron(III) and aluminium(III) aqua ions. If you had four unknown solutions, each of which contained one of these metal aqua ions, you could use the method above and the differences in their reactions to distinguish between them. Here's how:

Tip: In real life, the colours of the solutions would give you a big clue. In the exam, they might tell you the observations from various reactions, but not the initial colours.

Reactions with sodium hydroxide

All four metal-aqua ions will form precipitates with sodium hydroxide, but only the aluminium hydroxide precipitate will dissolve in an excess of sodium hydroxide. This is because it's amphoteric (see page 161).

solution containing Al^{3+} ions → white precipitate forms → precipitate dissolves in solution

Reactions with ammonia

All four metal-aqua ions will form precipitates with ammonia, but only the copper hydroxide precipitate will dissolve in an excess of ammonia. This is because it undergoes a ligand exchange reaction with excess ammonia (see page 144).

solution containing Cu^{2+} ions → blue precipitate forms → precipitate dissolves and deep blue solution forms

Reactions with sodium carbonate

All four metal-aqua ions will form precipitates with sodium carbonate. The solutions containing Al^{3+} or Fe^{3+} will also form bubbles as CO_2 is formed (see page 162). So if you're not sure whether a sample contains Fe^{2+} or Fe^{3+} ions, (which behave identically in the other two tests), you can use this test to decide — a sample containing Fe^{3+} ions will give off a gas (which you'll see as bubbles forming), whereas a sample containing Fe^{2+} ions won't.

green solution containing Fe^{2+} ions → green precipitate forms

yellow solution containing Fe^{3+} → brown precipitate forms and bubbles are given off

Tip: The solutions should be freshly made — if Fe^{2+} ions are left too long in contact with air, they will oxidise to Fe^{3+} ions.

Tip: In these tests with sodium hydroxide, ammonia and sodium carbonate, you could just look at the colour of the solution or precipitate to identify the ion. However, you need to know the other things that you'd expect to see, so you can't just learn the colours.

Complex ion solutions and precipitates

This handy table summarises all the compounds that are formed in the reactions on these pages. You need to know the formulas of all the complex ions, and their colours.

Metal-aqua ion	With $OH^-_{(aq)}$ or $NH_{3(aq)}$	With excess $OH^-_{(aq)}$	With excess $NH_{3(aq)}$	With $Na_2CO_{3(aq)}$
$[Cu(H_2O)_6]^{2+}$ blue solution	$Cu(OH)_2(H_2O)_4$ blue precipitate	no change	$[Cu(NH_3)_4(H_2O)_2]^{2+}$ deep blue solution	$CuCO_3$ green-blue precipitate
$[Fe(H_2O)_6]^{2+}$ green solution	$Fe(OH)_2(H_2O)_4$ green precipitate	no change	no change	$FeCO_3$ green precipitate
$[Al(H_2O)_6]^{3+}$ colourless solution	$Al(OH)_3(H_2O)_3$ white precipitate	$[Al(OH)_4(H_2O)_2]^-$ colourless solution	no change	$Al(OH)_3(H_2O)_3$ white precipitate and bubbles
$[Fe(H_2O)_6]^{3+}$ yellow solution	$Fe(OH)_3(H_2O)_3$ brown precipitate	no change	no change	$Fe(OH)_3(H_2O)_3$ brown precipitate and bubbles

Practice Question — Application

Q1 A student has an unknown metal-aqua ion. When she adds sodium carbonate to the aqueous metal-aqua ion a green-blue precipitate forms. What metal ion could be present in the solution?

Practice Questions — Fact Recall

Q1 What type of bonds hold metal-aqua ion complexes together?

Q2 Explain why metal-aqua 3+ ions are more acidic than metal-aqua 2+ ions.

Q3 Write equations to show what happens when OH^- ions are added to aqueous iron(III) ions.

Q4 What would you observe if you added a small amount of OH^- ions to aqueous aluminium(III) ions?

Q5 What would you observe if excess NH_3 was added to aqueous copper(II) ions?

Section Summary

Make sure you know...

- That the chemical properties of the transition metals are due to the incomplete d sub-level.
- That transition metal characteristics include complex ion formation, formation of coloured ions, catalytic activity, and variable oxidation states.
- That a complex ion is a metal ion surrounded by co-ordinately bonded ligands.
- That a ligand is an atom, ion or molecule that donates a pair of electrons to a central metal ion.
- The difference between monodentate (e.g. NH_3, H_2O, Cl^-), bidentate (e.g. $NH_2CH_2CH_2NH_2$, $C_2O_4^-$) and multidentate (e.g. $EDTA^{4-}$) ligands.
- That the co-ordination number is the number of co-ordinate bonds formed by the central metal ion.
- That complex ions with six co-ordinate bonds usually form octahedral complexes.
- That complex ions with four co-ordinate bonds can form tetrahedral or square planar complexes.
- That silver complexes can have two co-ordinate bonds and form linear complexes.
- That octahedral complexes can display optical isomerism with three bidentate ligands.
- That octahedral and square planar complexes can display *cis-trans* isomerism with monodentate ligands.
- That the anti-cancer drug cisplatin is a *cis* isomer.
- That energy from visible light can cause d electrons to jump from a lower energy orbital (ground state) to a higher energy orbital (excited state).
- That the energy difference between the ground state and excited state is given by $\Delta E = h\nu = hc/\lambda$.
- That transition metal ions can be identified by their colour.
- That frequencies of light which aren't absorbed are reflected and this gives complex ions colour.
- That changes in oxidation state, co-ordination number and ligand can cause changes in colour.
- How the concentration of a solution of complex ions can be determined using spectroscopy.
- That the exchange of similarly sized ligands occurs without change of co-ordination number.
- That the Cl^- ligand is larger than the uncharged ligands NH_3 and H_2O.

- That the exchange of the ligand H_2O by Cl^- can involve a change in co-ordination number because Cl^- is larger than H_2O.
- That substitution reactions may be incomplete.
- That haem is an iron(II) complex with a multidentate ligand.
- That oxygen forms a co-ordinate bond to Fe(II) in haemoglobin, enabling oxygen to be transported in the blood.
- That carbon monoxide is toxic because it replaces oxygen co-ordinately bonded to Fe(II) in haemoglobin.
- That the chelate effect is when complexes become more stable after monodentate ligands are replaced by bidentate and multidentate ligands, because there is a small change in enthalpy and a large, positive change in entropy.
- That vanadium species in oxidation states IV, III, and II are formed by the reduction of vanadate(V) ions by zinc in acidic solution
- That the redox potential for a transition metal ion changing from a higher to a lower oxidation state is influenced by pH and by the ligand.
- That the reduction of $[Ag(NH_3)_2]^+$ (Tollens' reagent) to metallic silver is used to distinguish between aldehydes and ketones.
- That transition metals can be used in titrations — specifically Fe^{2+} and $C_2O_4^{2-}$ with MnO_4^-.
- How to calculate the concentration or volume of a reagent using titration results.
- That the variable oxidation states of transition metals means they make good catalysts.
- That a heterogeneous catalyst is in a different phase from the reactants (and that the reaction occurs on its surface) and that a homogeneous catalyst is in the same phase as the reactants (and that the reaction proceeds through an intermediate species).
- That V_2O_5 acts as a heterogeneous catalyst in the Contact Process and that Fe is used as a heterogeneous catalyst in the Haber process.
- That a support medium can maximise the surface area of heterogenous catalysts and minimise the costs involved in reactions.
- That heterogeneous catalysts can become poisoned by impurities, leading to reduced efficiency, which increases the cost involved in reactions.
- How Fe^{2+} ions catalyse the reaction between $S_2O_8^-$ and I^-, and how Mn^{2+} ions autocatalyse the reaction between MnO_4^- and $C_2O_4^{2-}$.
- That Fe(II) and Cu(II) ions form metal-aqua ions $[M(H_2O)_6]^{2+}$ in solution.
- That Al(III) and Fe(III) ions form metal-aqua ions $[M(H_2O)_6]^{3+}$ in solution.
- That $[M(H_2O)_6]^{3+}$ is more acidic than $[M(H_2O)_6]^{2+}$ due to the difference in the charge/size ratio of the metal ions.
- That some metal hydroxides (e.g. hydroxides of Al^{3+}) show amphoteric character by dissolving in both acids and bases.
- The reactions of $Fe^{2+}_{(aq)}$, $Cu^{2+}_{(aq)}$, $Al^{3+}_{(aq)}$ and $Fe^{3+}_{(aq)}$ ions with the bases OH^-, NH_3 and CO_3^{2-} and be able to explain them.
- How to carry out simple test tube reactions to identify transition metal ions in aqueous solution.

Exam-style Questions

1   Which of the following shows an incorrect electron configuration for the given
     transition element?

     A   vanadium: $1s^2\ 2s^2\ 2p^6\ 3s^2\ 3p^6\ 3d^3\ 4s^2$

     B   chromium: $1s^2\ 2s^2\ 2p^6\ 3s^2\ 3p^6\ 3d^5\ 4s^1$

     C   manganese: $1s^2\ 2s^2\ 2p^6\ 3s^2\ 3p^6\ 3d^6\ 4s^1$

     D   iron: $1s^2\ 2s^2\ 2p^6\ 3s^2\ 3p^6\ 3d^6\ 4s^2$

                                                                    (1 mark)

2   Which of the following statements about the transition metal complex
     $[Cu(H_2O)_6]^{2+}_{(aq)}$ is untrue?

     A   When chloride ions are added, a square planar complex is formed.

     B   When $NaOH_{(aq)}$ is added, a blue precipitate is formed.

     C   When excess $NH_{3(aq)}$ is added, a deep blue solution is formed.

     D $[Cu(H_2O)_6]^{2+}_{(aq)}$ is octahedral and blue in solution.

                                                                    (1 mark)

3   A student is given an unknown solution containing a transition metal-aqua complex
     and asked to identify the ion present. The student carries out three tests on three
     separate samples, the results of which are shown below.

     Test 1: A few drops of $NaOH_{(aq)}$ are added to the unknown solution and a precipitate
             forms. More $NaOH_{(aq)}$ is added until it is in excess and no change is
             observed.

     Test 2: A few drops of $NH_{3(aq)}$ are added to the unknown solution and a precipitate
             forms. More $NH_{3(aq)}$ is added until it is in excess and no change is observed.

     Test 3: A few drops of $Na_2CO_{3(aq)}$ are added to the unknown solution and no gas
             bubbles were observed.

     What is the unknown transition metal ion?

     A   Al(III)

     B   Fe(II)

     C   Cu(II)

     D   Fe(III)

                                                                    (1 mark)

4   Brass is an alloy of mainly copper and zinc.

Dissolving brass in acid produces a solution which contains aqueous copper ions.

4.1   What colour is the aqueous Cu^{2+} ion?

(1 mark)

4.2   Write down the full electron configurations of the copper atom and the Cu^{2+} ion.

(2 marks)

4.3   Explain why the Cu^{2+} ion has the chemical properties associated with transition metal elements.

(1 mark)

In the solution, the $[Cu(H_2O)_6]^{2+}$ complex ion forms.
In this complex ion, water acts as a ligand.

(1 mark)

4.4   Draw the 3D structure of $[Cu(H_2O)_6]^{2+}$ and state its shape.

(2 marks)

4.5   What is the co-ordination number of this ion?

(1 mark)

4.6   Explain why transition metal complex ions have a colour.

(2 marks)

4.7   Give three factors which can affect the colour of a complex ion.

(3 marks)

5   Many complex ions exist as stereoisomers.

$CoCl_2(NH_3)_2$ exists as two stereoisomers.

5.1   Give the shape of the $CoCl_2(NH_3)_2$ ion.

(1 mark)

5.2   What type of stereoisomerism does $CoCl_2(NH_3)_2$ exhibit?

(1 mark)

5.3   Draw the two possible stereoisomers of $CoCl_2(NH_3)_2$.

(2 marks)

The ethanedioate ion is a bidentate ligand. When it binds to chromium(III) ions it forms a complex ion with stereoisomers. The structure of the ethanedioate ion is shown below.

Ethanedioate ion

5.4   What type of stereoisomerism does $[Cr(C_2O_4)_3]^{3-}$ exhibit?

(1 mark)

5.5   Describe how the ethanedioate ion bonds to the chromium ion.

(2 marks)

5.6   Draw two stereoisomers of $[Cr(C_2O_4)_3]^{3-}$.
You can simplify the structure of the ethanedioate ion if you wish.

(2 marks)

6 Transition metals and their oxides make good catalysts. Rhodium (Rh) is used in catalytic converters to catalyse the reaction shown below:

$$2CO_{(g)} + 2NO_{(g)} \rightarrow 2CO_{2(g)} + N_{2(g)}$$

6.1 Explain why transition metals make good catalysts.

(2 marks)

6.2 What type of catalyst is rhodium in this reaction?

(1 mark)

6.3 Explain why catalytic converters contain a ceramic lattice coated with a thin layer of rhodium rather than a solid rhodium block.

(3 marks)

6.4 The rhodium used in catalytic converters is vulnerable to catalytic poisoning. Explain what catalytic poisoning is.

(3 marks)

Fe^{2+} catalyses this reaction between $S_2O_8{}^{2-}$ and I^-:

$$S_2O_8{}^{2-}{}_{(aq)} + 2I^-{}_{(aq)} \rightarrow I_{2(aq)} + 2SO_4{}^{2-}{}_{(aq)}$$

6.5 Explain why this reaction is extremely slow in the absence of a catalyst.

(2 marks)

6.6 Write two equations to show how Fe^{2+} catalyses this reaction.

(2 marks)

7 Metal-aqua complex ions form when transition metal compounds dissolve in water.

7.1 Describe the bonding in a metal-aqua complex ion.

(2 marks)

7.2 Give the formula of the species formed when Fe^{2+} ions dissolve in water.

(1 mark)

7.3 Write an equation for the reaction of the iron-aqua complex ion and water.

(1 mark)

7.4 Explain why this solution will be less acidic than a solution of Al^{3+} ions dissolved in water.

(4 marks)

7.5 Describe the observation you would expect when a small amount of NaOH is added to the solution of Fe^{2+} ions and water.

(1 mark)

7.6 Identify the species formed when Fe^{3+} ions dissolve in water.

(1 mark)

7.7   Write an equation for the addition of carbonate ions to this species.

(1 mark)

7.8   Describe what you would observe when this reaction takes place.

(2 marks)

When aluminium dissolves in water, $[Al(H_2O)_6]^{3+}$ is formed.

7.9   Write an equation for the ligand substitution reaction between this species
and an excess of ethane-1,2-diamine $(NH_2CH_2CH_2NH_2)$.

(1 mark)

7.10   Explain why the metal complex formed in this reaction is
more stable than $[Al(H_2O)_6]^{3+}$.

(2 marks)

8   Aluminium hydroxide $(Al(OH)_3(H_2O)_{3(aq)})$ is amphoteric.

8.1   Define the term amphoteric.

(1 mark)

8.2   Describe the appearance of aluminium hydroxide.

(1 mark)

8.3   Write an equation for the reaction of aluminium hydroxide with OH^- ions.

(2 marks)

8.4   What type of acid is aluminium hydroxide acting as in this reaction?
Explain your answer.

(2 marks)

9   This question is all about the uses of transition metals.

The key component of Tollens' reagent is a complex ion.

9.1   Identify the complex ion present in Tollens' reagent, sketch it and describe
its structure.

(3 marks)

9.2   State what Tollens' reagent is used for and explain why it can be used for
this purpose.

(3 marks)

9.3   Transition metals can also be used in titrations. In one titration, 15.8 cm³ of
acidified potassium manganate(VII) was needed to completely react with
30.0 cm³ of a 0.150 mol dm⁻³ solution of acidified iron(II) sulfate. Calculate the
concentration of the potassium manganate (VII) solution used.

(4 marks)

9.4   What colour will the solution be at the end point?

(1 mark)

1. Optical Isomerism

Optical isomerism, as with all other isomerism, is to do with how molecules arrange in space. So, if you're struggling to picture what they look like, get your hands on some molecular models to play around with.

What is optical isomerism?

Optical isomerism is a type of **stereoisomerism**. Stereoisomers have the same structural formula, but have their atoms arranged differently in space. Optical isomers have a **chiral** carbon atom. A chiral (or asymmetric) carbon atom is one that has four different groups attached to it.

--- Example ---

The molecule below, 1-aminoethan-1-ol, has a chiral carbon atom.

This carbon is chiral because it has four different groups attached to it.

It's possible to arrange the groups in two different ways around chiral carbon atoms so that two different molecules are made — these molecules are called **enantiomers** or **optical isomers**. The enantiomers are mirror images and, no matter which way you turn them, they can't be superimposed. If molecules can be superimposed, they're **achiral** — and there's no optical isomerism.

--- Example ---

Here are the two enantiomers of 1-aminoethan-1-ol. It doesn't matter how many times you turn and twist them, they can't be superimposed.

mirror

You have to be able to draw optical isomers. Just follow these steps each time:

1. Locate the chiral centre — look for the carbon atom with four different groups attached.

2. Draw one enantiomer in a tetrahedral shape — put the chiral carbon atom at the centre and the four different groups in a tetrahedral shape around it. Don't try to draw the full structure of each group — it gets confusing. Just use the structural formulas.

3. Draw the mirror image of the enantiomer — put in a mirror line next to the enantiomer and then draw the mirror image of the enantiomer on the other side of it.

Figure 1: Left handed and right handed scissors are mirror images of each other — they can't be superimposed on each other.

Don't panic — here are some examples to help you get to grips with this.

Examples

Draw the two enantiomers of 2-hydroxypropanoic acid.
The structure of 2-hydroxypropanoic acid is shown below.

Tip: You can get molecules that contain more than one chiral carbon, but in your exam you'll only get asked about molecules with just one chiral centre.

1. Locate the chiral centre — the chiral carbon in this molecule is the carbon with the groups H, OH, COOH and CH_3 attached.

Tip: The chiral centre and the chiral carbon atom are the same thing.

2. Draw one enantiomer in a tetrahedral shape — put the chiral carbon atom at the centre and the groups H, OH, COOH and CH_3 in a tetrahedral shape around it.

3. Then draw its mirror image beside it.

Tip: Remember, those dashed lines mean the bond is pointing into the page, and the wedged lines mean the bond is pointing out of the page towards you.

Draw the two enantiomers of butan-2-ol.

1. Draw the structure of butan-2-ol and locate the chiral centre.

butan-2-ol

Tip: Remember the chiral carbon is the one with four <u>different</u> groups attached to it.

2. Draw one enantiomer in a tetrahedral shape.

3. Then draw its mirror image beside it.

Tip: Sometimes a chiral carbon is shown in a diagram by placing a star next to the chiral carbon atom, like this:

Optical activity

Optical isomers are optically active — they rotate **plane polarised light**.

Plane polarised light

Normal light vibrates in all directions — some of it vibrates up and down, some of it vibrates side to side and some wiggles all over the place.
If normal light is passed through a polarising filter it becomes plane polarised. This means all the light is vibrating in the same plane (for example, only up and down or only side to side).

Rotation of plane polarised light

When you pass plane polarised light through an optically active mixture, the molecules interact with the light and rotate the plane of the vibration of the light. The two enantiomers of an optically active molecule will rotate the plane polarised light in opposite directions. One enantiomer rotates it in a clockwise direction, and the other rotates it in an anticlockwise direction.

Racemates

A **racemate** (or racemic mixture) contains equal quantities of each enantiomer of an optically active compound. Racemates don't show any optical activity — the two enantiomers cancel each other's light-rotating effect.
Chemists often react two achiral things together and get a racemic mixture of a chiral product. This is because when two molecules react, there's normally an equal chance of forming each of the enantiomers.

┌─ **Examples** ─────────────────────

Here's the reaction between butane and chlorine:

butane   *2-chlorobutane*

A chlorine atom replaces one of the H groups on carbon 2, to give 2-chlorobutane. Either of the H's directly attached to carbon 2 can be replaced, so the reaction produces a mixture of the two possible enantiomers.

Tip: Butane is achiral because it doesn't have four *different* groups attached to the central carbon atom — two of the groups are hydrogen atoms.

Each hydrogen has an equal chance of being replaced, so the two optical isomers are formed in equal amounts — you get a racemic mixture (a racemate).

Here's the reaction between propanal and acidified KCN. The nitrile group adds to the carbonyl group to form 2-hydroxybutanenitrile.

propanal   *2-hydroxybutanenitrile*

Tip: The reaction between butane and chlorine will also produce 1-chlorobutane:

H−C−C−C−C−Cl (with H's)

But, 1-chlorobutane is made via a less stable intermediate, so it is the minor product. It also doesn't contain a chiral centre, so it doesn't produce an optical isomer.

2-hydroxybutanenitrile has two enantiomers (shown below). They are equally likely to form via this reaction and so the two enantiomers are formed in equal amounts — you get a racemic mixture.

Tip: See pages 178-180 for more detail on hydroxynitriles.

You can modify a reaction to produce a single enantiomer using chemical methods, but it's difficult and expensive.

Tip: Not all reactions that produce chiral compounds will produce racemates. Sometimes, one enantiomer will be favoured over another enantiomer and you'll get an <u>enantiomerically pure product</u> — a product that contains only one enantiomer.

Practice Questions — Application

Q1 Circle the chiral carbon in each of these molecules.

a)

b)

c)

d)

Q2 Draw the two enantiomers of the following molecules.

a)

b)

Q3 Here is an equation for the reaction between butanone and acidified KCN.

butanone   *2-hydroxy-2-methylbutanenitrile*

Draw the two optical isomers that can be formed via this reaction.

Tip: When you're drawing out the enantiomers for molecules just write out the structural formula of each group — don't try and draw the displayed formula for each one or your diagram will become too confusing.

Practice Questions — Fact Recall

Q1 What is optical isomerism?

Q2 What is a chiral carbon?

Q3 What does it mean if a molecule is 'optically active'?

Q4 Explain why racemic mixtures are not optically active.

Learning Objectives:

- Be able to apply IUPAC rules for naming aldehydes and ketones.
- Know that aldehydes are readily oxidised to carboxylic acids
- Know the chemical tests to distinguish between aldehydes and ketones, including Fehling's solution and Tollens' reagent.
- Know that aldehydes can be reduced to primary alcohols and ketones to secondary alcohols, using $NaBH_4$ in aqueous solution, and that these reactions are examples of nucleophilic addition.
- Be able to write overall equations for reduction reactions using [H] as the reductant.
- Be able to outline the nucleophilic addition mechanism for reduction reactions with $NaBH_4$ (the nucleophile should be shown as H⁻).

Specification Reference 3.3.1.1, 3.3.8

Tip: This is a recap of stuff you learnt at Year 1, so if it's not looking familiar, you might want to have a look back at your Year 1 notes.

Tip: When naming ketones, the carbonyl group is the highest priority, so you always number the carbons from the end that means the carbonyl group carbon has the lowest number.

2. Aldehydes and Ketones

Aldehydes and ketones are compounds that are made by oxidising alcohols. Aldehydes are made by oxidising primary alcohols and ketones are made by oxidising secondary alcohols. You met aldehydes and ketones in Year 1, but now it's time to cover them in a bit more detail.

What are aldehydes and ketones?

Aldehydes and **ketones** are both **carbonyl compounds** as they both contain the carbonyl functional group, C=O. The difference between aldehydes and ketones is that they've got their carbonyl groups in different positions. Aldehydes have their carbonyl group at the end of the carbon chain. Ketones have their carbonyl group in the middle of the carbon chain, see Figure 1.

Figure 1: The difference between an aldehyde and a ketone. 'R' represents a carbon chain of any length.

Nomenclature

Before you can study aldehydes and ketones you need to know how to name them. Aldehydes have the suffix -al. You don't have to say which carbon the functional group is on — it's always on carbon-1. Naming aldehydes follows very similar rules to the naming of alcohols, which you saw back in Year 1.

Example

2-ethylpentanal

The longest carbon chain containing the aldehyde functional group is 5 carbon atoms, so the stem is pentane.

There's an ethyl- group attached to the second carbon atom so there's a 2-ethyl- prefix.

So, the aldehyde is called 2-ethylpentanal.

The suffix for ketones is -one. For ketones with five or more carbons (or four-carbon ketones which are branched), you always have to say which carbon the functional group is on.

Example

3-methylbutan-2-one

The longest continuous carbon chain is 4 carbon atoms, so the stem is butane.

The carbonyl is found on the second carbon atom and there is a methyl group on the third carbon.

So, the ketone is called 3-methylbutan-2-one.

Testing for aldehydes and ketones

There are a few tests to distinguish between aldehydes and ketones. They all work on the idea that an aldehyde can be easily oxidised to a carboxylic acid, but a ketone can't. Aldehydes can be easily oxidised to carboxylic acids because there's a hydrogen attached to the carbonyl group:

The only way to oxidise a ketone would be to break a carbon-carbon bond so ketones are not easily oxidised:

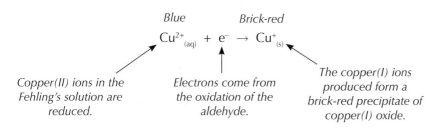

As an aldehyde is oxidised, another compound is reduced — so a reagent is used that changes colour as it's reduced. Two reagents that can be used to distinguish between aldehydes and ketones are Tollens' reagent and Fehling's solution.

Tollens' reagent

Tollens' reagent is a colourless solution of silver nitrate dissolved in aqueous ammonia. If it's heated in a test tube with an aldehyde, a silver mirror forms after a few minutes (see Figure 2). As the aldehyde is oxidised, the diaminesilver ions in the Tollens' reagent are reduced, producing silver and ammonia:

Colourless   *Silver*

$$Ag(NH_3)_2{}^+{}_{(aq)} + e^- \rightarrow Ag_{(s)} + 2NH_{3(aq)}$$

Diaminesilver ions in the Tollens' reagent are reduced.

Electrons come from the oxidation of the aldehyde.

The silver produced forms a silver mirror.

Ketones don't react with Tollens' reagent.

Fehling's solution

Fehling's solution is a blue solution of complexed copper(II) ions dissolved in sodium hydroxide. If it's heated with an aldehyde the copper(II) ions are reduced to a brick-red precipitate of copper(I) oxide (see Figure 3):

Blue   *Brick-red*

$$Cu^{2+}{}_{(aq)} + e^- \rightarrow Cu^+{}_{(s)}$$

Copper(II) ions in the Fehling's solution are reduced.

Electrons come from the oxidation of the aldehyde.

The copper(I) ions produced form a brick-red precipitate of copper(I) oxide.

Ketones also don't react with Fehling's solution.

Tip: In these equations [O] is used to represent an oxidising agent.

Figure 2: *Tollens' reagent. The test tube on the left shows the unreacted Tollens' reagent. The test tube on the right shows the result of a reaction of Tollens' reagent with an aldehyde.*

Tip: Aldehydes and ketones are flammable, so they must be heated in a water bath rather than over a flame. (See page 7 for methods of heating that don't involve a naked flame.) You also need to consider any other safety precautions before carrying out these tests.

Figure 3: *Fehling's solution. The test-tube on the left shows the unreacted Fehling's solution. The test tube on the right shows the result of the reaction of Fehling's solution with an aldehyde.*

Reducing aldehydes and ketones

In Year 1, you saw how primary alcohols can be oxidised to produce aldehydes and carboxylic acids, and how secondary alcohols can be oxidised to make ketones. Using a reducing agent you can reverse these reactions. $NaBH_4$ (sodium tetrahydridoborate(III) or sodium borohydride) is usually the reducing agent used (see Figure 4). But in equations, [H] is often used to indicate a hydrogen from a reducing agent. The equation below shows the reduction of an aldehyde to a primary alcohol:

Figure 4: $NaBH_4$ *powder. This is dissolved in water with methanol to produce a commonly used reducing agent.*

$$R-\overset{\displaystyle O}{\overset{\|}{C}}-H + 2[H] \longrightarrow R-\overset{\displaystyle OH}{\underset{\displaystyle H}{\overset{|}{C}}}-H$$

And here's the reduction of a ketone to a secondary alcohol:

$$R-\overset{\displaystyle O}{\overset{\|}{C}}-R + 2[H] \longrightarrow R-\overset{\displaystyle OH}{\underset{\displaystyle H}{\overset{|}{C}}}-R$$

Exam Tip
When you're writing equations like this in an exam, make sure you balance the [H]'s as well as the molecules.

Nucleophilic addition reactions

You need to understand the reaction mechanisms for the reduction of aldehydes and ketones back to alcohols. These are **nucleophilic addition** reactions — an H⁻ ion from the reducing agent acts as a nucleophile and adds on to the δ^+ carbon atom of a carbonyl group. Here's the mechanism...

Tip: In reaction mechanisms, the curly arrows show the movement of an electron pair.

1. The C=O bond is polar, meaning the carbon in the carbonyl group is slightly positive. So, the $C^{\delta+}$ attracts the negatively charged lone pair of electrons on the H⁻ ion.
2. The H⁻ ion attacks the slightly positive carbon atom and donates its lone pair of electrons forming a bond with the carbon.
3. As carbon can only have 4 bonds, the addition of the H⁻ ion causes one of the carbon-oxygen bonds to break. This forces a lone pair of electrons from the C=O double bond onto the oxygen.
4. The oxygen donates its lone pair of electrons to a H⁺ ion (this H⁺ ion usually comes from water but sometimes a weak acid is added as a source of H⁺).
5. A primary alcohol is produced.

Exam Tip
You need to be able to draw the mechanism for the reduction of any aldehyde or ketone — so make sure you understand all the steps of these nucleophilic addition reactions.

The mechanism for the reduction of a ketone is the same as for an aldehyde — you just get a secondary alcohol at the end instead of a primary alcohol:

This reaction mechanism can be applied to any aldehyde or ketone.

Examples

Propanal can be reduced to propan-1-ol:

Exam Tip
You <u>must</u> draw the curly arrows coming from the lone pair of electrons. If you don't — you won't get the marks for the mechanism in the exam.

Butanone can be reduced to butan-2-ol:

Practice Questions — Application

Q1 Name these molecules:

Q2 Draw the mechanisms for the reduction of each molecule in Q1 to an alcohol. Use H⁻ as the nucleophile.

Q3 Write an equation, using structural formulas, for the reduction of pentan-2-one to pentan-2-ol. Use [H] to represent a reducing agent.

Tip: Don't forget — aldehydes are reduced to primary alcohols and ketones are reduced to secondary alcohols.

Practice Questions — Fact Recall

Q1 What is the difference between an aldehyde and a ketone?

Q2 What type of compound is produced when an aldehyde is oxidised?

Q3 Explain why ketones cannot be easily oxidised.

Q4 Describe what you would observe if you used the following to distinguish between an aldehyde and a ketone:

a) Tollens' reagent.

b) Fehling's solution.

Q5 Identify a reducing agent which could be used to reduce an aldehyde to a primary alcohol.

Tip: Sometimes you might see primary and secondary alcohols written as 1° and 2° alcohols.

3. Hydroxynitriles

Aldehydes and ketones can be used to produce another set of molecules known as hydroxynitriles.

What are hydroxynitriles?

Hydroxynitriles are molecules which contain a hydroxyl group (OH) and a nitrile group (CN) — see Figure 1.

Figure 1: *The general structure of a hydroxynitrile.*

When naming hydroxynitriles the nitrile group is the most important so the suffix is -nitrile and the carbon that's attached to the nitrogen is always carbon-1. There's also a hydroxy- prefix because of the OH group. After that, naming hydroxynitriles is just the same as naming any other compound.

Example

2-hydroxy-3-methylbutanenitrile

The longest continuous carbon chain is 4 carbon atoms, so the stem is butane.
The OH group is on carbon-2 and there is a methyl group on carbon-3.

So, this is 2-hydroxy-3-methylbutanenitrile.

Producing hydroxynitriles

Hydroxynitriles can be produced by reacting aldehydes or ketones with potassium cyanide (KCN), followed by a dilute acid. This is another example of a nucleophilic addition reaction — a nucleophile attacks the molecule, causing an extra group to be added. Here's the mechanism for the reaction of aldehydes with KCN (for ketones, just replace the H with an R' group):

1. Potassium cyanide's an ionic compound.
   It dissociates in water to form K^+ ions and CN^- ions: $KCN \rightleftharpoons K^+ + CN^-$.
2. The CN^- ion from the KCN attacks the partially positive carbon atom and donates a pair of electrons, forming a bond with the carbon.
3. A pair of electrons from the C=O double bond is pushed onto the oxygen.
4. The oxygen bonds to a H^+ ion (from the dilute acid) to form the hydroxyl group (OH) and a hydroxynitrile is produced.

The overall reaction for an aldehyde is:

$$RCHO_{(aq)} + KCN_{(aq)} \xrightarrow{H^+_{(aq)}} RCH(OH)CN_{(aq)} + K^+_{(aq)}$$

Or for a ketone: $RCOR'_{(aq)} + KCN_{(aq)} \xrightarrow{H^+_{(aq)}} RC(OH)R'CN_{(aq)} + K^+_{(aq)}$

Learning Objectives:

- Be able to apply IUPAC rules for naming hydroxynitriles.
- Understand the nucleophilic addition reactions of carbonyl compounds with KCN, followed by dilute acid, to produce hydroxynitriles.
- Be able to outline the nucleophilic addition mechanism for the reaction of carbonyl compounds with KCN, followed by dilute acid.
- Be able to write overall equations for the formation of hydroxynitriles using HCN.
- Be able to explain why aldehydes and unsymmetrical ketones form mixtures of enantiomers when they react with KCN followed by dilute acid in nucleophilic addition reactions.
- Know the hazards associated with using KCN.

Specification Reference 3.3.1.1, 3.3.8

Tip: Don't forget to add a negative sign to the oxygen after step three.

Tip: This mechanism is exactly the same as the nucleophilic addition mechanism on page 176, except we're using CN^- instead of H^-.

Example

Propanone and acidified KCN react to form 2-hydroxy-2-methylpropanenitrile. The mechanism for this reaction is shown below:

You can also make hydroxynitriles by reacting aldehydes or ketones with hydrogen cyanide. The overall equations for these reactions are:

Aldehyde: RCHO + HCN → RCH(OH)CN

Ketone: RCOR′ + HCN → RC(OH)R′CN

Racemic mixtures of hydroxynitriles

Double bonds, such as C=O and C=C bonds, are planar. So, when nucleophiles attack atoms at double bonds, they can attack from either above or below the plane of the bond. Nucleophilic attack from each side of the bond will produce a different enantiomer.

The nucleophilic attack of cyanide ions (from e.g. KCN) on aldehydes or unsymmetric ketones can lead to a racemic mixture of hydroxynitriles. This is because nucleophilic attack of the $C^{\delta+}$, by CN:−, can occur from either above or below the plane of the C=O bond. Depending on which way the nucleophile attacks from, a different enantiomer will form. Usually, attack from both sides is equally likely, so a racemic mixture is formed.

Example

The products of the reaction of propanal with potassium cyanide, under weakly acidic conditions, are present as a racemic mixture. Explain this observation.

The reaction of acidified KCN with propanal involves the nucleophilic attack of CN− at the positive carbon centre. The CN− nucleophile can attack from two directions — from above the plane of the molecule, or from below it.

Depending on the direction from which the nucleophilic attack happens, one of two enantiomers is formed.

Because the C=O bond is planar, there is an equal chance that the nucleophile will attack from either of these directions. Therefore, equal amounts (a racemate) of the products of these reactions are formed.

Exam Tip
In the exam, you could be asked to apply this mechanism to show how any aldehyde or ketone reacts with KCN.

Tip: The mechanism for the reactions of aldehydes/ketones is exactly the same with HCN as with KCN. The only difference is that you don't need to add an acid as HCN is a source of H+ ions (since HCN ⇌ H+ + CN−).

Exam Tip
Unless a question asks otherwise, you can show overall equations using displayed formulas, if you find structural formulas hard to use.

Tip: Look back at pages 170-173 for more on enantiomers and racemic mixtures.

Tip: Try building these molecules with a molecular modelling kit if you're struggling to visualise the planar carbonyl group. It will make it so much clearer which directions the nucleophile can attack from.

Tip: This is just the same as the mechanism that you saw on the last page. Look back there for full details on all the steps.

Figure 2: Warning labels on the bottles of chemicals warn you if a chemical is dangerous.

Risk assessments

A **risk assessment** involves reviewing the hazards of the reacting chemicals, the products and any conditions needed, such as heat. You don't have to wrap yourself in cotton wool, but you do have to take all reasonable precautions to reduce the risk of an accident.

┌─ **Example** ─────────────────────────

Here's part of a risk assessment for reacting potassium cyanide with a carbonyl compound:

KCN is toxic but it can be stored safely. Acidified potassium cyanide is used for the reaction to supply the CN^- ions and also the H^+ ions needed. However, the reaction should be done in a fume cupboard as there is a risk of some HCN gas being released from the solution. Also, the organic compounds are flammable, so if you need to heat them use a water bath or electric mantle.

└──────────────────────────────────────

Practice Questions — Application

Tip: Remember — when drawing reaction mechanisms, curly arrows must go <u>from</u> a lone pair and <u>to</u> the atom the lone pair is going to.

Q1 a) Draw the structure of the hydroxynitrile that would be produced if 2-methylpropanal was reacted with acidified KCN.
The structure of 2-methylpropanal is shown below:

   b) Draw the mechanism for this reaction.

Q2 The diagram below shows a hydroxynitrile:

Tip: Look back at page 174 if you need a reminder on how to name certain carbonyl compounds.

   a) Name this hydroxynitrile.
   b) Draw the structure of the carbonyl compound that could be used to produce this hydroxynitrile.
   c) Name this carbonyl compound.
   d) Draw the mechanism for the production of this hydroxynitrile.

Q3 Butanone reacts with acidified potassium cyanide to produce a mixture of products.
   a) Draw the structures of the products from this reaction.
   b) Explain why this reaction doesn't produce a single product.

Practice Questions — Fact Recall

Tip: If a question asks you what a certain molecule is, you can always draw a picture to help you show its features.

Q1 What is a hydroxynitrile?
Q2 Name the mechanism for the production of hydroxynitriles from carbonyl compounds and acidified KCN.
Q3 a) What are the hazards associated with KCN?
   b) What safety precautions should be taken when using KCN?

4. Carboxylic Acids and Esters

Carboxylic acids and esters are two more types of carbonyl compound that you need to know about. Read on to learn all about them.

What are carboxylic acids?

Carboxylic acids contain the carboxyl functional group –COOH.

← This is the carboxyl functional group.

To name them, you find and name the longest alkane chain, take off the 'e' and add '–oic acid'. The carboxyl group is always at the end of the molecule and when naming it's more important than other functional groups — so all the other functional groups in the molecule are numbered starting from this carbon.

--- Example ---

4-hydroxy-2-methylbutanoic acid

The longest continuous carbon chain containing the carboxylic acid functional group is 4 carbon atoms, so the stem is butane.

Numbering of the carbons starts at the COOH group so there's a COOH group on carbon-1, a methyl group on carbon-2 and a hydroxyl group on carbon-4.

So, this is 4-hydroxy-2-methylbutanoic acid.

Dissociation of carboxylic acids

Carboxylic acids are weak acids — in water they partially dissociate into a carboxylate ion and an H^+ ion.

Carboxylic acid   *Carboxylate ion*

This reaction is reversible but the equilibrium lies to the left because most of the molecules don't dissociate.

Reaction with carbonates

Carboxylic acids react with carbonates (CO_3^{2-}) or hydrogen carbonates (HCO_3^-) to form a salt, carbon dioxide and water.

--- Examples ---

$$2CH_3COOH_{(aq)} + Na_2CO_{3(s)} \rightarrow 2CH_3COONa_{(aq)} + H_2O_{(l)} + CO_{2(g)}$$

Ethanoic acid   Sodium carbonate   Sodium ethanoate

$$HCOOH_{(aq)} + NaHCO_{3(s)} \rightarrow HCOONa_{(aq)} + H_2O_{(l)} + CO_{2(g)}$$

Methanoic   Sodium hydrogen   Sodium
acid   carbonate   methanoate

In these reactions, carbon dioxide fizzes out of the solution.

Learning Objectives:

- Know the structures of carboxylic acids and esters.
- Be able to apply IUPAC rules for naming carboxylic acids and esters.
- Know that carboxylic acids are weak acids but will liberate CO_2 from carbonates.
- Know that carboxylic acids and alcohols react, in the presence of an acid catalyst, to give esters.

Specification Reference 3.3.1.1, 3.3.9.1

Tip: A carboxyl group contains a carbonyl group and a hydroxyl group on the same carbon atom.

Tip: See page 97 for more on the dissociation of weak acids.

Tip: When you're writing equations for the reaction of carboxylic acids with carbonates, always remember to balance the equation at the end.

Esterification reactions

If you heat a carboxylic acid with an alcohol in the presence of a strong acid catalyst, you get an **ester**. It's called an **esterification** reaction.

The H⁺ ion catalyst comes from the strong acid.

This half of the ester comes from the carboxylic acid.

This half of the ester comes from the alcohol.

Carboxylic acid   Alcohol   Ester   Water

Concentrated sulfuric acid (H_2SO_4) is usually used as the acid catalyst, but other strong acids such as HCl or H_3PO_4 can also be used.

Naming esters

You've just seen that an ester is formed by reacting an alcohol with a carboxylic acid. Well, the name of an ester is made up of two parts — the first bit comes from the alcohol, and the second bit from the carboxylic acid.

To name an ester, just follow these steps:

1. Look at the alkyl group that came from the alcohol.
   This is the first bit of the ester's name.

2. Now look at the part that came from the carboxylic acid.
   Swap its '-oic acid' ending for 'oate' to get the second bit of the name.

3. Put the two parts together.

> **Example**
>
> Ethanoic acid reacts with methanol to produce the ester shown below:
>
>
>
> 1. This part of the ester came from the alcohol.
>   It's a methyl group so the first part of the ester's name is methyl-.
>
> 2. This part of the ester came from the carboxylic acid. It came from
>   ethanoic acid so the second part of the ester's name is - ethanoate.
>
>   So this ester is methyl ethanoate.

The same rules apply even if the carbon chains are branched or if the molecule has a benzene ring attached. Always number the carbons starting from the carbon atoms in the C–O–C bond.

> **Examples**
>
> This ester has a methyl group that came from the alcohol so the name begins with methyl-.
>
> There is a benzene ring that came from benzoic acid so the name ends in -benzoate.
>
> So this is methyl benzoate.

Tip: Making esters in the lab, by reacting an alcohol and a carboxylic acid under reflux, won't result in a pure product. You'll need to purify your ester using a separating funnel and distillation (see pages 193-194).

Tip: Esterification reactions are also <u>condensation reactions</u> because they release a small molecule (water) when the carboxylic acid and alcohol join.

Figure 1: *Model showing the structure of the ester ethyl ethanoate.*

Tip: Be careful — the name of the ester is generally written the opposite way round to the formula.

182   Unit 3: Section 5 Isomerism and Carbonyl Compounds

This ester has an ethyl group that came from the alcohol and a 2-methyl butanyl group that came from the acid so is called ethyl 2-methylbutanoate.

This ester has a 1-methylpropyl group that came from the alcohol and a methyl group that came from the acid so is called 1-methylpropyl methanoate.

Sometimes you may be asked to predict which alcohol and which carboxylic acid are needed to form a particular ester.

┌─ Example ─────────────────────────────

There are 3 carbons in the part of the molecule that came from the acid so the stem is propane. This part came from propanoic acid.

There is one carbon in the section that came from the alcohol so the stem is methane. This part of the molecule came from methanol.

Tip: The rules about naming esters only apply if the alcohol is a primary alcohol — if it's a secondary alcohol the first part of the name will be different. E.g. The alcohol that reacts with methanoic acid to form 1-methylpropyl methanoate is called butan-2-ol, not 1-methylpropan-1-ol.

Practice Questions — Application

Q1 Below are two carboxylic acids:

(i)

$$H-\overset{O}{\overset{\|}{C}}-OH$$

(ii)

a) Name these carboxylic acids.

b) Write a balanced equation for the reaction of carboxylic acid (i) with sodium carbonate (Na_2CO_3).

Q2 Below are two esters:

(i)

(ii)

a) Name these esters

b) State which carboxylic acid and which alcohol have reacted to form each of these esters.

Q3 1-methylethyl methanoate is an ester.

a) Draw the structure of this ester.

b) Write an equation, using structural formulas, to show the formation of this ester from an acid and an alcohol.

Exam Tip
Sometimes examiners will try and throw you by drawing esters the opposite way round, e.g.

Try not to get confused when naming esters — always think about the position of the O and C=O groups rather than just thinking about left and right. This ester is methyl propanoate.

Practice Questions — Fact Recall

Q1 Name the three products that are produced when a carboxylic acid reacts with a carbonate or a hydrogen carbonate.

Q2 Carboxylic acids react with alcohols to form esters.

a) What is the name given to this type of reaction?

b) What type of catalyst is used for this reaction? Give an example.

- Know the common uses of esters (e.g. in solvents, plasticisers, perfumes and food flavourings).

- Know that esters can be hydrolysed in acid or alkaline conditions to form alcohols and carboxylic acids or salts of carboxylic acids.

- Know that vegetable oils and animal fats are esters of propane-1,2,3-triol (glycerol).

- Know that vegetable oils and animal fats can be hydrolysed in alkaline conditions to give soap (salts of long-chain carboxylic acids) and glycerol.

- Know that biodiesel is a mixture of methyl esters of long-chain carboxylic acids.

- Know that biodiesel can be produced by reacting vegetable oils with methanol in the presence of a catalyst.

Specification Reference 3.3.9.1

Tip: The nice fragrances and flavours of lots of flowers and fruits come from esters.

Exam Tip
Don't worry, you don't need to know the mechanism for these reactions — just knowing the equations is enough.

5. Reactions and Uses of Esters

Esters are extremely useful molecules. In fact — you've probably used an ester at some point today without even realising it. Read on to find out more.

Useful properties of esters

Esters have a number of properties that make them very useful.

- Esters have a sweet smell — it varies from gluey sweet for smaller esters to a fruity 'pear drop' smell for the larger ones. This makes them useful in perfumes. The food industry uses esters to flavour things like drinks and sweets too.

- Esters are polar liquids so lots of polar organic compounds will dissolve in them. They've also got quite low boiling points, so they evaporate easily from mixtures. This makes them good solvents in glues and printing inks.

- Esters are used as plasticisers — they're added to plastics during polymerisation to make the plastic more flexible. Over time, the plasticiser molecules escape though, and the plastic becomes brittle and stiff.

Hydrolysis of esters

Hydrolysis is when a substance is split up by water — but using just water is often really slow, so an acid or an alkali is often used to speed it up. There are two types of hydrolysis of esters — acid hydrolysis and base hydrolysis. With both types you get an alcohol, but the second product in each case is different.

Acid hydrolysis

Acid hydrolysis splits the ester into an acid and an alcohol — it's the reverse of the reaction on page 182. You have to reflux the ester with a dilute acid, such as hydrochloric or sulfuric acid. The ester will then split back into the carboxylic acid and alcohol it was originally made from.

| Ester | Water | Carboxylic acid | Alcohol |

Example

Acid hydrolysis of methyl ethanoate produces ethanoic acid and methanol:

| Methyl ethanoate | Water | Ethanoic acid | Methanol |

As these acid hydrolysis reactions are reversible you need to use lots of water to push the equilibrium over to the right so you get lots of product.

Base hydrolysis

For a base hydrolysis reaction you have to reflux the ester with a dilute alkali, such as sodium hydroxide. OH^- ions from the base react with the ester and you get a carboxylate ion and an alcohol.

Tip: Make sure you know the difference between the two different types of hydrolysis — acid hydrolysis produces a carboxylic acid and base hydrolysis produces a carboxylate ion.

Example

Base hydrolysis of methyl ethanoate produces ethanoate ions and methanol:

Methyl ethanoate   Ethanoate ion   Methanol

Tip: The negatively charged carboxylate ions bond with the positively charged ions from the base (e.g. Na^+ ions if the base is NaOH) to form salts like the one shown below:

This is sodium ethanoate.

Fats and oils

Animal fats and vegetable oils are esters of glycerol and **fatty acids**. Fatty acids are long chain carboxylic acids. They combine with glycerol (propane-1,2,3-triol) to make fats and oils — see Figure 1. The fatty acids can be **saturated** (no double bonds) or **unsaturated** (with C=C double bonds). Most of a fat or oil is made from fatty acid chains — so it's these that give them many of their properties.

Figure 1: *Diagram showing the structure of a fat/oil.*

Figure 2: *Fats and oils are esters formed from glycerol (propane-1,2,3-triol) and long-chain carboxylic acids.*

'Fats' have mainly saturated hydrocarbon chains — they fit neatly together, increasing the van der Waals forces between them (see Figure 3). This means higher temperatures are needed to melt them and they're solid at room temperature.

Figure 3: *The arrangement of hydrocarbon chains in a fat.*

'Oils' have unsaturated hydrocarbon chains — the double bonds mean the chains are bent and don't pack together well, decreasing the effect of the van der Waals forces (see Figure 4). So they're easier to melt and are liquids at room temperature.

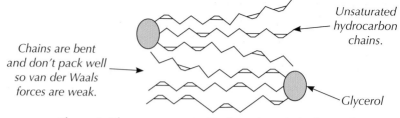

Unsaturated hydrocarbon chains.

Chains are bent and don't pack well so van der Waals forces are weak.

Glycerol

Figure 4: *The arrangement of hydrocarbon chains in an oil.*

Hydrolysis of fats and oils

Tip: See the previous page for more on the base hydrolysis of esters.

Like any ester, you can hydrolyse oils and fats by heating them with sodium hydroxide. This is a type of base hydrolysis. OH⁻ ions from the sodium hydroxide react with the fat/oil to form a carboxylate ion and an alcohol. The alcohol that is formed is glycerol (propane-1,2,3-triol) and the carboxylate ions combine with Na^+ ions from the sodium hydroxide to form a sodium salt. And you'll never guess what the sodium salt produced is — a soap.

Figure 5: *Student making soap by heating vegetable oil with sodium hydroxide.*

If you want to, you can then convert the sodium salt back into a long chain carboxylic acid (fatty acid) by adding an acid such as HCl. H^+ ions from the acid displace the Na^+ ions in the salt to form a carboxylic acid, which releases a free Na^+ ion. This reaction is shown below:

$$CH_3(CH_2)_{16}COO^-Na^+ + H^+ \rightarrow CH_3(CH_2)_{16}COOH + Na^+$$

sodium salt (soap)   fatty acid

Tip: You may get the chance to make soap and biodiesel in the lab. If you do, make sure you carry out a risk assessment before you start your experiment, and take any necessary safety precautions.

Biodiesel

Vegetable oils, e.g. rapeseed oil, make good vehicle fuels, but you can't burn them directly in engines. The oils must be converted into **biodiesel** first. This involves reacting them with methanol, using a strong alkali (e.g. potassium hydroxide or sodium hydroxide) as a catalyst. You get a mixture of methyl esters of long-chain fatty acids — this is biodiesel.

Exam Tip
Make sure you learn the equation for the formation of biodiesel — it could come up in your exam.

Fat/Oil   Methanol   Glycerol (propane-1,2,3-triol)   Methyl ester (biodiesel is a mixture of methyl esters)

Is biodiesel 100% carbon neutral?

Biodiesel can be thought of as carbon neutral, because when crops grow they absorb the same amount of CO_2 as they produce when they're burned. But it's not quite as simple as that — energy is used to make the fertilizer to grow the crops, and it's used in planting, harvesting and converting the oil. If this energy comes from fossil fuels, then the process won't be carbon neutral overall.

Figure 6: A biodiesel fuel pump.

Practice Questions — Application

Q1 Below is the ester methyl propanoate:

Write an equation to show:

a) the acid hydrolysis of this ester.

b) the base hydrolysis of this ester.

Q2 Stearic acid ($CH_3(CH_2)_{16}COOH$) is a long chain carboxylic acid found in most animal fats.

a) Draw the triester that would be produced if three molecules of stearic acid reacted with glycerol.

b) Write an equation for the production of soap from this triester.

c) Explain how soap could be converted back into glycerol and stearic acid.

Q3 Below is an ester commonly found in vegetable oils.

$$CH_2OOC(CH_2)_{14}CH_3$$
$$CH_2OOC(CH_2)_{14}CH_3$$
$$CH_2OOC(CH_2)_{14}CH_3$$

a) Write an equation for the conversion of this ester into biofuel.

b) Suggest a suitable catalyst for this reaction.

Exam Tip
If you don't recognise the structure of a molecule in your exam, try re-drawing it in a different way — it might start to look more familiar.

Practice Questions — Fact Recall

Q1 Give three common uses of esters.

Q2 What two products are produced when an ester is broken down by:

a) acid hydrolysis?

b) base hydrolysis?

Q3 What two things are fats and oils made of?

Q4 Explain why the properties of fats and oils are different.

Q5 Fats can be hydrolysed by heating them with NaOH. What are the products of this reaction?

Q6 How is biodiesel made?

Q7 Explain why biodiesel usually isn't 100% carbon neutral.

Learning Objectives:

- Know the structure of acyl chlorides.
- Be able to apply IUPAC rules for naming acyl chlorides.
- Be able to outline the nucleophilic addition-elimination reactions of water, alcohols, ammonia and primary amines with acyl chlorides.
- Be able to outline the mechanism of nucleophilic addition-elimination reactions of acyl chlorides with water, alcohols, ammonia and primary amines.

Specification Reference 3.3.1.1, 3.3.9.2

6. Acyl Chlorides

Acyl chlorides are a particularly useful type of carbonyl compound because they are good starting points for making lots of different types of molecule.

What are acyl chlorides?

Acyl (or **acid**) **chlorides** have the functional group COCl — their general formula is $C_nH_{2n-1}OCl$. Naming acyl chlorides is similar to naming carboxylic acids. All their names end in –oyl chloride and the carbon atoms are numbered from the end with the acyl functional group.

┌ **Example** ──────────────

2,3-dimethylpentanoyl chloride

The longest continuous carbon chain containing the acyl chloride functional group is 5 carbon atoms, so the stem is pentane.

There are methyl groups on carbon-2 and carbon-3.

So, it's 2,3-dimethylpentanoyl chloride.

Reactions of acyl chlorides

Acyl chlorides can react with a wide range of different molecules. In each of these reactions, Cl is substituted by an oxygen or nitrogen group and misty fumes of hydrogen chloride are given off. The key reactions involving acyl chlorides that you need to know are:

Reaction with water

Acyl chlorides react vigorously with cold water, producing a carboxylic acid.

Ethanoyl chloride   *Ethanoic acid*

Reaction with alcohols

Acyl chlorides react vigorously with alcohols at room temperature, producing an ester.

Ethanoyl chloride   Methanol   *Methyl ethanoate*

This irreversible reaction is a much easier, faster way to produce an ester than esterification (see page 182).

Reaction with ammonia

Acyl chlorides react vigorously with ammonia at room temperature, producing an amide.

Ethanoyl chloride   *Ethanamide*

Figure 1: *The reaction of an acyl chloride with water. You can see the misty fumes of HCl that are being given off.*

Tip: Amides are organic compounds with a C=O double bond and an –NH$_2$ group attached to the same carbon.

Reaction with primary amines

Acyl chlorides react vigorously with **primary amines** at room temperature, producing an **N-substituted amide**.

Tip: See pages 209-216 for more on amines and amides.

Ethanoyl chloride   *Methylamine*   *N-methylethanamide*

Nucleophilic addition-elimination

Tip: A nucleophile is a molecule that can donate a lone pair of electrons.

All of the reactions involving acyl chlorides shown on this page and the previous page follow the same mechanism — they are all **nucleophilic addition-elimination** reactions. Acyl chloride nucleophilic addition-elimination reactions have two steps:

1. The nucleophile adds onto the acyl chloride, displacing a Cl⁻ ion.
2. The hydrogen leaves to create an acyl chloride derivative.

Step 1:

In acyl chlorides, both the chlorine and the oxygen atoms draw electrons towards themselves, so the carbon has a slight positive charge — meaning it's easily attacked by nucleophiles.

2. A pair of electrons is transferred from the C=O bond onto the oxygen.

3. The pair of electrons on the oxygen reform the double bond and the chlorine is kicked off.

Exam Tip
Sometimes you will be asked to apply this mechanism to a nucleophilic reaction that you haven't studied before, so make sure you really understand it — it won't be enough to just learn the examples.

1. The nucleophile attacks the δ⁺ carbon on the acyl chloride.

4. This leaves a positively charged ion and a negatively charged chloride ion.

Step 2:

...and a hydrogen ion.

Tip: An acyl chloride derivative is just something that is made from an acyl chloride.

5. A pair of electrons is transferred onto the nucleophile from the bond

6. This leaves an acyl chloride derivative...

All the reactions that you need to know involving acyl chlorides work in exactly the same way. You just need to change the nucleophile (Nu) to whichever nucleophile is present in the reaction, for example water (H_2O:), an alcohol (e.g. $CH_3\ddot{O}H$), ammonia ($\ddot{N}H_3$) or an amine (e.g. $CH_3\ddot{N}H_2$).

Below is the mechanism for the reaction of ethanoyl chloride with methanol:

Step 1:

Methanol is the nucleophile here. It attacks the partially positive carbon on the ethanoyl chloride, and a pair of electrons from the C=O bond are transferred to the oxygen. Then the pair of electrons on the oxygen reform the double bond and the chlorine's kicked off.

Step 2:

The hydrogen in the hydroxyl group of the methanol leaves, leaving methyl ethanoate and a hydrogen ion.

Practice Questions — Application

Q1 Name the acyl chlorides that are shown below:

Q2 Draw the mechanisms for the following reactions:
    a) acyl chloride (a) with methanol.
    b) acyl chloride (b) with water.
    c) acyl chloride (c) with ammonia.
    d) acyl chloride (d) with methylamine.

Practice Questions — Fact Recall

Q1 What is the general formula for an acyl chloride?
Q2 What are the products when an acyl chloride is reacted with:
    a) water?   b) an alcohol?   c) ammonia?   d) an amine?
Q3 What is the name given to the mechanism for the reactions of acyl chlorides with water, alcohols, ammonia and amines?

7. Acid Anhydrides

Acid anhydrides are compounds that react in a similar way to acyl chlorides.

What are acid anhydrides?

An **acid anhydride** is made from two identical carboxylic acid molecules. The two carboxylic acid molecules are joined together via an oxygen with the carbonyl groups on either side. This oxygen has come from the OH group of one of the carboxylic acids. The other OH group and the spare hydrogen are released as water. The formation of an acid anhydride is shown below.

2 × Carboxylic acid   *Acid anhydride*   *Water*

If you know the name of the carboxylic acid, acid anhydrides are easy to name — just take away 'acid' and add 'anhydride'. So methanoic acid gives methanoic anhydride, ethanoic acid gives ethanoic anhydride, etc...

Example

2 × Ethanoic acid   *Ethanoic anhydride*   *Water*

Reactions of acid anhydrides

You need to know the reactions of water, alcohol, ammonia and primary amines with acid anhydrides. Luckily, they're almost the same as those of acyl chlorides — the reactions are just less vigorous and you get a carboxylic acid formed instead of HCl.

Examples

Acid anhydrides react with water, producing a carboxylic acid.

Ethanoic anhydride   *2 × Ethanoic acid*

Acid anhydrides react with alcohols, producing an ester.

Ethanoic anhydride Methanol   *Methyl ethanoate*   *Ethanoic acid*

Acid anhydrides react with ammonia, producing an amide.

Ethanoic anhydride   *Ethanamide*   *Ethanoic acid*

Acid anhydrides react with amines, producing an N-substituted amide.

Ethanoic anhydride   *Methylamine*   *N-methylethanamide*   *Ethanoic acid*

Tip: The carboxylic acid formed at the end of all these reactions is the same as the carboxylic acid that would have made the anhydride.

Tip: Aspirin is a drug used to relieve symptoms such as minor aches and pains, fever and swelling.

Figure 1: *Aspirin tablets.*

Tip: In these reactions salicylic acid is behaving like an alcohol so everything you've just learnt about the reactions of acid anhydrides/acyl chlorides with alcohols applies here too.

Manufacture of aspirin

Aspirin is an ester — it can be made by reacting salicylic acid (which has an alcohol group) with either ethanoic anhydride (see Figure 2) or ethanoyl chloride. Ethanoic anhydride is used in industry because it's cheaper than ethanoyl chloride. It's also safer to use than ethanoyl chloride as it's less corrosive, reacts more slowly with water, and doesn't produce dangerous hydrogen chloride fumes.

Salicylic Acid   *Ethanoic anhydride*   *Aspirin*   *Ethanoic acid*

Figure 2: *Using ethanoic anhydride to produce aspirin.*

Practice Questions — Application

Q1 Draw the following anhydrides:

  a) propanoic anhydride

  b) 2-ethylpentanoic anhydride

  c) 4-hydroxy-2,3-dimethylbutanoic anhydride

Q2 Write an equation for the following reactions:

  a) propanoic anhydride with water

  b) 2-ethylpentanoic anhydride with methanol

  c) 4-hydroxy-2,3-dimethylbutanoic anhydride with ammonia

Q3 Write the equation for the production of aspirin from salicylic acid and ethanoyl chloride.

Practice Questions — Fact Recall

Q1 What is produced when propanoic anhydride reacts with propanol?

Q2 Give two reason why ethanoic anhydride is used instead of ethanoyl chloride when producing aspirin.

8. Purifying Organic Compounds

Synthesising organic compounds is hardly ever as simple as it sounds. The products of organic reactions are almost always riddled with impurities. It's a good thing there are many ways of purifying them, outlined on these pages.

REQUIRED PRACTICAL **10**

Separation

If an organic product is insoluble in water, then you can use separation to remove any impurities that do dissolve in water, such as salts or water soluble organic compounds (e.g. alcohols).

The organic layer and the aqueous layer (which contains any water soluble impurities) are immiscible, i.e. they don't mix, so separate out into two distinct layers (see Figure 1). You can then open the tap and run each layer off into a separate container.

The organic layer is normally less dense than the aqueous layer so should float on top. Any water soluble impurities should have dissolved in the lower aqueous layer. You can then open the stopper on the separating funnel, run off the aqueous layer and collect your product.

impure product

aqueous layer containing some impurities

***Figure 1:** Separating apparatus.*

Solvent extraction

If your product and impurities are all dissolved in a solution together, you can use another form of separation known as **solvent extraction**. This involves vigorously shaking your impure product with an immiscible solvent, so they temporarily mix. Your product needs to be more soluble in the added immiscible solvent than the one it was initially dissolved in. If this is the case, the product will dissolve in the added solvent, and separate from the solution containing the impurities. The solvent containing the product can then be run off using a separating funnel, as shown above.

Drying agents

If you use separation to purify a product, the organic layer will end up containing trace amounts of water, so it has to be dried. To do this you can add an anhydrous salt such as magnesium sulfate ($MgSO_4$) or calcium chloride ($CaCl_2$). The salt is used as a **drying agent** — it binds to any water present to become hydrated.

When you first add the salt to the organic layer it will form clumps. This means you need to add more. You know that all the water has been removed when you can swirl the mixture and it looks like a snow globe. You can filter the mixture to remove the solid drying agent.

Learning Objectives:

- Be able to prepare a pure organic solid and test its purity (Required Practical 10).
- Be able to prepare a pure organic liquid (Required Practical 10).

Specification Reference 3.3.9.2

Tip: Water soluble impurities might include salts (such as NaCl) or short-chain organic compounds that are capable of forming hydrogen bonds (such as alcohols, carbonyls and carboxylic acids).

Tip: Your product won't necessarily be pure after separation — any organic impurities that don't dissolve in water will still be in the organic layer alongside your product. You'll probably need to remove them by redistillation (see page 195).

***Figure 2:** A student using a separating funnel to separate an organic and an aqueous layer.*

Washing

The product of a reaction can be contaminated with unreacted reagents or unwanted side products. You can remove some of these by washing the product.

Example

An excess of aqueous sodium hydrogen carbonate solution can be used to remove acid from an organic product.

Any acid is reacted with the sodium hydrogen carbonate to give CO_2 gas, a salt and water. This leaves an aqueous solution of the excess aqueous sodium hydrogen carbonate, salt and water. The organic product (assuming it's insoluble in the aqueous layer) can be easily removed using a separating funnel.

Distillation

Distillation separates liquids with different boiling points. It works by gently heating a mixture in distillation apparatus. The substances will evaporate out of the mixture in order of increasing boiling point.

A thermometer is placed at the neck of the condenser and shows the boiling point of the substance that is evaporating at any given time. If you know the boiling point of your pure product, you can use the thermometer to tell you when it's evaporating and therefore when it's condensing.

If the product of a reaction has a lower boiling point than the starting materials, then the reaction mixture can be heated in distillation apparatus so that the product evaporates from the reaction mixture as it forms. If the starting materials have a higher boiling point than the product, so as long as the temperature is controlled, they won't evaporate out from the reaction mixture.

Figure 3: *Distillation apparatus.*

Example

Hexan-1-ol reacts with acidified dichromate(VI) solution to form hexanal. However, hexanal can be further oxidised by acidified dichromate(VI) to form hexanoic acid.

By heating the reaction in distillation apparatus at a temperature of around 131 °C (the boiling point of hexanal), any hexanal that is produced will immediately evaporate out of the reaction mixture. Hexan-1-ol, which has a boiling point of about 155 °C, won't evaporate so stays in the reaction mixture and can react fully to form hexanal. The hexanal that is distilled out of the reaction mixture can be collected in a separate vessel. This prevents it from being oxidised further to hexanoic acid.

Redistillation

Mixtures that contain volatile liquids can be purified using a technique called **redistillation**. If a product and its impurities have different boiling points, then redistillation can be used to separate them. You just use the same distillation apparatus as shown on the previous page, but this time you're heating an impure product, instead of the reaction mixture.

When the liquid you want boils (this is when the thermometer is at the boiling point of the liquid), you place a flask at the open end of the condenser ready to collect your product. When the thermometer shows the temperature is changing, put another flask at the end of the condenser because a different liquid is about to be delivered.

Recrystallisation

If the product of an organic reaction is a solid, then the simplest way of purifying it is a process called **recrystallisation**. First you dissolve your solid in a hot solvent to make a saturated solution. Then you let it cool. As the solution cools, the solubility of the product falls. When it reaches the point where it can't stay in solution, it starts to form crystals. Here's how it's done:

1. Add very hot solvent to the impure solid until it just dissolves — it's really important not to add too much solvent.

2. This should give a saturated solution of the impure product.

3. Leave the solution to cool down slowly. Crystals of the product form as it cools.

4. The impurities stay in solution. They're present in much smaller amounts than the product, so they'd take much longer to crystallise out.

5. Remove the crystals by filtration and wash them with ice-cold solvent. The crystals then need to be dried — leaving you with crystals of your product that are much purer than the original solid.

Testing purity

You can use melting point apparatus to accurately determine the melting point of an organic solid.

Pack a small sample of the solid into a glass capillary tube and place it inside the heating element. Increase the temperature until the sample turns from solid to liquid. You usually measure a melting range, which is the range of temperatures from where the solid begins to melt to where it has melted completely.

You can look up the melting point of a substance in data books and compare it to your measurements. Impurities in the sample will lower the melting point and increase the melting range.

Figure 4: *Melting point apparatus.*

Tip: In a saturated solution, the maximum possible amount of solid is dissolved in the solvent.

Tip: When you recrystallise a product, you must use an appropriate solvent for that particular substance. It will only work if the solid is very soluble in the hot solvent, but nearly insoluble when the solvent is cold.

Tip: You can separate out the crystals using <u>filtration under reduced pressure</u> — see page 8 for details on this technique.

Tip: You can also use melting point analysis to identify an unknown substance. For example, if you have an unknown ester, you could hydrolyse it and purify the carboxylic acid using recrystallisation. You could then use melting point analysis to work out the identity of the carboxylic acid. Working out the identity of the alcohol as well would let you identify the ester.

Practice Questions — Application

Q1 Hexane is insoluble in water and has a boiling point of 68 °C. Ethanol is soluble in water and has a boiling point of 78 °C. Suggest how you could separate a mixture of hexane and ethanol into its component parts.

Q2 A student wants to make the compound 4-hydroxypentan-2-one by heating pentan-2,4-diol with acidified potassium dichromate. If the reaction is left for too long, the starting material ends up being oxidised twice to form a compound with two carbonyl groups. Suggest a method the student could use to prevent the starting material from being over-oxidised.

Exam Tip
Always remember to label diagrams if you have to draw them in the exam.

Practice Questions — Fact Recall

Q1 Name two compounds that can be used as drying agents.

Q2 Draw a labelled diagram of the apparatus used to carry out a distillation.

Q3 What physical property is used to separate compounds in redistillation?

Q4 Will a pure product have a wide or a narrow melting point range?

Section Summary

Make sure you know...

- That optical isomerism is a form of stereoisomerism.
- That chiral carbon atoms are carbon atoms with four different groups attached, and that optical isomers have chiral carbon atoms.
- That enantiomers (optical isomers) are molecules with a chiral carbon atom and the same structural formula that exist as non superimposable mirror images.
- How to draw optical isomers.
- That enantiomers rotate plane polarised light in opposite directions.
- That a racemic mixture contains equal quantities of each enantiomer of an optically active compound.
- That racemic mixtures are optically inactive.
- The difference between aldehydes and ketones — aldehydes have their carbonyl group at the end of the carbon chain and ketones have their carbonyl group in the middle.
- How to name aldehydes and ketones.
- That aldehydes are easily oxidised to form carboxylic acids but ketones aren't.
- How Tollens' reagent and Fehling's solution can be used to distinguish between aldehydes and ketones.
- That aldehydes and ketones can be reduced to primary and secondary alcohols respectively, using reducing agents such as $NaBH_4$.
- The nucleophilic addition reaction mechanism for the reduction of aldehydes and ketones.
- What hydroxynitriles are and how to name them.
- That aldehydes and ketones react with KCN to produce hydroxynitriles.

- How to write the overall eqautions to show the reaction of aldehydes and ketones with HCN and acidified KCN.
- That the production of hydroxynitriles using aldehydes/ketones and KCN is an example of nucleophilic addition.
- That the reaction between KCN and aldehydes or unsymmetrical ketones leads to enantiomers.
- The hazards of using KCN in a reaction.
- What carboxylic acids are and how to name them.
- That carboxylic acids are weak acids that partially dissociate in water.
- That carboxylic acids react with carbonates and hydrogen carbonates to form a salt, CO_2 and H_2O.
- That carboxylic acids react with alcohols in the presence of a strong acid catalyst (e.g. HCl, H_2SO_4 or H_3PO_4) to form esters — this is called an esterification reaction.
- What esters are and how to name them.
- That esters can have pleasant smells so are often used in perfumes and as food flavourings.
- That esters can also be used as plasticisers and solvents.
- That esters can undergo acid hydrolysis to give carboxylic acids and alcohols.
- That esters can undergo base hydrolysis to give carboxylate ions and alcohols.
- That fats/oils are esters of glycerol (propane-1,2,3-triol) and long chain carboxylic acids (fatty acids).
- The difference between fats and oils — fats contain mainly saturated fatty acids while oils contain mostly unsaturated fatty acids.
- Why fats are solid at room temperature when oils are liquid.
- That fats and oils can be hydrolysed to form glycerol and sodium salts which can be used as soap.
- That vegetable oils react with methanol in the presence of a KOH catalyst to form methyl esters which are used in biodiesel.
- That biodiesel is sometimes referred to as carbon neutral, but it actually is not.
- What acyl chlorides are and how to name them.
- The reactions of acyl chlorides with water, alcohols, ammonia and primary amines — including the nucleophilic addition-elimination mechanism for these reactions.
- What acid anhydrides are and how to name them.
- The reactions of acid anhydrides with water, alcohols, ammonia and primary amines.
- That aspirin can be made by reacting salicylic acid with ethanoic anhydride or ethanoyl chloride.
- That ethanoic anhydride is used in industry to produce aspirin because it is cheaper and safer to work with than ethanoyl chloride.
- That you can use a separating funnel to separate an organic product from impurities that dissolve in a solvent that's immiscible with the organic product.
- That solvent extraction is a form of separation that involves the vigorous shaking of a product with an immiscible solvent.
- That drying agents remove water from an organic product.
- That washing is a technique used to purify organic products.
- That distillation is a technique that uses the difference in boiling points of different substances to isolate a product from a reaction as it forms.
- That redistillation uses differences in boiling points to purify volatile liquids.
- That organic solids can be purified by recrystallisation.
- That you can test the purity of a product using melting point apparatus.

Exam-style Questions

1 Which of the following molecules have optical isomers?

molecule **x**   molecule **y**   molecule **z**

- **A** **x** and **z** only
- **B** **y** only
- **C** **x**, **y** and **z**
- **D** **y** and **z** only

(1 mark)

2 Which of the following methods could be used to purify a solid organic product?
- **A** Redistillation
- **B** Washing
- **C** Reflux
- **D** Recrystallisation

(1 mark)

3 Which of the options shows the molecule with the correctly labelled chiral carbon atom?

A

B

C

D

(1 mark)

4   The two compounds, A and B, shown below are structurally very similar, but a simple test can be used to distinguish between them.

         Compound A   Compound B

4.1 Give the IUPAC names for these two compounds.

                                                                    (2 marks)

4.2 Describe a test that could be used to differentiate between these compounds.

                                                                    (2 marks)

         Compound A can be reduced to form a primary alcohol.

4.3 Suggest a suitable reducing agent for this reaction.

                                                                    (1 mark)

4.4 Outline the mechanism for this reduction reaction.

                                                                    (4 marks)

         Compound B can react with acidified potassium cyanide (KCN).

4.5 Name and outline the mechanism for this reaction.

                                                                    (5 marks)

4.6 Give the IUPAC name for the product formed.

                                                                    (1 mark)

4.7 Compound A can also react with acidified KCN. What effect will the product of this reaction have on plane polarised light? Explain your answer.

                                                                    (3 marks)

5   2-methylbutanoic acid is a carboxylic acid.

5.1 Draw the structure of this carboxylic acid.

                                                                    (1 mark)

5.2 2-methylbutanoic acid is optically active. Draw the two enantiomers of 2-methylbutanoic acid, and mark the chiral centre on each molecule with a *.

                                                                    (2 marks)

5.3 Write an equation for the reaction of 2-methylbutanoic acid with sodium carbonate (Na_2CO_3).

                                                                    (2 marks)

Carboxylic acids react with alcohols to form esters.

5.4   Draw the structure of the ester that would be formed if 2-methylbutanoic acid reacted with methanol.

(1 mark)

5.5   Give the IUPAC name for this ester.

(1 mark)

5.6   Suggest a suitable catalyst for this reaction.

(1 mark)

5.7   Write an equation for the hydrolysis of this ester with dilute alkali. Show the structure of the reactants and products in your answer.

(2 marks)

5.8   Give one common use of esters.

(1 mark)

6   Fats and oils are esters formed from glycerol (propane-1,2,3-triol) and fatty acids (long chain carboxylic acids).

6.1   Explain why fats are usually solid at room temperature while oils are normally liquid.

(3 marks)

6.2   The structure below shows a naturally occurring triester commonly found in fats and oils.

$$CH_2OOC(CH_2)_{16}CH_3$$
$$CH_2OOC(CH_2)_{16}CH_3$$
$$CH_2OOC(CH_2)_{16}CH_3$$

Write an equation to show how this ester could be converted to a sodium salt.

(3 marks)

6.3   Suggest a use for this sodium salt.

(1 mark)

Biodiesel can be produced from fats and oils.

6.4   What is biodiesel?

(1 mark)

6.5   Write an equation to show how biodiesel could be produced from the ester shown in part **6.2**.

(3 marks)

6.6   What is the role of KOH in this reaction?

(1 mark)

7 This question is about acyl chlorides and acid anhydrides.

The structure below shows the acyl chloride 2,3-dimethylbutanoyl chloride.

7.1 Write an equation to show the reaction of this acyl chloride with ammonia.

(2 marks)

7.2 Name and outline the mechanism for this reaction.

(6 marks)

Acid anhydrides have very similar properties to acyl chlorides but they are structurally very different.

7.3 Draw the structure of ethanoic anhydride.

(1 mark)

7.4 Write an equation to show the reaction of this acid anhydride with water.

(2 marks)

Ethanoic anhydride can be reacted with salicylic acid to produce aspirin. The structure of salicylic acid is shown below.

Salicylic acid has an OH group and behaves like an alcohol when reacting with ethanoic anhydride.

7.5 Using your knowledge of the reactions of acid anhydrides with alcohols, write an equation showing the formation of aspirin from ethanoic anhydride and salicylic acid.

(2 marks)

7.6 Aspirin can also be produced by reacting ethanoyl chloride with salicylic acid.

Which method of aspirin production is favoured in industry?
Explain your answer.

(3 marks)

7.7 In the lab, aspirin forms as a solid organic product which contains trace impurities. Outline a method that could be used to purify aspirin made in the lab.

(3 marks)

Learning Objectives:

▪ Be able to describe the nature of the bonding in a benzene ring, limited to its planar structure and bond length intermediate between single and double.

▪ Understand that the delocalisation of p electrons makes benzene more stable than the theoretical molecule cyclohexa-1,3,5-triene.

▪ Be able to use thermochemical evidence from enthalpies of hydrogenation to account for the extra stability of the benzene ring.

▪ Be able to apply IUPAC rules for nomenclature to name organic compounds limited to chains and rings with up to six carbon atoms each.

▪ Be able to apply IUPAC rules for nomenclature to draw the structure of an organic compound from the IUPAC name limited to chains and rings with up to six carbon atoms each.

Specification Reference
3.3.1.1, 3.3.10.1

Tip: Have a look at your Year 1 notes for a recap on p-orbitals.

1. Aromatic Compounds

Aromatic compounds all contain a benzene ring. Benzene's a bit of a funny thing — it contains a very stable ring of delocalised electrons, and this affects its properties. Read on and all shall be revealed...

The structure of benzene

Benzene has the formula C_6H_6. It has a planar cyclic structure (which is just a complicated way of saying that its six carbon atoms are joined together in a flat ring). Each carbon atom forms single covalent bonds to the carbons on either side of it and to one hydrogen atom. The final unpaired electron on each carbon atom is located in a p-orbital that sticks out above and below the plane of the ring. The p-orbitals on each carbon atom combine to form a ring of delocalised electrons (see Figure 1). The electrons in the ring are said to be delocalised because they don't belong to a specific carbon atom. All the bonds in the ring are the same, so they are the same length — 140 pm. This lies in between the length of a single C–C bond (147 pm) and a double C=C bond (135 pm).

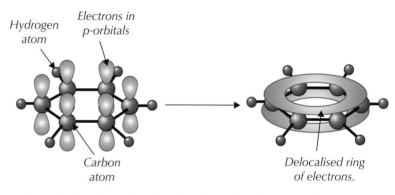

Figure 1: The formation of a delocalised ring of electrons in benzene.

The delocalised ring of electrons can be represented by a circle in the ring of carbon-carbon single bonds rather than as alternating double and single bonds (see Figure 3).

Figure 2: The structure of benzene according to the delocalised model.

Figure 4 shows another representation of benzene that you may come across. Don't get confused by this drawing — those aren't really alternating single and double bonds between the carbon atoms. Scientists used to think this was the structure, and their way of drawing it has just stuck around.

Figure 3: *Another representation of a benzene ring.*

Figure 4: *A computer graphic showing the structure of benzene.*

Stability of benzene

Benzene is far more stable than the theoretical compound cyclohexa-1,3,5-triene would be (where the ring would be made up of alternating single and double bonds). You can see this by comparing the enthalpy change of hydrogenation for benzene with the enthalpy change of hydrogenation for cyclohexene. Cyclohexene has one double bond. When it's hydrogenated, the enthalpy change is -120 kJ mol^{-1}. If benzene had three double bonds, you'd expect it to have an enthalpy of hydrogenation of -360 kJ mol^{-1}. But the experimental enthalpy of hydrogenation of benzene is -208 kJ mol^{-1} — 152 kJ mol^{-1} less exothermic than expected (see Figure 5).

Tip: See page 20 for more on enthalpies.

Tip: Cyclohexa-1,3,5-triene (a six-carbon ring with three double bonds) is a theoretical molecule (it doesn't actually exist), so we can't measure its enthalpy of hydrogenation directly. We can only predict it from the enthalpy of hydrogenation for cyclohexene.

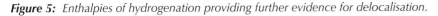

Figure 5: *Enthalpies of hydrogenation providing further evidence for delocalisation.*

Energy is put in to break bonds and released when bonds are made. So more energy must have been put in to break the bonds in benzene than would be needed to break the bonds in a theoretical cyclohexa-1,3,5-triene molecule. This difference indicates that benzene is more stable than cyclohexa-1,3,5-triene would be. This is thought to be due to the delocalised ring of electrons. In a delocalised ring the electron density is shared over more atoms, which means the energy of the molecule is lowered and it becomes more stable.

Q1 The graph below shows the enthalpies of hydrogenation of cyclohexene and benzene.

Use the graph to explain why benzene does not have the structure of the theoretical molecule cyclohexa-1,3,5-triene.

Tip: Aromatic compounds are also known as <u>arenes</u>, so don't get confused if you see this term around.

Naming aromatic compounds

Aromatic compounds all contain a benzene ring, but naming them isn't that simple. They're named in two ways:

1. In some cases, the benzene ring is the main functional group and the molecule is named as a substituted benzene ring — the suffix is -benzene and there are prefixes to represent any other functional groups.

<u>Examples</u>

Chlorobenzene   Nitrobenzene   Methylbenzene   Chloromethylbenzene

Tip: Non-aromatic molecules are called aliphatic molecules — don't get the terms aromatic and aliphatic mixed up.

2. In other cases, the benzene ring is not the main functional group and the molecule is named as having a phenyl group (C_6H_5) attached. Phenyl- or phen- are used as a prefixes to show the molecule has a benzene ring and the suffix comes from other functional groups on the molecule (e.g. -ol if it's an alcohol, -amine if it's an amine).

<u>Examples</u>

Phenylamine   Phenol   Phenylethanone   Phenylethene

Unfortunately, there's no simple rule to help remember which name to use — you just have to learn which are '-benzene' and which are 'phenyl-'

Numbering the benzene ring

If there is more than one functional group attached to the benzene ring you have to number the carbons to show where the groups are. If all the functional groups are the same, pick any group to start from and count round either clockwise or anticlockwise — whichever way gives the smallest numbers. If the functional groups are different, start from whichever functional group gives the molecule its suffix (e.g. the –OH group for a phenol) and continue counting round whichever way gives the smallest numbers. If there's no suffix from a functional group, start numbering from whichever group is first alphabetically.

Tip: If there is only one functional group you don't have to number the carbons because all the positions around the carbon ring are the same.

--- Examples ---

This benzene ring only has methyl groups attached so it will be named as a substituted benzene ring.

Starting from the methyl group at the top and counting clockwise there is another methyl group on carbon-3.

So this is 1,3-dimethylbenzene.

This benzene ring has an OH group attached so the stem is phenol.

Starting from the OH group (the group which gives the molecule its name) and counting anticlockwise there are chlorines on carbon-2 and carbon-4.

So this is 2,4-dichlorophenol.

Exam Tip
You're unlikely to be asked to name anything too complicated in the exams. If you need to give the product of a reaction, don't try and name it unless they specifically ask for the name — giving the structure should be enough to get the marks.

Practice Question — Application

Q1 Name these aromatic compounds:

a)   b)   c)

Practice Questions — Fact Recall

Q1 What are aromatic compounds?

Q2 Describe the structure of benzene.

- Know that electrophilic attack on benzene rings results in substitution, limited to monosubstitutions.

- Be able to explain why substitution reactions occur at a benzene ring in preference to addition reactions.

- Be able to outline the electrophilic substitution mechanism of nitration, including the generation of the nitronium ion.

- Understand that nitration is an important step in synthesis, including for the manufacture of explosives and formation of amines.

- Be able to outline the electrophilic substitution mechanism of acylation using $AlCl_3$ as a catalyst.

- Understand that Friedel-Crafts acylation reactions are important steps in synthesis.

Specification Reference
3.3.10.1, 3.3.10.2

Tip: Don't get confused between electrophiles and nucleophiles. Just remember, <u>electro</u>philes love <u>electro</u>ns.

Exam Tip
In your exams, you might be asked to write out the equation for the formation of the nitronium ion before giving the rest of the mechanism for nitration — so make sure you learn it.

2. Reactions of Aromatics

You need to know some of the main reactions of aromatic compounds — plus, there's another reaction mechanism for you to learn.

Electrophilic substitution

The benzene ring is a region of high electron density, so it attracts **electrophiles**. Electrophiles are electron pair acceptors — they are usually a bit short of electrons so are attracted to areas of high electron density. Common electrophiles include positively charged ions (e.g. H^+ or NO_2^+), and polar molecules (e.g. carbonyl compounds), which have a partial positive charge.

As the benzene ring's so stable, it doesn't undergo electrophilic addition reactions, which would destroy the delocalised ring of electrons. Instead, it undergoes **electrophilic substitution** reactions where one of the hydrogen atoms (or another group on the ring) is substituted for the electrophile.

1. The electron-dense region at the centre of the benzene ring attracts an electrophile (El^+).
2. The electrophile steals a pair of electrons from the centre of the benzene ring and forms a bond with one of the carbons.
3. This partially breaks the delocalised electron ring and gives the molecule a positive charge.
4. To regain the stability of the benzene ring, the carbon which is now bound to the electrophile loses a hydrogen.
5. So you get the substitution of an H^+ with the electrophile.

You need to know two electrophilic substitution mechanisms for benzene — the nitration reaction (below) and Friedel-Crafts acylation (page 207).

Nitration

When you warm benzene with concentrated nitric acid and concentrated sulfuric acid, you get nitrobenzene. The overall equation for this reaction is:

Nitric acid   *Benzene*   *Nitrobenzene*

Sulfuric acid acts as a catalyst — it helps to make the nitronium ion, NO_2^+, which is the electrophile. The formation of the nitronium ion is the first step of the reaction mechanism. The equation for this step is:

$$HNO_3 + H_2SO_4 \rightarrow HSO_4^- + NO_2^+ + H_2O$$

Once the nitronium ion has been formed, it can react with benzene to form nitrobenzene. This is the electrophilic substitution step in the reaction.

Here's the mechanism for the electrophilic substitution part of the reaction:

| The nitronium ion attacks the benzene ring. | An unstable intermediate forms. | An H+ ion is lost. | This H+ ion reacts with HSO_4^- to reform the catalyst, H_2SO_4. |

Exam Tip
If you're asked how the catalyst reforms, here's the reaction:
$$H^+ + HSO_4^- \rightarrow H_2SO_4$$

If you only want one NO_2 group added (mononitration), you need to keep the temperature below 55 °C. Above this temperature you'll get lots of substitutions.

Uses of nitration reactions

Nitro compounds can be reduced to form aromatic amines (see page 216). These are used to manufacture dyes and pharmaceuticals. Nitro compounds decompose violently when heated, so they are used as explosives — such as 2,4,6-trinitromethylbenzene (trinitrotoluene (TNT) — see Figures 1 and 2).

Figure 1: TNT.

Figure 2: Blocks of TNT explosive.

Friedel-Crafts acylation

Many useful chemicals such as dyes and pharmaceuticals contain benzene rings, but because benzene is so stable, it's fairly unreactive. Friedel-Crafts acylation reactions are important in the synthesis of these compounds, as they are used to add an acyl group (–C(=O)–R) to the benzene ring. The products of the reaction are HCl and a phenylketone. The reactants need to be heated under reflux in a non-aqueous solvent (like dry ether) for the reaction to occur. Here's the equation for the reaction:

| Acyl chloride | Benzene | Phenylketone |

Once an acyl group has been added, the side chains can be modified by further reactions to produce useful products.

An electrophile has to have a pretty strong positive charge to be able to attack the stable benzene ring — most just aren't polarised enough. But some can be made into stronger electrophiles using a catalyst called a **halogen carrier**.

Friedel-Crafts acylation uses an acyl chloride to provide the electrophile and a halogen carrier such as $AlCl_3$. $AlCl_3$ accepts a lone pair of electrons from the acyl chloride. As the lone pair of electrons is pulled away, the polarisation in the acyl chloride increases and it forms a **carbocation**. This makes it a much, much stronger electrophile, and gives it a strong enough charge to react with the benzene ring. The formation of the carbocation is the first step in the reaction mechanism and is shown below:

Figure 3: Charles Friedel — co-developer of Friedel-Crafts acylation.

Tip: There are other types of halogen carrier, but $AlCl_3$ is the only one you need to know about.

Exam Tip
The formation of the carbocation is part of the reaction mechanism so make sure you include it in the exams.

Acyl chlorides are weak electrophiles.

The halogen carrier accepts a lone pair of electrons from the acyl chloride.

The carbocation generated is a much stronger electrophile than the acyl chloride.

And here's the second step in the reaction mechanism, the electrophilic substitution bit:

Exam Tip
You could draw out the full structure of benzene when writing out this equation — but these simplified diagrams are a lot quicker and could save you valuable time in your exams.

Electrons in the benzene ring are attracted to the positively charged carbocation. Two electrons from the benzene bond with the carbocation. This partially breaks the delocalised ring and gives it a positive charge.

The negatively charged $AlCl_4^-$ ion is attracted to the positively charged ring. One chloride ion breaks away from the aluminium chloride ion and bonds with the hydrogen. This removes the hydrogen from the ring, forming HCl. It also allows the catalyst to reform. Any acyl chloride can react with benzene in this way.

Exam Tip
When drawing the intermediates of these reactions, make sure the horseshoe in the middle of the benzene ring only extends from carbon-2 to carbon-6.

Example

Ethanoyl chloride reacts with benzene to produce phenyl ethanone:

$$CH_3COCl + AlCl_3 \rightarrow CH_3CO^+ + AlCl_4^-$$

Exam Tip
When drawing these mechanisms in your exams, make sure your curly arrows clearly go from the delocalised ring of electrons to the carbocation and from the C-H bond back to the delocalised electron ring. Just drawing your curly arrows to/from the centre of benzene won't be enough to get you all the marks.

Practice Questions — Application

Q1 Phenylmethanal can be produced using Friedel-Crafts acylation.
  a) Suggest a suitable catalyst for this reaction.
  b) Write out an equation for this reaction.
  c) Name and outline the mechanism for this reaction.

Q2 a) Draw the mechanism for the formation of nitrobenzene from benzene and concentrated nitric acid.
  b) What two conditions are needed to produce nitrobenzene with this reaction?

Practice Questions — Fact Recall

Q1 Explain why electrophiles are attracted to aromatic compounds.

Q2 Give two uses of nitro compounds produced by nitration of benzene.

Q3 Explain how $AlCl_3$ acts as a catalyst in Friedel-Crafts acylation.

3. Amines and Amides

Amines and amides are produced from ammonia (NH_3). You met amines in Year 1, where you saw that they can be formed when halogenoalkanes react with ammonia. Now you need to know a bit more about them. The next few pages are all about amines, amides and why they're useful.

What are amines?

If one or more of the hydrogens in ammonia (NH_3) is replaced with an organic group such as an alkyl or aromatic group, you get an **amine**. If one hydrogen is replaced, you get a primary amine, if two are replaced it's a secondary amine, and three means it's a tertiary amine. If a fourth organic group is added you get a quaternary ammonium ion (see Figure 1).

Ammonia   Primary amine   Secondary amine   Tertiary amine   Quaternary ammonium ion

Figure 1: *Diagram showing the different types of amine.*

Because quaternary ammonium ions are positively charged, they will hang around with any negative ions that are near. The complexes formed are called quaternary ammonium salts — like tetramethylammonium chloride (($CH_3)_4N^+Cl^-$). Small amines smell similar to ammonia, with a slightly 'fishy' twist. Larger amines smell very 'fishy'. (Nice.)

Naming amines

Naming amines is similar to naming other organic compounds. The suffix is -amine (or -amine ion if it's a quaternary ammonium ion). The prefix depends on what organic groups are attached. If the organic groups are all the same you also need to add di- for secondary amines, tri- for tertiary amines and tetra- for quaternary ammonium ions.

┌─ Examples ──

Propylamine   Diethylamine   Trimethylamine   Tetramethylamine ion

└──

If the amine has more than one type of organic group attached, you list the different groups in alphabetical order.

┌─ Example ───

This is a secondary amine. It has a methyl group and a propyl group attached.
So this is methylpropylamine.

└──

You can also get aromatic amines. See page 204 for how to name these.

Learning Objectives:

- Be able to apply IUPAC rules for nomenclature to name organic compounds limited to chains and rings with up to six carbon atoms each.

- Be able to apply IUPAC rules for nomenclature to draw the structure of an organic compound from the IUPAC name limited to chains and rings with up to six carbon atoms each.

- Be able to describe the use of quaternary ammonium salts as cationic surfactants.

- Know that amines are weak bases.

- Be able to describe and explain the difference in base strength between ammonia, primary aliphatic and primary aromatic amines in terms of the availability of the lone pair of electrons on the N atom.

- Be able to recognise the structures of amides.

Specification Reference 3.3.1.1, 3.3.9.2, 3.3.11.2, 3.3.11.3

Tip: Have a look at your Year 1 notes for the general rules for naming organic compounds.

Tip: Aliphatic amines are amines without a benzene ring. Aromatic amines are amines where the nitrogen atom is directly bonded to a benzene ring.

Cationic surfactants

Surfactants are compounds which are partly soluble and partly insoluble in water. Some quaternary ammonium compounds can be used as **cationic surfactants** (surfactants which are positively charged). These compounds are quaternary ammonium salts with at least one long hydrocarbon chain (see Figure 2).

Figure 2: *A cationic surfactant.*

The long hydrocarbon chain is insoluble in water, but will bind to non-polar substances such as grease, whilst the positively charged head group is soluble in water. This makes cationic surfactants useful in detergents, as the non-polar end will bind to grease, and the polar head group will dissolve in water, allowing spots of grease to mix with water and be washed away (see Figure 3).

Tip: Cationic surfactants form induced dipole-dipole interactions with non-polar substances and hydrogen bonds with water.

Figure 3: *How cationic surfactants can help non-polar substances such as grease mix with water.*

Figure 4: *Fabric softeners contain cationic surfactants.*

Cationic surfactants are used in things like fabric conditioners and hair products. When hair or fabric get wet they pick up negative charges on their surface. The positively charged part of the surfactant is attracted to these negatively charged surfaces and forms a coating over the surface. This coating prevents the build-up of static electricity. In fabric conditioners this is important to keep the fabric smooth and in hair products it helps to keep hair flat.

Amines as bases

Tip: See page 97 for more on acids and bases.

Amines act as weak bases because they accept protons. There's a lone pair of electrons on the nitrogen atom that forms a **co-ordinate** (dative covalent) bond with an H^+ ion (see Figure 5).

Tip: A co-ordinate bond is a type of covalent bond where both of the electrons have been provided by the same atom (in this case the nitrogen atom).

Figure 5: *Formation of a dative bond between a primary amine and an H^+ ion.*

The strength of the base depends on how available the nitrogen's lone pair of electrons is. A lone pair of electrons will be more available if its electron density is higher. The more available the lone pair is, the more likely the amine is to accept a proton, and the stronger a base it will be.

Primary aromatic amines are weak bases. This is because the benzene ring draws electrons towards itself and the nitrogen's lone pair gets partially delocalised onto the ring. So the electron density on the nitrogen decreases. This makes the lone pair much less available.

Primary aliphatic amines are strong bases. This is because alkyl groups push electrons onto attached groups. So the electron density on the nitrogen atom increases. This makes the lone pair more available.

The strength of ammonia as a base lies somewhere in between. This is because ammonia doesn't have an aromatic group to pull the lone pair of electrons away, or an alkyl group to push the lone pair of electrons forward — see Figure 6.

Exam Tip
You need to be able to explain the difference in base strength between ammonia, primary aromatic amines and primary aliphatic amines — so make sure you understand these explanations.

Tip: The effect of an alkyl group on a lone pair of electrons is sometimes called the inductive effect.

● Areas of highest electron density

Weakest Base — **Strongest Base**

Lone pair least available ⟶ Lone pair most available

The benzene ring draws electrons towards itself, making the lone pair of electrons less available.

The alkyl group pushes electrons away from itself, making the lone pair of electrons more available.

Figure 6: *Diagram showing why primary aromatic amines are weaker bases than ammonia and why primary aliphatic amines are stronger bases than ammonia.*

Tip: Don't get confused between amides and amines. Just remember, amides contain nitrogen bonded directly to a carbon with a C=O double bond — amines contain no double bonds.

Amides

Amides are derivatives of carboxylic acids. They contain the functional group $-CONH_2$. The carbonyl group pulls electrons away from the NH_2 group, so amides behave differently from amines. Here's the general structure of an amine:

The carbonyl group pulls electrons away from the NH_2 group.

Carbonyl group

NH_2 group

Tip: Amides can be made by reacting acyl chlorides with ammonia See page 188 for more.

Naming amides is pretty easy — the suffix is always -amide and the prefix comes from the acyl group (R–C=O).

┌─ **Examples** ───────────────────────────────

Methanamide   *Ethanamide*   *Methylpropanamide*

Tip: N-substituted amides can be made by reacting acyl chlorides with amines. There's more about this on page 189.

You can also get **N-substituted amides**. These are amides where one of the hydrogens attached to the nitrogen has been substituted with an alkyl group. When naming N-substituted amides, you have to add an extra bit onto the beginning of the name. The name starts with N-something (e.g. N-methyl, N-ethyl, N-propyl) — whatever the alkyl group that's been added onto the nitrogen is.

┌─ **Examples** ──────────────────────────────

This molecule is based on ethanamide.
One of the hydrogens attached to the nitrogen has been substituted with a methyl group.
So this is N-methylethanamide.

This is based on propanamide.
One of the hydrogens attached to the nitrogen has been substituted with an ethyl group.
So this is N-ethylpropanamide.

Exam Tip
You don't need to know much about amides. As long as you can name them and know how they can be produced from acyl chlorides (see pages 188-189) or acid anhydrides (see page 192) you should be fine in your exams.

Practice Questions — Application

Q1 Name these amines:

Q2 Ammonia, phenylamine and ethylamine, shown below, can all act as bases:

Ammonia *Phenylamine* *Ethylamine*

a) Which of these is the strongest base? Explain your answer.

b) Which of these is the weakest base? Explain your answer.

Q3 Name these amides:

Practice Questions — Fact Recall

Q1 What is a quaternary ammonium ion?

Q2 a) What type of ammonium compound can be used as a cationic surfactant?

b) Give one use of cationic surfactants.

Q3 Amines can act as bases. What determines the strength of the base?

4. Reactions of Amines

The last few pages talked about amines and why they are useful. This section covers how amines are made from other organic compounds, and how they can react.

Formation of amines from halogenoalkanes

There are two ways to produce aliphatic amines — the first uses halogenoalkanes in a nucleophilic substitution reaction you met in Year 1. Amines can be made by heating a halogenoalkane with excess ethanolic ammonia (ammonia dissolved in ethanol).

Example

Ethylamine can be produced by heating bromoethane with ammonia:

But, things aren't that simple. You'll actually get a mixture of primary, secondary and tertiary amines, and quaternary ammonium salts, as more than one hydrogen is likely to be substituted.

Example

When producing ethylamine you'll actually get a mixture of ethylamine, diethylamine, triethylamine and tetraethylamine ions:

The formation of amines from halogenoalkanes is a **nucleophilic substitution** reaction. Here's the general mechanism for this reaction:

X = any halogen

Figure 1: *The nucleophilic substitution mechanism for the reaction between ammonia and a halogenoalkane.*

1. NH_3 (the nucleophile) attacks the δ^+ carbon on the halogenoalkane and donates its lone pair of electrons, forming a bond with the carbon.
2. As carbon can only have four bonds, the addition of ammonia causes the C–X bond to break, releasing a negatively charged halide ion and leaving an alkylammonium salt.
3. A second ammonia molecule then donates its lone pair of electrons to one of the hydrogens attached to the nitrogen.
4. This hydrogen breaks off from the alkyl ammonium salt and joins ammonia to form an NH_4^+ ion.
5. This leaves a primary amine. The NH_4^+ ion forms an ionic bond with the X$^-$ ion to produce $NH_4^+X^-$.

Learning Objectives:

- Know that primary aliphatic amines can be prepared by the reaction of ammonia with halogenoalkanes and by the reduction of nitriles.

- Be able to describe and outline the mechanisms of the nucleophilic substitution reactions of ammonia and amines with halogenoalkanes to form primary, secondary and tertiary amines and quaternary ammonium salts.

- Know that amines are nucleophiles.

- Be able to describe and outline the mechanism of the nucleophilic addition-elimination reactions of ammonia and primary amines with acyl chlorides.

- Be able to describe the nucleophilic addition-elimination reactions of ammonia and primary amines with acid anhydrides.

- Know that aromatic amines can be prepared by the reduction of nitro compounds, and are used in the manufacture of dyes.

Specification Reference 3.3.11.1, 3.3.11.3

Tip: The nitrogen in the amine has a lone pair of electrons on it. This means it can accept a hydrogen and form an alkylammonium salt — so the conversion of an alkylammonium salt to an amine is reversible.

Exam Tip
You could be asked to name and outline the mechanism for the production of any amine from a halogenoalkane, so make sure you understand this mechanism — just learning the example won't be enough.

Tip: The number of further substitutions that happen can be reduced by increasing the concentration of ammonia relative to the halogenoalkane — the higher the concentration of ammonia, the less likely it is that a halogenoalkane will meet and react with an amine rather than ammonia.

Tip: Amines and ammonia can both act as nucleophiles in nucleophilic substitution reactions because they both have a lone pair of electrons.

Tip: Forming amines by reducing nitriles is useful if you just want the primary amine because you can't get further substitutions — the primary amine is the only product.

Tip: [H] means any reducing agent.

Example

Here's the mechanism for the formation of ethylamine from ammonia and bromoethane:

The amine product still has a lone pair of electrons on the nitrogen, so it is still a nucleophile. This means that further substitutions can take place. They keep happening until you get a quaternary ammonium salt, which can't react any further as it doesn't have a lone pair of electrons (see Figure 2).

Figure 2: *Further substitutions lead to the formation of secondary, tertiary and quaternary amines.*

The mechanism for these further substitutions is the same — you just use an amine instead of ammonia.

Example

Here's the mechanism for the formation of dimethylamine from methylamine and bromomethane:

Formation of amines from nitriles

The second way to produce aliphatic amines uses nitriles. You can reduce a nitrile to an amine using a strong reducing agent such as lithium aluminium hydride ($LiAlH_4$) in dry ether, followed by some dilute acid.

Example

Here's the equation for the formation of ethylamine from ethanenitrile:

$$CH_3C\equiv N \quad + \quad 4[H] \xrightarrow[\text{2. Dilute acid}]{\text{1. } LiAlH_4} CH_3CH_2NH_2$$

Ethanenitrile   *Ethylamine*

This is great in the lab, but $LiAlH_4$ is too expensive for industrial use. Industry uses a metal catalyst such as platinum or nickel at a high temperature and pressure — it's called **catalytic hydrogenation**.

Example

Here's the equation for the formation of ethylamine from ethanenitrile using catalytic hydrogenation:

$$CH_3C \equiv N \ + \ 2H_2 \xrightarrow[\text{High temp \& pressure}]{Ni} CH_3CH_2NH_2$$

Ethanenitrile   *Ethylamine*

Amines as nucleophiles

Acyl chlorides react with ammonia to form primary amides, and with primary amines to form N-substituted amides. These reactions occur via a **nucleophilic addition-elimination** mechanism. The general mechanism is:

> **Tip:** Remember, nucleophiles are lone pair donors. The lone pair on the nitrogen atom in aliphatic amines lets them act as nucleophiles.

Step 1:

1. The lone pair of electrons on the nitrogen atom of the amine attacks the δ⁺ carbon on the acyl chloride.

4. This leaves a positively charged amide ion and a negatively charged chloride ion.

2. A pair of electrons is transferred from the C=O bond onto the oxygen.

3. The pair of electrons on the oxygen reform the double bond and the chlorine is kicked off.

> **Tip:** The mechanism for the reaction with ammonia is exactly the same, but an amide containing a -C(O)NH₂ group is formed

Step 2:

5. The Cl⁻ ion bonds with a hydrogen on the nitrogen atom.

7. This leaves an amide...

...and HCl has been eliminated.

6. A pair of electrons is transferred onto the nitrogen atom from the bond.

> **Tip:** There's lots more detail about acyl chlorides and their reactions on pages 188-189.

Examples

Ethanolychloride   *Ammonia*   *Ethanamide*   *Hydrogen chloride gas*

Ethanoylchloride   *Methylamine*   *N-methylethanamide*   *Hydrogen chloride gas*

Figure 3: *The reaction of an amine (the orange liquid in the pipette) with an acyl chloride, to produce an amide and hydrogen chloride gas.*

Tip: Acid anhydrides have the general formula RC(O)OC(O)R'. There's more about them and their reactions on pages 191-192.

Acid anhydrides also react with primary amines or ammonia to form amides and a carboxylic acid. The reaction with primary amines produces and N-substituted amide, whilst the reaction with ammonia produces a primary amide. The general reactions is:

Figure 4: *The general reaction of an amine (if R' is an organic group) or ammonia (if R' is an H atom) with an acid anhydride.*

Tip: See page 206 for more on nitrobenzene and how it is made.

Formation of aromatic amines

Aromatic amines are produced by reducing a nitro compound, such as nitrobenzene. There are two steps to the method:

- First, a of a nitro compound, tin metal and concentrated hydrochloric acid is heated under reflux — this makes a salt.
- Then to turn the salt into an aromatic amine, an alkali, such as sodium hydroxide solution, is added to the mixture.

Figure 5: *The reflux equipment used to make phenylamine.*

> ## Example
>
> Phenylamine can be made by reducing nitrobenzene:
> - Mixing nitrobenzene with tin and concentrated HCl and heating under reflux produces the salt $C_6H_5NH_3^+$ Cl^-.
> - Adding NaOH to this salt then releases phenylamine.
>
> Here's the overall equation for the reaction:
>
> $$NO_2 \text{ (benzene ring)} + 6[H] \xrightarrow[\text{2. } NaOH_{(aq)}]{\substack{\text{1. } Sn, \text{ conc. } HCl \\ \text{reflux}}} NH_2 \text{ (benzene ring)} + 2H_2O$$
>
> *Nitrobenzene*   *Phenylamine*

Producing aromatic amines is important in industry — for example, they're used in the manufacture of dyes.

Practice Questions — Application

Q1 a) Write an equation to show the formation of methylamine from chloromethane.

   b) Name and outline the mechanism for this reaction.

Q2 a) Write an equation to show the formation of propylamine from propanenitrile by catalytic hydrogenation.

   b) What conditions are required for this reaction?

Q3 Write an equation to show the formation of 3-methylphenylamine from 3-methylnitrobenzene.

Q1 a) How can amines be produced from halogenoalkanes?

b) Explain why a mixture of primary, secondary and tertiary amines, and quaternary ammonium salts are produced in these reactions.

Q2 a) Give two ways that amines can be produced from nitriles.

b) Which of these methods is used in industry, and why?

Q3 Name the type of organic product(s) formed when ammonia reacts with:

a) a chloroalkane   b) an acyl chloride   c) an acid anhydride

Q4 Describe how aromatic amines can be produced.

Section Summary

Make sure you know...

- That benzene has the chemical formula C_6H_6 with six carbons joined together in a planar (flat) ring.
- That the carbon-carbon bonds in benzene are all the same length (intermediate between double and single bonds).
- That the delocalisation of p electrons makes benzene more stable than a theoretical cyclohexa-1,3,5-triene molecule.
- That enthalpies of hydrogenation provide evidence for the extra stability of benzene compared to a theoretical cyclohexa-1,3,5-triene molecule.
- What aromatic compounds are and how to name them.
- That the benzene ring is a region of high electron density so it attracts electrophiles.
- That electrophilic attack on benzene rings usually results in substitution because the ring is so stable.
- That Friedel-Crafts acylation and nitration are both electrophilic substitution reactions, and how to draw the mechanism for these reactions.
- That nitration is used to add nitro groups onto benzene rings, using HNO_3 and an H_2SO_4 catalyst.
- That nitro compounds are used to make explosives and aromatic amines (which are used to manufacture dyes and pharmaceuticals).
- That Friedel-Crafts acylation adds an acyl group onto benzene rings, producing a phenylketone.
- The role of halogen carriers such as $AlCl_3$ as catalysts in Friedel-Crafts acylation.
- What amines are and how to name them.
- That quaternary ammonium salts can be used as cationic surfactants, and the uses of these surfactants.
- That amines can accept protons, so are able to act as weak bases.
- Why aromatic amines are weaker bases than ammonia and why aliphatic amines are stronger bases.
- What amides are and how to name them.
- That amines can be formed by heating a halogenoalkane with an excess of ethanolic ammonia.
- That nucleophilic substitution reactions produce a mixture of primary, secondary and tertiary amines and quaternary ammonium salts because more than one hydrogen is likely to be substituted.
- The mechanism for nucleophilic substitution reactions of amines and ammonia with halogenoalkanes.
- That amines can also be formed by reducing nitriles.
- The mechanism for the nucleophilic addition-elimination reactions of ammonia and primary amines with acyl chlorides and acid anhydrides to produce amides.
- That aromatic amines are formed by reducing nitro compounds such as nitrobenzene.

Exam-style Questions

1 Which of the following statements about cationic surfactants is correct?

    A   Cationic surfactants can be made by reacting tertiary amines with halogenoalkanes.

    B   Cationic surfactants can cause a build-up of static electricity on hair and clothing.

    C   Cationic surfactants contain an amine group, so can act as bases.

    D   The long hydrocarbon chain in cationic surfactants allows the molecule to dissolve in water.

(1 mark)

2 Benzene is an extremely important molecule in the synthesis of aromatic compounds. The benzene ring is very stable and as a result benzene is fairly unreactive. Friedel-Crafts acylation reactions are used to add acyl side chains onto the benzene ring which can then be modified to make useful products.

  2.1   Write an equation to show the production of phenylpropanone by Friedel-Crafts acylation. Include all the reagents and conditions required for this reaction.

(2 marks)

  2.2   Friedel-Crafts acylation uses an $AlCl_3$ catalyst. Explain its role.

(2 marks)

  2.3   Outline the mechanism for this reaction.

(4 marks)

Nitro groups can be added to the benzene ring via nitration reactions, where an aromatic compound is heated with concentrated nitric and sulfuric acids.

  2.4   Outline the mechanism for the addition of one nitro group onto the benzene ring of methylbenzene. Your mechanism should include an equation to show the formation of a nitronium ion from concentrated nitric and sulfuric acids.

(4 marks)

Nitro compounds can be reduced to give aromatic amines.

  2.5   Write an equation to show the reduction of nitrobenzene to phenylamine. Describe the conditions needed for this reaction.

(5 marks)

3 What type of reactions will typically take place at a benzene ring?

    A Electrophilic addition

    B Electrophilic substitution

    C Nucleophilic addition-elimination

    D Nucleophilic substitution

(1 mark)

4 The diagrams below show two amines (**X** and **Y**).

                X   **Y**

4.1 Give the IUPAC names for these two amines.

(2 marks)

Aliphatic amines such as amine **X** can be produced by heating halogenoalkanes with an excess of ethanolic ammonia.

4.2 Write an equation to show the formation of amine **X** from a bromoalkane.

Name and outline the mechanism for this reaction.

(7 marks)

Preparations of amine **X** from a halogenoalkane are usually impure and contain a number of different products.

4.3 State why a mixture of different products can be produced in these reactions.

Draw the structure of one of the other products likely to be in the mixture with amine **X**.

(2 marks)

4.4 Suggest how the amount of amine **X** in the mixture could be increased.

(1 mark)

Amine **X** can also be made by reducing a nitrile with a strong reducing agent such as $LiAlH_4$.

4.5 Write an equation to show the reduction of a nitrile to amine **X**.

Explain why the amine **X** produced via this reaction is purer than the amine **X** made from a halogenoalkane.

(2 marks)

Amines **X** and **Y** can both act as bases.

4.6 State why amines are able to act as bases.

Which of these two amines is the stronger base? Explain your answer.

(5 marks)

Learning Objectives:

- Know that condensation polymers are formed by reactions between dicarboxylic acids and diols, dicarboxylic acids and diamines or between amino acids.

- Be able to describe the repeating units in polyesters (e.g. Terylene™) and polyamides (e.g. nylon 6,6 and Kevlar®) and the linkages between these repeating units.

- Be able to describe some typical uses of polyesters (e.g. Terylene™) and polyamides (e.g. nylon 6,6 and Kevlar®).

- Know that polyesters and polyamides can be broken down by hydrolysis.

- Be able to explain the nature of the intermolecular forces between molecules of condensation polymers.

Specification Reference
3.3.12.1, 3.3.12.2

1. Condensation Polymerisation

In Year 1, you met addition polymerisation which is where lots of alkenes join up together to form one long molecule. Now it's time for another type of polymerisation — condensation polymerisation.

Condensation polymers

Condensation polymerisation usually involves two different types of monomer. Each monomer has at least two functional groups. Each functional group reacts with a group on another monomer to form a link, creating polymer chains. Each time a link is formed, a small molecule is lost (usually water) — that's why it's called condensation polymerisation.

Examples of condensation polymers include polyamides, polyesters and polypeptides (or proteins). In polyesters, an ester link (–COO–) is formed between the monomers. In polyamides and polypeptides, amide links (–CONH–) are formed between the monomers. In polypeptides, these amide links are usually called peptide bonds.

Polyamides

Reactions between dicarboxylic acids and diamines make **polyamides**. The carboxyl groups of dicarboxylic acids react with the amino groups of diamines to form **amide links**. A water molecule is lost each time an amide link is formed — it's a condensation reaction (see Figure 1).

Figure 1: *The formation of an amide link.*

Dicarboxylic acids and diamines have functional groups at both ends, which means that they can each form two amide links and long chains can form. There are two polyamides you need to learn the reactions for:

- Nylon 6,6 — made from 1,6-diaminohexane and hexanedioic acid:

Tip: Figure 2 shows the formation of nylon 6,6. The product shown has brackets around it and an 'n' after it — this is the formula of the polymer. The repeating unit is this formula without the brackets, and without the 'n'.

Nylon 6,6

Figure 2: *The formation of nylon 6,6.*

Nylon 6,6 is strong and resistant to abrasion so is used to make clothing, carpet, rope, airbags and parachutes.

- Kevlar® — made from benzene-1,4-dicarboxylic acid and 1,4-diaminobenzene:

Benzene-1,4-dicarboxylic acid   *1,4-diaminobenzene*

Figure 3: *Kevlar® is used to make bulletproof clothing.*

Kevlar®

Figure 4: *The formation of Kevlar®.*

Kevlar® is both light and very strong, so it's used in bulletproof vests, boat construction, car tyres and lightweight sports equipment.

Exam Tip
If you're asked to draw the repeating unit of Kevlar® you should leave off the square brackets and the '*n*'.

Peptides

Amino acids contain an amine functional group and a carboxylic acid functional group. These groups can react in condensation polymerisation reactions to form polyamides. Polymers between amino acids are more commonly called **peptides**, though — see page 235 for more information.

Figure 5: *The formation of a peptide link.*

Polyesters

The carboxyl groups of dicarboxylic acids can react with the hydroxyl groups of diols to form **ester links** — it's another condensation reaction (see Figure 6).

Tip: The formation of polyesters is very similar to the formation of polyamides and polypeptides.

Figure 6: *The formation of an ester link.*

Polymers joined by ester links are called polyesters — an example is Terylene™ (PET). Terylene™ is formed from benzene-1,4-dicarboxylic acid and ethane-1,2-diol.

Figure 7: *The containers that microwave meals come in are made of Terylene™.*

Benzene-1,4-dicarboxylic acid   *Ethane-1,2-diol*

Terylene™

Figure 8: *The formation Terylene™.*

Some forms of Terylene™ are stable at both cold and hot temperatures, making them useful for creating containers for ready meals. Other forms are used to make plastic bottles, clothing, sheets and sails.

Hydrolysis of polyesters and polyamides

The ester or amide link in polyesters and polyamides can be broken down by **hydrolysis** — water molecules are added back in and the links are broken. The products of the hydrolysis are the monomers that were used to make the polymer — you're basically reversing the condensation reaction that was used to make them:

$$n(\text{monomers}) \underset{\text{hydrolysis}}{\overset{\text{condensation}}{\rightleftharpoons}} \text{polymer} + \text{water}$$

Tip: In hydrolysis reactions, a molecule of water breaks down a large molecule into two smaller molecules.

Water hydrolyses the amide links in polyamides, resulting in the formation of diamine and dicarboxylic acid molecules:

Figure 9: *The hydrolysis of a polyamide.*

Water hydrolyses the ester links in polyesters, resulting in the formation of diol and dicarboxylic acid molecules:

Figure 10: *The hydrolysis of a polyester.*

In practice, hydrolysis with just water is far too slow, so in the lab, the reaction is done with an acid or alkali. Polyamides are hydrolysed more easily in acidic conditions, and polyesters are hydrolysed more easily in basic conditions.

Bonding between polymer chains

Condensation polymers are generally stronger and more rigid than addition polymers (see your Year 1 notes). This is because condensation polymers are made up of chains containing polar bonds, e.g. C=O and C–N or C–O. So, as well as induced dipole-dipole forces, there are permanent dipole-dipole forces and very strong hydrogen bonds between the polymer chains (Figure 11).

hydrogen bonds

Figure 11: *Intermolecular forces between condensation polymer chains.*

Tip: You met all the different types of intermolecular force in Year 1. Have a look back at your notes if it all seems a bit hazy.

Tip: Hydrogen bonds are the strongest type of intermolecular force, so need lots of energy to be broken. This makes condensation polymers more rigid than addition polymers.

Practice Questions — Fact Recall

Q1 Suggest two types of molecule that can react together to form:

a) polyamides

b) polyesters

Q2 What type of reaction gives rise to polyamides and polyesters?

Q3 Draw the repeating units of:

a) Nylon 6,6

b) Kevlar®

c) Terylene™

Q4 What are the products when you hydrolyse:

a) a polyamide,

b) a polyester?

Q5 a) What is the strongest type of intermolecular force that can form between the chains of a condensation polymer?

b) Draw a diagram to show the formation of these bonds between two sections of polymer chains.

Tip: If your monomers are a dicarboxylic acid and a diol, you follow the same steps, but in step two you take an H from one of the oxygen atoms of your diol, and in the third step, you join the C and the O together to make an ester link.

Tip: Even if you've got a dicarboxylic acid and a diol, the -OH group is always lost from the carboxylic acid.

Tip: The formula of a polymer is just its repeating unit with square brackets round it and an *n* at the end.

Tip: If you've got a diol rather than a diamine, the process is exactly the same except you end up with a polyester rather than a polyamide.

2. Monomers & Repeating Units

You need to be able to look at a polymer and work out its repeating unit and what monomers it's made from, or look at some monomers and figure out the repeating unit of the polymer they'll form. Luckily for you, help is here...

Repeating units

Condensation polymers are made up of **repeating units** (a bit of molecule that repeats over and over again). If you know the formulas of a pair of monomers that react together in a condensation polymerisation reaction, you can work out the repeating unit of the condensation polymer that they would form. Here are the steps you should take to find the repeating unit of the polyamide that forms when a diamine and a dicarboxylic acid react together:

- Draw out the two monomer molecules next to each other.
- Remove an OH from the dicarboxylic acid, and an H from one of the nitrogen atoms in the diamine — that gives you a water molecule.
- Join the C=O and the N together to make an amide link.
- Take an H off the other nitrogen atom, and an OH off the other -COOH group at the ends of your molecule.

--- **Example** ---

Draw the repeating unit of the condensation polymer that is made from 1,4-diaminobutane, $H_2N(CH_2)_4NH_2$, and decanedioic acid, $HOOC(CH_2)_8COOH$.

If you draw out the monomers next to each other, this makes it easier to see which groups will be lost to form the water molecule:

Draw a bond between the C and the N that have lost groups to the water molecule:

To get the repeating unit, all that needs to be done now is to remove another -OH and -H from the groups at the ends of the molecule.

$$-N-(CH_2)_4-N-\overset{\overset{\textstyle O}{\|}}{C}-(CH_2)_8-\overset{\overset{\textstyle O}{\|}}{C}-$$

If you start by drawing the monomers the other way round, your repeating unit may end up looking slightly different:

This would cause your repeating unit to look like this:

$$-\overset{\overset{\displaystyle O}{\|}}{C}-(CH_2)_8-\overset{\overset{\displaystyle O}{\|}}{C}-\underset{\underset{\displaystyle H}{|}}{N}-(CH_2)_4-\underset{\underset{\displaystyle H}{|}}{N}-$$

Tip: It doesn't matter which way round you draw the repeating unit — both are correct.

You might also have to find the repeating unit from a longer section of a polyester or polyamide chain. Here's how you do it:

- Look along the chain and find the repeating pattern. Starting from one end, write out the chain until you get to the end of the repeating section.
- The repeating unit should have a C=O from an ester or amide link at one end, and the -O- or -NH- part of the link at the other. If the section you've written out doesn't, just find an ester or amide link, break it, and move the bit you've broken off from one end of the unit to the other.

--- Example ---

A section of a polymer chain is shown below. Draw its repeating unit.

Starting from the first $(CH_2)_2$, the repeating pattern goes to the second -NH-:

Move the $-(CH_2)_2$-NH- section from the start to the end, to get a C=O from an amide link at one end and the corresponding -NH- at the other:

So the repeating unit looks like this:

$$-\overset{\overset{\displaystyle O}{\|}}{C}-(CH_2)_4-\overset{\overset{\displaystyle O}{\|}}{C}-\underset{\underset{\displaystyle H}{|}}{N}-(CH_2)_2-\underset{\underset{\displaystyle H}{|}}{N}-$$

Tip: As before, you could write the repeating unit the other way round — you'd get the alternative version by moving the final -NH- from the end of the repeating section to the beginning instead of moving the $-(CH_2)_2$-NH- section.

Identifying monomers

In your exam, you might be asked to identify the monomers that formed a particular condensation polymer. To do this just follow these steps:

- If you're given a section of the polymer chain, first find the repeating unit, as shown above.
- Remove the bond in the middle of the central amide or ester link — that's the bond between the -C=O group and the -NH group in polyamides or the bond between the -C=O group and the oxygen in polyesters.
- Add –OH groups on to the -C=O groups to make carboxyl groups.
- For polyamides, add hydrogens to the -NH groups to make -NH$_2$ groups.
- For polyesters, add hydrogens on to the oxygens to make -OH groups and add -OH groups on to any terminal carbon atoms.

Exam Tip
Don't be caught out — there won't necessarily be two different monomers. There could be one monomer with a COOH and an NH$_2$ group on it. See the next page for an example of this.

Tip: This example is a polyamide. You do exactly the same for a polyester but you end up with a dicarboxylic acid and a diol.

Tip: The monomers are just the products of hydrolysing the polymer with water. This means it's easy to check that you've added enough -H and -OH groups. For a repeating unit containing two monomers, you should add in two H atoms and two -OH groups (which makes up two H_2O molecules).

Example

Draw the monomers that formed this condensation polymer:

This is a polyamide so if you remove the bond in the middle of the amide link you get:

 and

Adding an OH group on to the C=O groups gives you:

And adding a hydrogen on to each of the NH groups gives you:

So these must be the monomers that joined to form the polymer.

More complex condensation polymers

Not all condensation polymers are made from a dicarboxylic acid and a diamine or diol.

For example, if a molecule contains a carboxylic acid group and either an alcohol or an amine group, it can polymerise with itself to form a condensation polymer with only one monomer. This is the case for amino acids, which contain an amine and a carboxylic acid group, and polymerise to form peptides (see page 235).

Tip: When a molecule can form a condensation polymer with itself, it's called 'self-polymerisation'.

Tip: Amino acids contain a carboxylic acid group and an amine group, so they can react with themselves to form polymers containing only one monomer. More usually, they react with other amino acids to form a protein with a long sequence of different amino acids all joined together by peptide bonds (p.235).

Example

3-aminopropanoic acid contains both an amine and a carboxylic acid group. It can react with itself to form a condensation polymer:

3-aminopropanoic acid

Molecules that contain both an amine and an alcohol group can react with dicarboxylic acids in a condensation polymerisation reaction. The polymers they form contain both amide and ester links.

Tip: You could also draw the repeat unit so that the ester link is in the middle and the amide link is split between the repeat units — both ways are correct.

Example

4-aminobutan-1-ol contains an amine group and an alcohol group. It can react with dicarboxylic acids, such as butanedioic acid, in a condensation polymerisation reaction:

The ester link goes between the repeating units.

Exam Tip
It's easy to get in a muddle when you draw repeating units of condensation polymers, so make sure you practise these types of questions.

Practice Questions — Application

Q1 Identify whether the following are formulas of polyesters or polyamides and draw the monomer(s) they were formed from.

Q2 Draw the repeating units of the polymers that would be formed from these monomers:

Learning Objectives:

- Know that polyalkenes are chemically inert and non-biodegradable.

- Know that polyesters and polyamides can be broken down by hydrolysis and are biodegradable.

- Be able to explain why polyesters and polyamides can be hydrolysed but polyalkenes cannot.

- Be able to describe the advantages and disadvantages of different methods of disposal of polymers, including recycling.
  Specification Reference 3.3.12.2

Tip: You met addition polymers (polyalkenes) back in Year 1. They form when the double bonds in alkenes open up and join together.

Tip: A ton is just over 1000 kg (1016.047 kg to be exact) so 3 million tons is an awful lot of plastic to dispose of.

3. Disposing of Polymers

Polymers are really useful — loads of things are made from them. But unfortunately, disposing of polymers once they've been used can be a tad tricky. Read on to find out why.

The widespread use of polymers

Synthetic polymers have loads of advantages, so they're incredibly widespread these days — we take them pretty much for granted. Just imagine what you'd have to live without if there were no polymers (see Figure 1).

Figure 1: *Some of the many items that are made out of synthetic polymers.*

Biodegradability of polymers

Polyalkenes such as poly(ethene) and polystyrene are chemically inert (very unreactive). This is because the bonds between the repeating units are non-polar, so they aren't susceptible to attack by nucleophiles. Being chemically inert is an advantage when polymers are being used (e.g. a polystyrene cup won't react with your coffee), but it has the disadvantage of making them **non-biodegradable** (the bonds in the polymer can't be hydrolysed and won't break down naturally).

Condensation polymers such as PET (a polyester that's used to make fizzy drinks bottles and carrier bags amongst other things) and nylon (a polyamide) can be broken down by hydrolysis. This is because the bonds between the repeating units are polar and so are susceptible to attack by nucleophiles such as water. Because the bonds in condensation polymers can be hydrolysed, these polymers are **biodegradable** (they will break down naturally), although the process is very slow.

Disposing of waste plastics

It's estimated that in the UK we throw away over 3 million tons of plastic (i.e. synthetic polymers) every year. Because plastics either take a very long time to biodegrade or are non-biodegradable, the question of what to do with all those plastic objects when we've finished using them is an important one. The options are burying, burning or sorting for reusing or recycling (Figure 2).

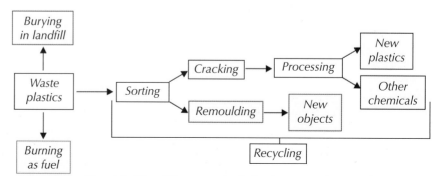

Figure 2: *The different methods for disposing of waste plastic.*

None of these methods is an ideal solution — they all have advantages and disadvantages associated with them.

Burying waste plastic

Landfill is one option for dealing with waste plastics. It is generally used when the plastic is difficult to separate from other waste, not in sufficient quantities to make separation financially worthwhile or too difficult technically to recycle. Landfill is a relatively cheap and easy method of waste disposal, but there are disadvantages to burying waste plastic too:

- It requires areas of land.
- As the waste decomposes it can release methane — a greenhouse gas.
- As the waste decomposes it can release toxins which can be washed away and contaminate water supplies.

The amount of waste we generate is becoming more and more of a problem, so there's a need to reduce landfill as much as possible.

Figure 3: *A landfill site — burying waste plastic is one way of disposing of it.*

Burning waste plastic

Waste plastics can be burned and the heat used to generate electricity. This process needs to be carefully controlled to reduce toxic gases. For example, polymers that contain chlorine (such as PVC) produce HCl when they're burned — this has to be removed. So, waste gases from the combustion are passed through scrubbers which can neutralise gases such as HCl by allowing them to react with a base. But, the waste gases, e.g. carbon dioxide, will still contribute to the greenhouse effect.

Recycling plastics

Because many plastics are made from non-renewable oil fractions, it makes sense to recycle plastics as much as possible. There's more than one way to recycle plastics. After sorting into different types some plastics (poly(propene), for example) can be melted and remoulded, while others can be cracked into monomers which can be used to make more plastics or other chemicals. Plastic products are usually marked to make sorting easier. The different numbers show different polymers.

Figure 4: *The recycling symbol on the bottom of a plastic bottle.*

┌─ **Examples** ─────────────────────

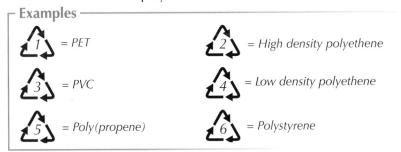

Like other disposal methods, there are advantages and disadvantages to recycling plastics:

Advantages	Disadvantages
It reduces the amount of waste going into landfill.	It is technically difficult to recycle plastics.
It saves raw materials — which is important because oil is non-renewable.	Collecting, sorting and processing the plastic is more expensive than burning/landfill.
The cost of recycling plastics is lower than making the plastics from scratch.	You often can't remake the plastic you started with — you have to make something else.
It produces less CO_2 emissions than burning the plastic.	The plastic can be easily contaminated during the recycling process.

Exam Tip
When answering a question on the advantages and disadvantages of recycling plastics, don't just say cost — you need to justify your answer because the cost can be an advantage and a disadvantage.

Section Summary

Make sure you know...

- What condensation polymers are.
- How polyamides, polyesters and polypeptides are formed.
- The typical uses of polyesters and polyamides.
- How polyamides and polyesters can be hydrolysed back to their constituent monomers using acid or base hydrolysis.
- That condensation polymers can form strong hydrogen bonds between the polymer chains.
- How to draw the repeating unit(s) of condensation polymers from monomer structures or from a section of a polymer chain.
- How to draw the monomer structure(s) from a section of a condensation polymer chain.
- Why addition polymers are non-biodegradable and condensation polymers are biodegradable.
- The advantages and disadvantages of disposing of waste plastic in landfill and burning waste plastic.
- The advantages and disadvantages of recycling waste plastics.

Exam-style Questions

1   Which of the options below shows the correct monomers that are formed when the
general polymer shown below is hydrolysed by water?

	Monomer 1	Monomer 2
A	HO–R'–OH	HOOC–R–COOH
B	HO–R–OH	HOOC–R'–COOH
C	HO–R'–COOH	HOOC–R–OH
D	HO–R'–$CONH_2$	H_2NOC–R–OH

(1 mark)

2   The diagram below shows the repeating unit formed when two amino acids
polymerise to form a peptide:

2.1   Draw the two amino acids which have joined together to make this repeating unit.

(2 marks)

2.2   What type of polymerisation occurs between the amino acids to form this polymer?

(1 mark)

2.3   What is the name of the link that forms between two amino acids?

(1 mark)

3   Nylon 6,6 is made from hexanedioic acid and 1,6-diaminohexane.

3.1   What type of condensation polymer is nylon 6,6?

(1 mark)

3.2   Draw the repeating unit of nylon 6,6.

(1 mark)

3.3   Is nylon 6,6 biodegradable or non-biodegradable? Explain your answer.

(4 marks)

3.4   Discuss the advantages and disadvantages of recycling objects made
from nylon 6,6.

(4 marks)

Learning Objectives:

- Understand that amino acids have both acidic and basic properties.
- Be able to apply IUPAC rules for naming amino acids.
- Understand that amino acids can form zwitterions.
- Be able to draw the structures of amino acids as zwitterions, and the ions formed from amino acids in acid and alkaline solution.
- Know that mixtures of amino acids can be separated and identified by thin-layer chromatography.
- Know that amino acids can be located on a chromatogram using developing agents such as ninhydrin or ultraviolet light and identified by their R_f values.
- Be able to calculate R_f values from a chromatogram.

Specification Reference
3.3.1.1, 3.3.13.1, 3.3.13.2

Tip: The only amino acid that isn't chiral is glycine because its organic side chain is just H — so there are two hydrogens attached to the central carbon.

Tip: See pages 170-173 for more on optical isomerism and chirality.

1. Amino Acids

This is where chemistry and biology start to overlap. Amino acids are the building blocks of all living organisms. Read on to find out all about them.

What are amino acids?

An **amino acid** has two functional groups — an amine (or amino) group (NH_2) and a carboxyl group (COOH). The structure of all amino acids is the same apart from an organic side chain (R) that is different in each. The general structure of an amino acid is given in Figure 1.

Organic side group
Carboxyl group
Amino group
Hydrogen atom
Central carbon atom

Figure 1: The general structure of an amino acid.

Amino acids are interesting molecules because they are **amphoteric** — this means they've got both acidic and basic properties. They can act as acids because the carboxyl group is acidic — it can donate a proton:

$$\text{-COOH} \rightleftharpoons \text{-COO}^- + \text{H}^+$$

They can act as bases because the amino group is basic — it can accept a proton:

$$\text{-NH}_2 + \text{H}^+ \rightleftharpoons \text{-NH}_3^+$$

Amino acids are chiral molecules because the carbon usually has four different groups attached. So a solution of a single amino acid enantiomer will rotate polarised light — see Figure 2.

mirror

Figure 2: The two different amino acid enantiomers.

Naming amino acids

Amino acids often have a common and a systematic name. There's no way of working out the common names, but you can work out the systematic names. To name an amino acid systematically just follow these steps:

1. Find the longest carbon chain that includes the carboxylic acid group and write down its name.
2. Number the carbons in the chain starting with the carbon in the carboxylic acid group as number 1.
3. Write down the positions of any NH₂ groups and show that they are NH₂ groups with the word 'amino'.
4. Write down the names of any other functional groups and say which carbon they are on.

Tip: 'Carboxylic acid groups' and 'carboxyl groups' are the same thing.

Exam Tip
Don't worry about learning the common names of the amino acids. If you're asked to name an amino acid in your exam just give the systematic name — you can work this out without having to memorise them all.

─ **Examples** ─────────────

The common name for this amino acid is glycine.
The longest carbon chain is two carbons long so the stem is ethane and the amino group is on carbon-2.
So the systematic name is 2-aminoethanoic acid.

The common name for this amino acid is valine.
The longest carbon chain is four carbons long so the stem is butane. The amino group is on carbon-2 and there is a methyl group on carbon-3.
So this is 2-amino-3-methylbutanoic acid.

Exam Tip
The amino acid side chains can get really complicated, but don't worry — you won't be asked to name anything too complicated in your exam.

Zwitterions

Amino acids can exist as **zwitterions**. A zwitterion is a dipolar ion — it has both a positive and a negative charge in different parts of the molecule. Zwitterions only exist near an amino acid's **isoelectric point**. This is the pH where the overall charge on the amino acid is zero. It's different for different amino acids — it depends on their R-group.

An amino acid becomes a zwitterion when its amino group is protonated to NH_3^+ and its COOH group is deprotonated to COO^-.

- In conditions more acidic than the isoelectric point, the $-NH_2$ group is likely to be protonated but the $-COOH$ group will be unchanged — so the amino acid will carry a positive charge but not a negative charge.
- In conditions more basic than the isoelectric point, the $-COOH$ group is likely to lose its proton but the $-NH_2$ group will be unchanged — so the amino acid will carry a negative charge but not a positive charge.
- Only at or near the isoelectric point are both the carboxyl group and the amino group likely to be ionised — forming a zwitterion (see Figure 3).

Tip: 'Protonated' just means 'has gained a proton' or 'has gained an H^+'. 'Deprotonated' means the opposite.

Exam Tip
You need to be able to draw amino acids at different pHs in your exam, so make sure you understand why amino acids have different charges at different pHs.

Zwitterion

Low pH

Isoelectric point

High pH

Figure 3: Formation of a zwitterion.

Separating mixtures of amino acids

Since different amino acids have different 'R' groups, they will all have different solubilities in the same solvent. This means you can easily separate and identify the different amino acids in a mixture using **thin-layer chromatography** (see Figure 4). Thin-layer chromatography (TLC) is covered in more detail on pages 265-267.

Thin-layer chromatography (TLC) is covered in more detail on pages 265-267.

Tip: The thin-layer chromatography plate is usually a piece of plastic or glass covered with a thin layer of silica (silicon dioxide) gel or alumina (aluminium oxide) powder.

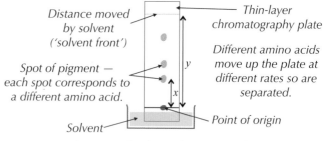

Distance moved by solvent ('solvent front')

Thin-layer chromatography plate

Different amino acids move up the plate at different rates so are separated.

Spot of pigment — each spot corresponds to a different amino acid.

Solvent

Point of origin

Figure 4: *Thin-layer chromatography.*

Amino acids aren't coloured — you need to do something to make them visible. You could spray ninhydrin solution on the plate, which causes the amino acids to turn purple. Alternatively, you could use a special plate that has a fluorescent dye added to it. The dye glows when UV light shines on it. Where there are spots of chemical on the plate, they cover the fluorescent dye — so the spots appear dark. You can put the plate under a UV lamp and draw around the dark patches to show where the spots are.

Figure 5: *Ninhydrin can also be used to detect fingerprints as it reacts with the amino acids in the fingerprint, turning them purple and making the print visible.*

Identifying amino acids

You can identify what amino acids you've got in the mixture by using the chromatogram to calculate R_f values. You work out the R_f value of each amino acid spot using this formula:

$$R_f = \frac{x}{y} = \frac{\text{distance travelled by spot}}{\text{distance travelled by solvent}}$$

Tip: When finding the value of x, measure from the point of origin to the middle of the spot of pigment.

Tip: There's more on calculating R_f values on page 266.

There's more on calculating R_f values on page 266.

Using a table of known amino acid R_f values, you can identify the amino acids in the mixture.

Practice Question — Application

Q1 a) Below are two amino acids (**A** and **B**). Name these amino acids.

   b) Draw species **A** at:
   (i) low pH   (ii) its isoelectric point   (iii) high pH

Practice Questions — Fact Recall

Q1 Explain why amino acids are said to be amphoteric.

Q2 What is a zwitterion?

Q3 What is the formula used to calculate the R_f value of an amino acid?

Q4 Why would ninhydrin solution, or a fluorescent dye with UV light be used in thin-layer chromatography involving amino acids?

2. Proteins

Amino acids are just the starting point for making living things — next come proteins. They're used in loads of different ways, and make up loads of different things, in your body and other animals and plants.

What are proteins?

Proteins are condensation polymers of amino acids — they are made up of lots of amino acids joined together by peptide links. The chain is put together by condensation reactions and broken apart by hydrolysis reactions. Here's how two amino acids join together to make a dipeptide:

If the two amino acids that are combining are different, then two different dipeptides will be formed because the amino acids can join either way round.

┌─ **Example** ───
A molecule of alanine and a molecule of glycine could join to form either of these dipeptides:

└──

The dipeptide still has an NH_2 group at one end and a COOH group at the other. This means the dipeptides can undergo further condensation reactions with amino acids or other peptides to make longer peptide chains.

To break up the protein into its individual amino acids (hydrolysis) you need to use pretty harsh conditions. One way of hydrolysing proteins is to add aqueous 6 mol dm^{-3} hydrochloric acid, and then heat the mixture under reflux for 24 hours. Proteins are condensation polymers, so to work out the formulas of the amino acids that a protein chain was made from, you can use the same method as on page 225 — just break each of the peptide links down the middle, then add either an H atom or an OH group to each of the broken ends to get the amino acids back.

Protein structure

Proteins are big, complicated molecules. They're easier to explain if you describe their structure in four 'levels' — primary, secondary, tertiary and quaternary. You don't need to know about the quaternary structure though, so only the first three are explained here.

Learning Objectives:

- Know that proteins are sequences of amino acids joined by peptide links.
- Be able to draw the structure of a peptide formed from up to three amino acids.
- Know that hydrolysis of the peptide link produces the constituent amino acids.
- Be able to draw the structure of the amino acids formed by hydrolysis of a peptide.
- Know the primary, secondary (α-helix and β-pleated sheets) and tertiary structure of proteins.
- Be able to identify primary, secondary and tertiary structures in diagrams, and explain how these structures are maintained by hydrogen bonding and S–S bonds.
- Understand the importance of hydrogen bonding and sulfur-sulfur bonding in proteins.

Specification Reference 3.3.13.2

Tip: A condensation reaction is a reaction which joins two molecules together and releases a small molecule (often water). A hydrolysis reaction is a reaction that splits a larger molecule into two smaller molecules using water.

Primary structure

The primary structure is the sequence of amino acids in the long chain that makes up the protein (the polypeptide chain).

Tip: Proteins are really just polyamides — the monomers are joined by amide groups. But in proteins these are called peptide links.

┌─ Example ───

The diagram below shows the primary structure of a polypeptide chain, showing individual amino acids.

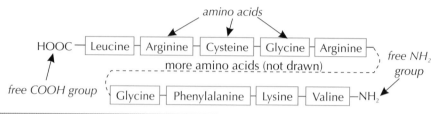

amino acids

HOOC — Leucine — Arginine — Cysteine — Glycine — Arginine

free NH₂ group

more amino acids (not drawn)

free COOH group   Glycine — Phenylalanine — Lysine — Valine —NH₂

Secondary structure

Tip: Proteins often have a mixture of different types of secondary structure — see Figure 1.

The peptide links can form hydrogen bonds with each other (see the next page), meaning the chain isn't a straight line. The shape of the chain is called its secondary structure. The most common secondary structure is a spiral called α-helix. Another common type of secondary structure is a β-pleated sheet. This is a layer of protein folded like a concertina.

Tip: The letter 'α' is read as 'alpha', and the letter 'β' is read as 'beta'

┌─ Examples ───

These are the two main forms of secondary structure of proteins.

α-helix   β-pleated sheet

Figure 1: *A computer model showing the secondary structure of the protein tyrosine phosphatase. The α-helices are shown in blue and the β-pleated sheets are shown in purple.*

Tertiary structure

The chain of amino acids is itself often coiled and folded in a characteristic way that identifies the protein. Extra bonds can form between different parts of the polypeptide chain, which gives the protein a kind of three-dimensional shape (see Figure 2). This is its tertiary structure.

α-helix chain coiled into tertiary structure

Figure 2: *An example of tertiary structure.*

Figure 3: *A molecular model showing the tertiary structure of the protein of the hepatitis B virus.*

Intermolecular forces in proteins

The secondary and tertiary structures of proteins are formed by intermolecular forces causing the amino acid chains to fold or twist. These intermolecular forces are really important, because the three-dimensional shape of a protein is vital to how it functions. For example, changing the shape of an enzyme can stop it working (see page 239). There are two main types of bond that hold proteins in shape — hydrogen bonds and disulfide bonds.

1. Hydrogen bonding

Hydrogen bonding is one type of force that holds proteins in shape. Hydrogen bonds only exist between polar groups such as –OH and –NH_2. These groups contain electronegative atoms which induce a partial positive charge on the hydrogen atom. The hydrogen is then attracted to lone pairs of electrons on adjacent polar groups and a hydrogen bond is formed — see Figure 3.

Tip: Hydrogen bonding was covered in Year 1, so get your old notes out if you need a bit of a reminder.

Hydrogen bonds form

Lone pair of electrons on an electronegative oxygen atom.

Hydrogen is partially positively charged due to electronegative nitrogen.

Figure 4: *Hydrogen bonding.*

2. Disulfide bonding

An amino acid that's part of a protein is called a residue. Disulfide bonding (or sulfur-sulfur bonding) occurs between residues of the amino acid cysteine. Cysteine contains a thiol group (–SH) and this thiol group can lose its H atom and join together to form a disulfide –S–S– bond with another thiol group. These disulfide bonds link together different parts of the protein chain, and help to stabilise the tertiary structure — see Figure 5.

Tip: Don't be put off by the term 'residue' — it's just the term for an amino acid that's part of a protein. So cysteine, when it's part of a protein, is a 'cysteine residue'. You may also hear it called an 'amino acid residue'.

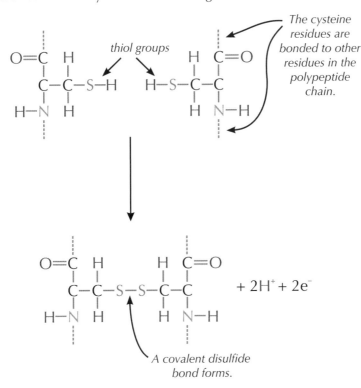

thiol groups

The cysteine residues are bonded to other residues in the polypeptide chain.

$+ 2H^+ + 2e^-$

A covalent disulfide bond forms.

Figure 5: *Disulfide bonding between two cysteine residues.*

amino acid chain

hydrogen bonds

disulfide bond

Figure 6: *An amino acid chain folds and can form both hydrogen and disulfide bonds.*

Tip: Remember — the primary structure of a protein is held together by covalent bonds. The secondary structure is formed by hydrogen bonds. The tertiary structure is the result of hydrogen bonds <u>and</u> disulfide bonds.

Factors such as temperature and pH can affect hydrogen bonding and the formation of disulfide bonds and so can change the shape of proteins.

Practice Question — Application

Q1 The amino acids cysteine and serine are shown below. There are two possible dipeptides that could form when one cysteine molecule reacts with one serine molecules. Draw the structures of both of these dipeptides.

cysteine   serine

Q2 The diagram below shows a tripeptide. Draw the structure of the molecules that would form when the tripeptide is fully hydrolysed.

Q3 Below is a simplified diagram of part of a protein. The side groups are represented by the letter R.

a) What types of protein structure are shown in this diagram?

b) What type of bond is represented by the dashed lines in the diagram?

c) i) Name a type of bonding that helps maintain the structure of proteins that isn't shown in the diagram above.

   ii) What type of structure would these bonds result in?

Practice Questions — Fact Recall

Q1 What is a protein?

Q2 Give two common secondary structure of proteins.

Q3 What is a cysteine residue?

Q4 Explain how disulfide bonds and hydrogen bonds maintain the three-dimensional structure of proteins.

3. Enzymes

Enzymes are a type of protein that work wonders in your body all the time. They help speed up chemical reactions, and each has a very specific purpose.

Biological catalysts

Enzymes speed up chemical reactions by acting as biological **catalysts**. They catalyse every metabolic reaction in the bodies of living organisms. They are proteins, but some also have non-protein components. The molecules that enzymes act upon are known as **substrates**.

Every enzyme has an area called its active site. This is the part that the substrate fits into so that it can interact with the enzyme. The active site is three-dimensional — it's part of the tertiary structure of the enzyme protein (see page 236).

Specificity

Enzymes are a bit picky. They only work with specific substrates — usually only one. This can be explained by the 'lock-and-key' model. This states that, for an enzyme to work, the substrate has to fit into the active site. If the substrate's shape doesn't match the active site's shape then the reaction won't be catalysed. The lock-and-key model is a simplified model of what actually happens, but it does a good job of explaining an enzyme's specificity.

enzyme   *enzyme-substrate complex*   *enzyme is unchanged after the reaction*

substrate

active site   *products*

Figure 1: *An example of how an enzyme interacts with a substrate.*

The active sites of enzymes are **stereospecific** — they'll only work on one enantiomer of a substrate. The other enantiomer won't fit properly in the active site, so the enzyme can't work on it — it's a bit like how your left shoe doesn't fit on your right foot properly.

Inhibitors

Molecules that have a similar shape to the substrate act can as enzyme inhibitors. They compete with the substrate to bond with the active site, but no reaction follows. Instead they block the active site, so no substrate can fit in it (see Figure 3).

enzyme

substrate (the inhibitor is a similar shape to this)

inhibitor fits into active site

active site

Figure 3: *Diagram showing how an inhibitor affects an enzyme.*

Learning Objectives:

- Know that enzymes are proteins.
- Understand the action of enzymes as catalysts, including the concept of a stereospecific active site that binds to a substrate molecule.
- Be able to explain why a stereospecific active site can only bond to one enantiomeric form of a substrate or drug.
- Understand the principle of a drug acting as an enzyme inhibitor by blocking the active site.
- Know that computers can be used to help design such drugs.

Specification Reference 3.3.13.3

Tip: Figure 1 shows an enzyme breaking up a substrate, but they can do lots of other things as well. For example, they can be used to combine two substrates, or add a functional group to a substrate.

Figure 2: *A computer model showing an inhibitor (purple) binding to the active sites of two enzyme molecules (green), preventing them from binding to a substrate molecule.*

The amount of inhibition that happens depends on the relative concentrations of inhibitor and substrate — if there's a lot more of the inhibitor, it'll take up most of the active sites and very little substrate will be able to get to the enzyme. The amount of inhibition is also affected by how strongly the inhibitor bonds to the active site.

Use of inhibitors as drugs

Some drugs are inhibitors that block the active site of an enzyme and stop it from working. For example, some antibiotics work by blocking the active site of an enzyme in bacteria that helps to make their cell walls. This causes their cell walls to weaken over time, so the bacteria eventually burst.

The active site of an enzyme is very specific, so it takes a lot of effort to find a drug molecule that will fit into the active site. It's even trickier if the drug molecule is chiral — then only one enantiomer will fit into the active site, because the active sites of enzymes are usually stereospecific. Often, new drug molecules are found by trial and error. Scientists will carry out experiments using lots of compounds to see if they work as inhibitors for a particular enzyme. They'll then adapt any that work to try and improve them. This process takes a long time. One way that scientists are speeding this process up is by using computers to model the shape of the enzyme's active site and predict how well potential drug molecules will interact with it. They can quickly test hundreds of molecules to look for ones that might be the right shape before they start testing anything in the laboratory.

Figure 4: Tamiflu® is an example of an enzyme inhibitor drug — it is used to treat people with the flu.

Practice Questions — Fact Recall

Q1 Describe the 'lock and key' model.

Q2 What is a stereospecific active site?

Q3 a) How does an enzyme inhibitor work?

b) Give one use of inhibitors.

4. DNA

DNA is the stuff that makes you, you. It's pretty complicated stuff, but after everything it's done for you, the least you could do is learn the basics...

Nucleotides

DNA stands for **d**eoxyribo**n**ucleic **a**cid. It contains all the genetic information of an organism. DNA is made up of lots of monomers called **nucleotides**, which are in turn made up of three components — a phosphate group, the pentose sugar 2-deoxyribose, and a base.

1. Phosphate group

The phosphate group is an ion, due to the negative charge on one of the oxygens.

Figure 1: A phosphate ion.

2. Pentose sugar

A pentose sugar is a sugar made up of five carbons. All pentose sugars in DNA are 2-deoxyribose.

Figure 2: 2-deoxyribose

3. Base

Each nucleotide in DNA contains one of four different bases: adenine (A), cytosine (C), guanine (G) and thymine (T).

adenine

guanine

cytosine

thymine

Figure 3: The four bases found in DNA.

The circled nitrogens in Figure 3 are the atoms that bond with the 2-deoxyribose molecule (see the next page).

Luckily, you don't need to learn the structures of the phosphate ion and 2-deoxyribose, or of the bases — they'll all be in your data booklet. But you do need to know how they are arranged to form nucleotides (see Figure 4).

Tip: When the phosphate and the sugar bond, a molecule of water is lost. Similarly, when the sugar and the base bond, a molecule of water is lost. Remembering this can help you work out what atoms bonds are formed between when the phosphate, sugar and base join together to form a nucleotide.

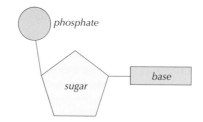

Figure 4: *Simplified structure of a nucleotide.*

Once you know the basic structure of a nucleotide (a phosphate ion bonded to a pentose sugar bonded to a base), you can use the structures in the data booklet to work out the structures of the four nucleotides in DNA. And here they are:

adenine nucleotide

guanine nucleotide

Exam Tip
You should be able to work out these structures from the info in the exam data booklet if you need to, so you don't have to learn them. But you do need to know where the phosphate group and the bases join to the sugar.

cytosine nucleotide

thymine nucleotide

Figure 5: *The four nucleotides that are found in DNA.*

Polynucleotides

Tip: The polynucleotide chain formed by nucleotides joining together is a <u>single strand of DNA</u>.

The nucleotides join together to form a **polynucleotide chain**. Covalent bonds form between the phosphate group of one nucleotide and the sugar of another — this makes what's called the sugar-phosphate backbone of the chain (see Figure 6).

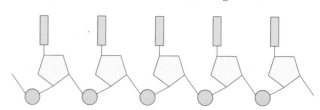

Figure 6: *The sugar-phosphate polymer chain that makes up DNA.*

Unit 3: Section 8 Amino Acids, Proteins and DNA

The sugar-phosphate backbone of DNA is formed by condensation polymerisation — a molecule of water is lost and a covalent phosphodiester bond is formed. There are still OH groups at either end of the chain, so further links can be made — see Figure 7. This allows the nucleotides to form a polymer made up of an alternating sugar-phosphate-sugar-phosphate chain.

Tip: In this polymerisation reaction the monomer units are the nucleotides. Hence the name 'polynucleotides'.

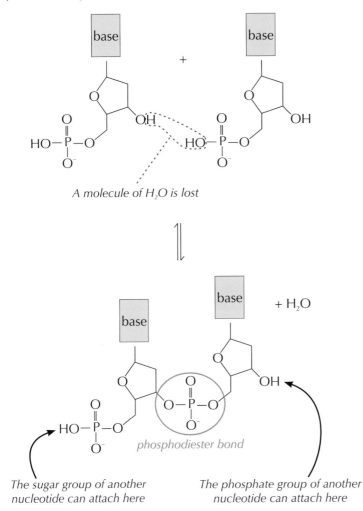

Figure 7: The condensation polymerisation of two nucleotides.

DNA structure

DNA is formed of two polynucleotide strands. The two strands spiral together to form a **double helix** structure, which is held together by hydrogen bonds between the bases. Each base can only join with one particular partner — adenine always pairs with thymine (A – T) and cytosine always pairs with guanine (C – G). So the two strands of DNA are complementary — whenever there is an adenine base on one strand, there'll be a thymine base on the other, and whenever there's a guanine base on one strand, there's a cytosine base on the other.

Tip: To help remember which bases go together, just think of us folk <u>at CG</u>P. We're always here to help...

Figure 8: *James Watson and Francis Crick discovered the double helix structure of DNA in 1953.*

Tip: A double helix looks a bit like a twisted ladder. Imagine holding a ladder at one end and twisting the other end so that the two sides start coiling around each other — that's a bit like the shape of a DNA molecule.

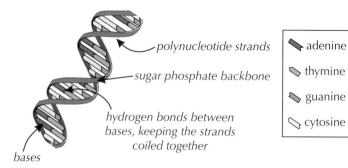

polynucleotide strands

sugar phosphate backbone

hydrogen bonds between bases, keeping the strands coiled together

bases

adenine

thymine

guanine

cytosine

Figure 9: *Double helix structure of DNA.*

The complementary base pairing is due to the arrangement of atoms in the base molecules that are capable of forming hydrogen bonds. A hydrogen bond forms between a hydrogen atom with partial positive charge (a hydrogen attached to anything highly electronegative, such as a nitrogen atom) and a lone pair of electrons on a nearby oxygen, nitrogen or fluorine atom. To bond, the two atoms have to be the right distance apart.

Adenine and thymine have the right atoms in the right places to each form two hydrogen bonds, so they can pair up. Cytosine and guanine can each form three hydrogen bonds, so they can pair up too (see Figure 10). These are the only possible base combinations. Other base pairings would put the partially charged atoms too close together (they'd repel each other), or too far apart, or the bonding atoms just wouldn't line up properly. The DNA double helix has to twist so that the bases are in the right alignment and at the right distance apart for the complementary base pairs to form.

Figure 10: *Two hydrogen bonds join adenine and thymine together, three hydrogen bonds join cytosine and guanine together.*

Practice Questions — Fact Recall

Q1 a) Name the components of a nucleotide of DNA,

b) Sketch a labelled diagram to show how the components are arranged within a nucleotide.

Q2 Nucleotides join together to form polynucleotides.

a) What type of bond is formed between two nucleotides?

b) What parts of the nucleotide react to form these bonds?

Q3 a) Name the four bases found in DNA.

b) State which bases form complementary pairs, and how many hydrogen bonds form between the bases in each pair.

5. Cisplatin

Cancer is caused by cells in the body dividing and reproducing uncontrollably.
Cisplatin is an anticancer drug that works by combating this reproduction.

What is cisplatin?

Cisplatin is a complex of platinum(II) with two chloride ion ligands and two ammonia ligands in a square planar shape. The two chloride ions are next to each other, making it cisplatin. If they were opposite each other, that would be transplatin, which has different biological effects (see pages 138-139 for more on *cis/trans* isomerism).

Figure 1: *The molecular structure of cisplatin.*

Cisplatin as an anticancer drug

Cancer is caused when cells mutate and start dividing uncontrollably to form tumours. In order for a cell to divide it has to replicate its DNA. The two strands of the DNA double helix have to unwind so that they can be copied. Cisplatin stops this happening properly, so the tumour cells stop reproducing. Here's how it works:

- A nitrogen atom on a guanine base in DNA forms a co-ordinate bond with cisplatin's platinum ion, replacing one of the chloride ion ligands (see Figure 2). This is a ligand replacement reaction.

Figure 2: *A guanine molecule replaces a chloride ion in cisplatin*

- A second nitrogen atom from a nearby guanine molecule (either on the same strand of the DNA, or the opposite strand) can bond to the platinum and replace the second chloride ion too (see Figure 4).

Learning Objectives:

- Know that the Pt(II) complex cisplatin is used as an anticancer drug.

- Be able to explain that cisplatin prevents DNA replication in cancer cells by a ligand replacement reaction with DNA in which a bond is formed between platinum and a nitrogen atom on guanine.

- Be able to explain why drugs such as cisplatin can have adverse effects.

- Be able to appreciate that society needs to assess the balance between the benefits and the adverse effects of drugs, such as the anticancer drug cisplatin.

Specification Reference 3.3.13.5

Tip: See pages 134-136 for more on ligands and the shapes of complex ions and pages 144-147 for more on ligand replacement reactions.

Figure 3: *Cisplatin is used as part of chemotherapy treatment of some cancers.*

Tip: The sugar-phosphate backbones in this reaction could be on separate polynucleotide strands, or they could be two parts of the same polynucleotide strand.

Figure 4: *A second guanine molecule replaces the other chloride ion in cisplatin.*

- The presence of the cisplatin complex bound to the DNA strands causes the strands to kink. This means that the DNA strands can't unwind and be copied properly — so the cell can't replicate properly.

Tip: The damage to the DNA caused by the cisplatin binding to it also triggers mechanisms that lead to the death of the cell.

Adverse effects

Unfortunately, cisplatin can bind to DNA in normal cells as well as cancer cells. This is a problem for any healthy cells that replicate frequently, such as hair cells and blood cells, because cisplatin stops them from replicating in the same way as it does the cancer cells. This means that cisplatin can cause hair loss and suppress the immune system (which is controlled by white blood cells). It can also cause kidney damage.

These side effects can be lessened by giving patients very low dosages of cisplatin. They can also be reduced by targeting the tumour directly — i.e. using a method that delivers the drug only to the cancer cells, so it doesn't get the chance to attack healthy cells.

Despite the side effects of cisplatin, it is still used as a chemotherapy drug. This is because the balance of the long-term positive effects (curing cancer) outweigh the negative short-term effects.

Tip: The balance of the benefits and the adverse effects must be assessed before deciding whether any drug should be used, not just cisplatin.

Practice Questions — Fact Recall

Q1 Draw the structure of cisplatin.

Q2 a) Outline how cisplatin binds to DNA strands and prevents DNA replication in cancer cells.

b) What are the disadvantages of using cisplatin as an anticancer drug?

Section Summary

Make sure you know...

- What amino acids are and how to name them.
- That amino acids are amphoteric — they have both acidic and basic properties.
- That amino acids can form zwitterions and what a zwitterion is.
- How to draw the structures of amino acids as zwitterions.
- How to draw the structures formed when amino acids are in acid and alkaline conditions.
- That mixtures of amino acids can be separated using thin-layer chromatography.
- That developing agents, such as ninhydrin, and ultraviolet light can be used to locate amino acids on a chromatogram.
- How to calculate R_f values and how to identify amino acids by their R_f values.
- That proteins are sequences of amino acids joined by peptide links.
- That proteins can be hydrolysed and this produces the constituent amino acids.
- How to draw the peptide formed from specified amino acids and vice versa.
- That protein structure can be described by looking at the primary, secondary and tertiary structures.
- That the primary structure of a protein is the chain of amino acids.
- That the secondary structure of proteins is often an α-helix or a β-pleated sheet.
- That the tertiary structure of proteins describes how the chain folds to form its 3D shape.
- That hydrogen bonding and disulfide bonding are important in maintaining the 3-dimensional structure of proteins.
- That enzymes are proteins that can be used as biological catalysts.
- That enzymes recognise specific substrate molecules using the 'lock and key' model.
- That enzymes are stereospecific — only one enantiomer of a chiral substrate will fit in the active site.
- That molecules with a similar shape to an enzyme's substrate can work as inhibitors by blocking the active site of the enzyme.
- That many drugs are enzyme inhibitors.
- That a nucleotide is made up of a phosphate ion, 2-deoxyribose and a base.
- That there are four bases found in DNA — adenine (A), thymine (T), cytosine (C) and guanine (G).
- That a polynucleotide is a polymer made up of nucleotide monomers, joined together by covalent bonds, in a sugar-phosphate-sugar-phosphate backbone.
- That DNA is formed from two complementary polynucleotide strands linked by hydrogen bonds and arranged in a double helix shape.
- That adenine and thymine are complementary bases that form 2 hydrogen bonds, and cytosine and guanine are complementary bases that form 3 hydrogen bonds.
- That cisplatin is a platinum(II) complex with two ammonia and two chloride ion ligands.
- That cisplatin can be used as an anticancer drug.
- How cisplatin works as an anticancer drug.
- What the adverse effects of cisplatin are, and why society needs to assess the benefits and adverse effects of any drug before making it available.

Exam-style Questions

1 What is the skeletal formula of the amino acid, 2-amino-3-hydroxybutanoic acid?

(1 mark)

2 Adenine (A), cytosine (C), guanine (G) and thymine (T) are the four bases found in DNA. Which pairing is formed by two hydrogen bonds?

    A   A-G

    B   A-T

    C   C-G

    D   C-T

(1 mark)

3 A group of researchers are trying to find out which amino acids are present in a mixture by using thin-layer chromatography. Their observations are recorded in Table 1 below. The R_f values of some amino acids are shown in Table 2.

Mark on plate	Distance from point of origin (in cm)
Solvent front	6.5
Spot A	3.6
Spot B	1.0

Table 1

Amino acid	R_f value
Arginine	0.32
Cystine	0.15
Isoleucine	0.73
Proline	0.48
Tyrosine	0.55
Valine	0.66

Table 2

3.1 Which of the amino acids in Table 2 could be present in this mixture?

(1 mark)

The diagrams below shows the amino acids methionine and histidine.

methionine   histidine

3.2 They react to form a dipeptide known as Met-His. In Met-His, the free –NH$_2$ group is from the methionine. Draw Met-His.

(1 mark)

The dipeptide Met-His has an isoelectric point of around 6.5.

3.3 What is the isoelectric point of an amino acid?

(1 mark)

3.4 Draw the structure of Met-His when in a solution of pH 13.

(1 mark)

4 The diagram below shows a dipeptide formed from two different amino acids.

4.1 What type of reaction could be used to break down the dipeptide into its component amino acids?

(1 mark)

4.2 Draw the structures of the two amino acids that the dipeptide breaks down into.

(2 marks)

Proteins are made up of many amino acids put together.

4.3 This dipeptide forms part of the protein FIH. The structure of FIH can be described in terms of its primary, secondary and tertiary structure. Explain what is meant by each of these terms. Include details on the shapes resulting from each level of structure and the bonding present in each level.

(7 marks)

Tip: You'll almost always have to use a solvent in organic synthesis as most organic reactions only happen in solution.

Exam Tip
You will be asked to recall some of the synthetic routes in your exam, so it's important that you know all the reactions on the next page. Don't panic, though — there's nothing new to learn there, it's just a summary of what you've already learnt.

1. Organic Synthesis

Organic synthesis deals with how to make organic compounds using different chemical reactions. Organic synthesis is important as it provides ways to create materials and chemicals like pharmaceutical drugs, fertilisers and plastics.

Synthetic routes

Chemists have got to be able to make one compound from another. It's vital for things like designing medicines. It's also good for making imitations of useful natural substances when the real things are hard to extract. Chemists use **synthetic routes** to show the reagents, conditions and any special procedures needed to get from one compound to another.

Designing synthetic routes

Chemists try to design synthetic routes that use non-hazardous starting materials — this limits the potential for accidents and environmental damage. Chemists are also concerned with designing processes that are not too wasteful. Processes with high atom economies and high percentage yields are preferred because they convert more of the starting materials into useful products.

Waste can be reduced by designing synthesis routes that have as few steps as possible. However, it's not always possible to synthesise one chemical straight from another — a synthetic route can involve multiple steps. For example, you can't synthesise an aldehyde directly from a halogenoalkane. You'd have to carry out a two step reaction and first synthesise an alcohol.

─ Example ──────────────

Avoiding using solvents wherever possible is one way of reducing both the hazards associated with a process and the amount of waste created by a synthetic route. Solvents are often flammable and toxic so can pose safety risks. Having to separate solvents from products or dispose of solvents after the reaction is complete can create a lot of waste too.

Organic synthesis in the exam

In your exam you could be asked to provide a step-wise synthesis for the production of one chemical from another. You might have to use any of the reactions you've learnt in Year 1 or Year 2 chemistry, so it's important that you learn them all really well. If you're asked how to make one compound from another in the exam, make sure you include:

■ Any special procedures, such as refluxing.

■ The conditions needed, e.g. high temperature or pressure, or the presence of a catalyst.

■ Any safety precautions, e.g. do it in a fume cupboard. (If there are toxic gases like hydrogen chloride or hydrogen cyanide around, you really don't want to go breathing them in. Stuff like bromine and strong acids and alkalis are corrosive, so you don't want to splash them on your bare skin.)

The reaction diagrams on the next two pages summarise the organic reactions you've come across in the Year 1 and Year 2 chemistry course.

Synthetic routes for making organic compounds

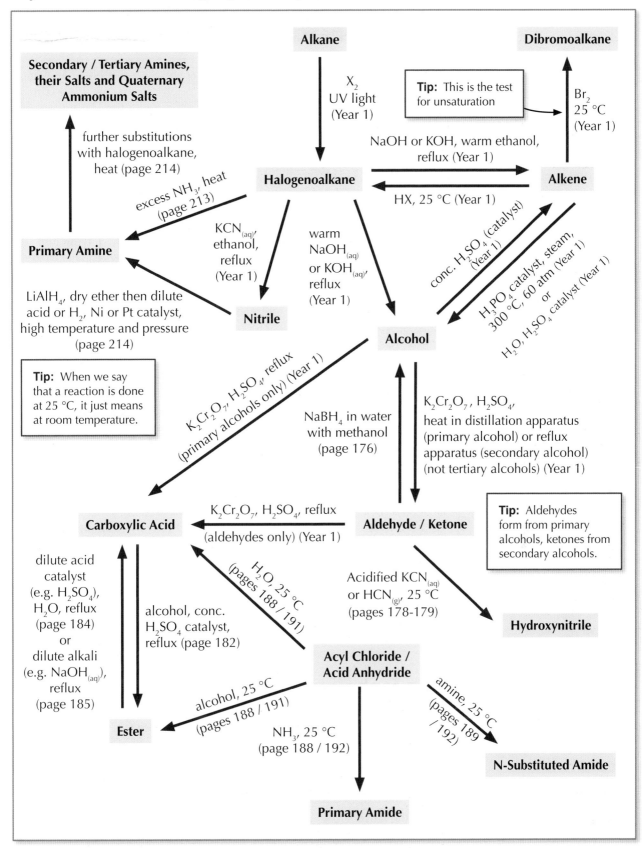

Synthetic routes for aromatic compounds

There are not so many of these reactions to learn, but it's still just as important that you know all the itty-bitty details. If you can't remember any of the reactions, look back to the relevant pages and take a quick peek over them.

Exam Tip
When you're writing down a step-wise synthesis in the exam, don't forget to put the conditions as well as the reagents. You might lose marks if you don't.

Exam Tip
For acylation questions in the exam, don't just put RCOCl — you need to specify what the R group is.

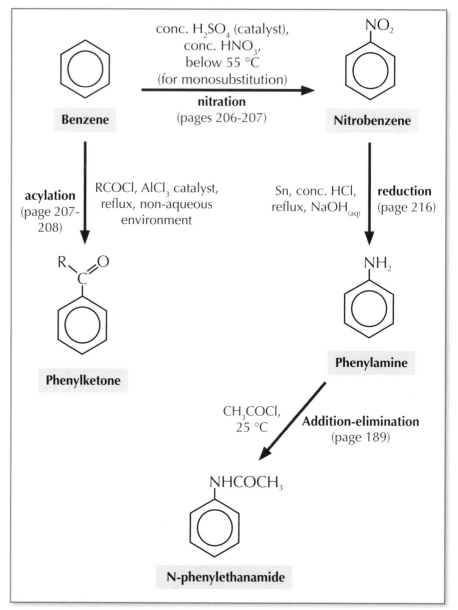

conc. H_2SO_4 (catalyst), conc. HNO_3, below 55 °C (for monosubstitution)

nitration (pages 206-207)

Benzene → **Nitrobenzene** (NO_2)

acylation (page 207-208)

RCOCl, $AlCl_3$ catalyst, reflux, non-aqueous environment

Phenylketone ($R\text{–}C\text{=}O$)

Sn, conc. HCl, reflux, $NaOH_{(aq)}$ | **reduction** (page 216)

Phenylamine (NH_2)

CH_3COCl, 25 °C | **Addition-elimination** (page 189)

N-phenylethanamide ($NHCOCH_3$)

Exam technique

In the exam you may be asked to 'identify' the name of a reagent used in a synthesis step. A reagent is just a chemical that can be used straight out of a bottle or container, for example, hydrochloric acid (HCl) or potassium cyanide (KCN). You must be really careful about this...

Figure 1: Reagents are chemicals that can be taken from bottles or containers. For example, NaOH can come as a solution or a solid.

Example

Suggest the reagents used to transform a halogenoalkane into a nitrile.

Giving the reagent CN^- in this case would be incorrect as you can't just take it out of a bottle. A correct answer could be KCN and ethanol.

Q1 Write down the reagents and conditions you would use to carry out the following organic syntheses.

   a) Making ethanol from ethene.

   b) Forming chloromethane from methane.

   c) Creating phenylethanone from benzene.

Q2 The following syntheses require a two-step organic synthesis. Write down the reagents and conditions you would use to carry out each step in the following organic syntheses, and state the organic product formed after the first step.

   a) Forming phenylamine from benzene.

   b) Creating propanal from 1-bromopropane.

   c) Turning ethane into propanenitrile.

   d) Making methyl butanoate from butanal.

Q3 Give a three-step synthesis of N-phenylethanamide starting from benzene. In your second synthesis step you should form phenylamine. For each step, give the reagents and conditions you would use to carry out the reaction, and state the organic product formed.

Q4 Give a three-step synthesis of propyl ethanoate starting from chloroethane. For each step, give the reagents and conditions you would use to carry out the reaction, and state the organic product formed.

Exam Tip
For questions like these you don't have to give the mechanisms or equations for the reactions.

Exam Tip
You need to be specific when you're talking about reagents in the exam. Make sure you write down exactly what you need to use — writing 'an alcohol' when you really mean 'ethanol' just won't get you all of the marks.

Q1 Give one reason why chemists try to avoid using hazardous starting materials when designing organic synthesis processes.

Q2 Give two ways a chemist can reduce the amount of waste produced in organic synthesis.

Q3 Explain why chemists try to design organic synthesis processes that not require a solvent.

Q4 Write down the reagents and conditions needed to carry out the following organic syntheses.

   a) Making a halogenoalkane from an alkene.

   b) Making a hydroxynitrile from an aldehyde.

   c) Making a carboxylic acid from an ester.

   d) Making a primary amine from a nitrile.

Q5 What reagents and conditions are needed to turn an acyl chloride into:

   a) an N-substituted amide?

   b) an ester?

   c) a primary amide?

2. NMR Spectroscopy

NMR spectroscopy is just one of several techniques that scientists have come up with to help determine the structure of a molecule. It provides information on the different environments of atoms in molecules.

Types of NMR spectroscopy

There are two types of nuclear magnetic resonance (NMR) spectroscopy that you need to know about — ^{13}C NMR, which gives you information about how the carbon atoms in a molecule are arranged, and ^1H (or proton) NMR, which tells you how the hydrogen atoms in a molecule are arranged.

Nuclear environments

A nucleus is partly shielded from the effects of an external magnetic field by its surrounding electrons. Any other atoms and groups of atoms that are around a nucleus will also affect the amount of electron shielding. So the overall effect of the external magnetic field on each nucleus is different, depending on its environment within the molecule.

The size of the energy gap between a nucleus being aligned with or against an external magnetic field is determined by the strength of the magnetic field. Nuclei in different environments will therefore absorb at different frequencies. It's these differences in absorption of energy between environments that you're looking for in NMR spectroscopy.

--- Example ---

If a carbon atom bonds to a more electronegative atom (like oxygen) the amount of electron shielding around its nucleus will decrease.

These electrons provide the carbon atoms with shielding from a magnetic field.

These electrons are pulled further away from the carbon atom by the electronegative oxygen atom. The carbon atom is less shielded.

This means that carbon 1 and carbon 2 are in different environments.

An atom's environment depends on all the groups that it's connected to, going right along the molecule — not just the atoms it's actually bonded to.

--- Examples ---

Chloroethane has 2 carbon environments — each of its two carbons are bonded to different atoms.

1-chlorobutane has 4 carbon environments — the carbons in the CH_2 groups are different distances from the electronegative Cl atom, so their environments are different.

Figure 1: *An NMR spectrometer.*

2-chloropropane has 2 carbon environments —
it's symmetrical, so the carbons in CH_3 groups on
each end are in the same environment.

Chemical shift

NMR spectroscopy measures differences in the energy absorbed
by nuclei in different environments relative to a standard substance
— the difference is called the **chemical shift** (δ).
Chemical shift is measured in parts per million (or ppm) relative to
a standard. The standard substance is tetramethylsilane (TMS).

tetramethylsilane (TMS)

Tip: Here's the ^{13}C
NMR spectrum for TMS:

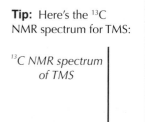

*^{13}C NMR spectrum
of TMS*

chemical shift (δ)

TMS has 12 hydrogen atoms all in identical environments and 4
carbon atoms all in identical environments. This means that, in both ^1H NMR
and ^{13}C NMR, it will produce a single absorption peak, well away from most
other absorption peaks. The single peak produced by TMS is given a chemical
shift value of 0. You'll often see a peak at $\delta = 0$ on spectra because TMS is
added to the test compound for calibration purposes. Tetramethylsilane is
inert (so it doesn't react with the sample), non-toxic, and volatile (so it's easy
to remove from the sample).

Practice Questions — Fact Recall

Q1 What is chemical shift (δ) measured in?

Q2 Explain why TMS is used as the standard substance used in NMR.

3. ^{13}C NMR Spectroscopy

Learning Objective:

- Be able to use ^{13}C NMR spectra and chemical shift data from the Chemistry Data Booklet to suggest possible structures or part structures for molecules.

Specification Reference 3.3.15

Time for some more information about carbon-13 NMR. This topic's all about working out where the carbon atoms in an organic molecule are.

^{13}C NMR

The number of peaks on a ^{13}C NMR spectrum tells you how many different carbon environments are present in a particular molecule. The spectrum will have one peak on it for each carbon environment in the molecule. The carbon atoms which are closer to more electronegative atoms (for example, oxygen, nitrogen or chlorine) will be less shielded and have a higher chemical shift.

Examples

Ethanol

There are two carbon atoms in a molecule of ethanol:

Because they are bonded to different atoms, each has a different amount of electron shielding — so there are two carbon environments in the ethanol molecule and two peaks on its ^{13}C NMR spectrum.

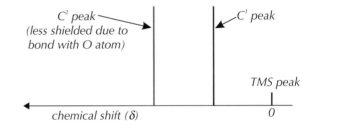

Tip: You'll often see a peak at $\delta = 0$ on spectra because TMS is added to the test compound for calibration purposes. You can ignore this peak when interpreting NMR spectra.

Ethane

Both carbon nuclei in ethane have the same environment. Each C has 3 Hs and a CH_3 group attached. So ethane has one peak on its ^{13}C NMR spectrum.

Exam Tip
Watch out for the scale on ^{13}C spectra in the exam — the chemical shift <u>increases</u> from <u>right to left</u>.

Propanone

There are two different carbon environments. The end carbons both have the same environment — they each have 3 Hs and a $COCH_3$ attached. The centre carbon has 2 CH_3 groups and an O attached by a double bond. So propanone's ^{13}C NMR spectrum has 2 peaks.

Tip: Remember, carbons next to more electronegative atoms will have a higher chemical shift and will be further to the left on the spectrum.

Cyclohexane-1,3-diol

In cyclohexane-1,3-diol there are four different carbon environments — each different carbon environment is shown in a different colour on the diagram below. If you think about the symmetry of the molecule you can see why this is.

So cyclohexane-1,3-diol's ^{13}C NMR spectrum will have 4 peaks.

^{13}C NMR spectrum
of cyclohexhane-1,3-diol

chemical shift (δ)

TMS peak

0

Chemical shifts on ^{13}C NMR spectra

In your exam you'll get a data sheet that will include a table like the one in Figure 1. The table shows the chemical shifts experienced by carbon–13 nuclei in different environments. You can match up the peaks in a ^{13}C NMR spectrum with the chemical shifts in the table to work out which carbon environments they could represent.

^{13}C NMR Chemical Shifts Relative to TMS	
Chemical shift, δ (ppm)	Type of Carbon
5 – 40	C—C
10 – 70	R—C—Cl or R—C—Br
20 – 50	R—C—C— (with O double bonded to middle C)
25 – 60	R—C—N (amines)
50 – 90	C—O (alcohols, ethers or esters)
90 – 150	C=C (alkenes)
110 – 125	R—C≡N
110 – 160	aromatic
160 – 185	carbonyl (ester or carboxylic acid) R—C— (with O double bonded)
190 – 220	carbonyl (ketone or aldehyde) R—C— (with O double bonded)

Figure 1: *Chemical shifts of different carbon environments.*

Tip: When you're thinking about the chemical shift of different carbon atoms you have to take into account all the atoms they're near — not just the ones right next to them.
For example, in 1-chlorobutane all of the carbons are in different environments:

Carbon-2 and carbon-3 look like they might be in the same environment. But carbon-2 is much closer to the electronegative chlorine atom — so it will have a higher chemical shift.

Exam Tip
You'll get a table like this in the exam, so you don't need to learn it (phew). Just read up from any chemical shift value to find what groups could be causing a peak there.

Matching peaks to the groups that cause them isn't always straightforward, because the chemical shifts can overlap. For example, a peak at $\delta \approx 30$ might be caused by C–C, C–Cl or C–Br. A peak at $\delta \approx 210$, is due to a C=O group in an aldehyde or a ketone — but you don't know which.

Interpreting ^{13}C NMR spectra

If you have a sample of a chemical that contains carbon atoms you can use a ^{13}C NMR spectrum of the molecule to help work out what it is. The spectrum gives you information about the number of carbon atoms that are in a molecule, and the environments that they are in.

Here are the three steps to follow to interpret a ^{13}C NMR spectrum:

1. Count the number of peaks in the spectrum (excluding the TMS peak) — this tells you the number of carbon environments in the molecule.

2. Use a table of chemical shift data to work out what kind of carbon environment is causing each peak. A table of typical chemical shift data for carbon-13 NMR is shown in Figure 1.

3. Use this information to figure out the structure of the molecule.

─ **Example** ────────────────

The carbon-13 NMR spectrum of a straight-chain molecule with the molecular formula $C_5H_{10}O$ is shown below. Use the spectrum, along with the data in Figure 1 to identify the molecule.

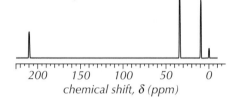

chemical shift, δ (ppm)

1. The spectrum has three peaks (and a TMS peak at $\delta = 0$), so the molecule must have three carbon environments.

2. The peak at $\delta = 10$ ppm represents carbon atoms in C–C bonds. Looking at the molecular formula, the peak at $\delta = 35$ ppm must also be due to carbons in C–C bonds (rather than C–Cl or C–Br bonds), as the molecule only contains C, H, and O atoms. The carbons causing this peak have a different chemical shift to those causing the first peak, so they must be in a slightly different environment.
The peak at $\delta = 210$ ppm is due to a carbon atom in a C=O group.

3. You know you're looking for a straight-chain carbonyl with the formula $C_5H_{10}O$ that has three different carbon environments. The only one that fits the bill is pentan-3-one:

^{13}C NMR spectra of cyclic molecules

The number of peaks on the ^{13}C spectrum of a cyclic compound depends on the symmetry of the molecule. There's an example on the next page to show how it works.

Example

The ^{13}C NMR spectrum of a cyclic molecule with the formula $C_6H_4Cl_2$ is shown below.
Identify the molecule that produced this spectrum.

chemical shift, δ (ppm)

1. The spectrum has four peaks, so it must have four carbon environments.

2. All four peaks are between $\delta = 125$ ppm and $\delta = 140$ ppm. Looking at the chemical shift table these can only be due to alkene groups or carbons in a benzene ring. The question tells you that the molecule is cyclic with six carbons, so these carbons must be in a benzene ring, as a six-carbon cyclic molecule with three double bonds does not exist.

3. There are only three aromatic molecules with the formula $C_6H_4Cl_2$ — they're all isomers of dichlorobenzene (see below).

1,2-dichlorobenzene

1,3-dichlorobenzene

1,4-dichlorobenzene

If you look at the symmetry of the molecules you can see that 1,2-dichlorobenzene has three carbon environments, while 1,3-dichlorobenzene has four and 1,4-dichlorobenzene only has two. So the spectrum must have been produced by 1,3-dichlorobenzene.

> **Tip:** If a cyclic molecule is symmetrical, you can draw a mirror line (like the dashed lines on the molecules on the left) across it. Atoms or groups that are in the same place on opposite sides of the line will be in the same environment.

Practice Question — Application

Q1 How many peaks would you see on a ^{13}C NMR spectrum of:
  a) butanal?   b) pentane?
  c) 2-methylpropane? d) 4-chlorocyclohexanone?

Q2 The carbon-13 NMR spectrum of a compound with the molecular formula C_5H_{12} is shown below.

chemical shift, δ (ppm)

Use the spectrum to identify the structure of the molecule. Explain your reasoning.

Q3 The carbon-13 NMR spectrum of a molecule with the formula $C_4H_{10}O$ is shown on the right. Identify the structure of the molecule.

chemical shift, δ (ppm)

> **Tip:** Use the chemical shift data table from page 257 to help you with these questions.

> **Tip:** Make sure you use any information that you're given about what atoms are in the molecule — for instance if you're told that the molecule's a hydrocarbon, then it will only have carbon and hydrogen in it. This will help you narrow down the options for what type of environment each shift could represent.

- Know that integrated spectra indicate the relative numbers of ¹H atoms in different environments.

- Be able to use integration data from ¹H NMR spectra to determine the relative numbers of equivalent protons in the molecule.

- Be able to use the n+1 rule to deduce the spin-spin splitting patterns of adjacent, non-equivalent protons, limited to doublet, triplet and quartet formation in aliphatic compounds.

- Know that ¹³C NMR gives simpler spectra than ¹H NMR.

- Know that ¹H NMR spectra are obtained using samples dissolved in deuterated solvents or CCl_4.

- Be able to use ¹H NMR spectra and chemical shift data from the Chemistry Data Booklet to suggest possible structures or part structures for molecules.

Specification Reference 3.3.15

Exam Tip
It can be difficult to work out how many hydrogen environments you have in a molecule. Sometimes it helps if you highlight all the hydrogens that are in the same environment the same colour — then you can go back and count up how many environments there are.

4. ¹H NMR Spectroscopy

¹H NMR works in pretty much the same way as ¹³C NMR except this time the spectra tell you about the different hydrogen environments in a molecule.

Hydrogen environments

¹H NMR is all about how hydrogen nuclei react to a magnetic field. The nucleus of a hydrogen atom is a single proton. So ¹H NMR is also known as 'proton NMR' — and you might see the hydrogen atoms involved being called 'protons'. Each peak on a ¹H NMR spectrum is due to one or more hydrogen nuclei (protons) in a particular environment — this is similar to a ¹³C NMR spectrum (which tells you the number of different carbon environments). But, with ¹H NMR, the relative area under each peak also tells you the relative number of H atoms in each environment.

─ Examples ───────────────────

The spectrum below is the ¹H NMR spectrum of ethanoic acid (CH_3COOH).

ethanoic acid

There are two peaks so there are H atoms in two different environments.

ratio of areas under peaks = 1 : 3

Peak due to TMS — set at δ = 0.

Chemical shift, δ (ppm)

There are two peaks — so there are two hydrogen environments. The numbers above the peaks tell you the area ratio between the hydrogens in each environment, which here is 1 : 3 — so there's 1 H atom in the environment at δ = 11.5 ppm to every 3 H atoms in the other environment. If you look at the structure of ethanoic acid, this makes sense:

3 H atoms attached to CH₂COOH.

1 H atom attached to COOCH₃.

How many peaks will be present on the ¹H NMR spectrum of 1-chloropropanone? Predict the ratio of the areas of these peaks.

By looking at the structure of 1-chloropropanone we can see that there are two different hydrogen environments, which means there will be 2 peaks on the ¹H NMR spectrum.

There are 2 hydrogens in one environment and 3 hydrogens in the other, so the ratio of the peak areas will be 2 : 3.

Two different hydrogen environments.

1-chloropropanone

Integration traces

¹H NMR spectra can get quite cramped and sometimes it's not easy to see the ratio of the areas — so an **integration trace** is often shown. The height increases shown on the integration trace are proportional to the areas of the peaks.

Example

Here's the spectrum for ethanoic acid again:

The integration trace (shown in green on the diagram) has a peak around 11.5 ppm and one around 2 ppm.

Chemical shift, δ (ppm)

The heights of the vertical lines are in the ratio 1 : 3 — this means that for every one hydrogen in the first environment there, are three in the second environment.

Tip: If the ratio of areas isn't given to you, you can use a ruler to measure the ratios off the integration trace. Measure the heights of the trace peaks and divide the measurements by the smallest peak height, et voilà — you've got your area ratio.

Tip: Don't worry if the relative areas are not always whole numbers — they are ratios and not exact numbers.

Chemical shift

You use a table like the one in Figure 1 to identify which functional group each peak in a ¹H NMR spectrum is due to. Don't worry — you'll be given one in your exam, so you don't need to memorise it, you just need to learn how to use it.

¹H NMR Chemical Shifts Relative to TMS	
Chemical shift, δ (ppm)	Type of H atom
0.5 – 5.0	ROH
0.7 – 1.2	RCH₃
1.0 – 4.5	RNH₂
1.2 – 1.4	R₂CH₂
1.4 – 1.6	R₃CH
2.1 – 2.6	R—C—C— (with O double bonded and H)
3.1 – 3.9	R—O—C—H
3.1 – 4.2	RCH₂Br or RCH₂Cl
3.7 – 4.1	R—C—O—C—H (with O double bonded)
4.5 – 6.0	R,H C=C H
9.0 – 10.0	R—C(=O)—H
10.0 – 12.0	R—C(=O)—O—H

The hydrogen atoms that cause the shift are highlighted in red.

R stands for the rest of the organic molecule.

Empty bonds just mean that there are other things attached to the carbon too. (So this group could be COCH₃, COCH₂R, or COCHR₂.)

Exam Tip
The copy of this table you get in your exam may look a little different, and have different values — they depend on the solvent, temperature and concentration.

Exam Tip
Try and get your hands on a copy of the data sheet that you'll get in the exam before the day (you can download one from AQA's website). That way you'll know exactly what's given to you and what you'll be expected to know.

Figure 1: *Chemical shifts of different hydrogen environments.*

─ Example ─────────────────────────────

According to the table, ethanoic acid (CH_3COOH) should have a peak at 10.0 – 12.0 ppm due to R-COOH, and a peak at 2.1 – 2.6 ppm due to $R-COCH_3$. You can see these peaks on ethanoic acid's spectrum below.

R—COCH₃

R—COOH

Peak due to TMS

Chemical shift, δ (ppm)

──

Tip: Neighbouring carbons are carbons one along in the carbon chain from the carbon the hydrogen's attached to. In the diagram below C^2 is the neighbouring carbon to C^1, so the peak for the red H atom is split into the number of purple H atoms, plus one.

Splitting patterns

The peaks on a ¹H NMR spectrum may be split into smaller peaks (this is called spin-spin splitting). These split peaks are called **multiplets**. Peaks always split into the number of hydrogens on the neighbouring carbon(s), plus one. It's called the **n+1 rule**. Some of the different **splitting patterns** you'll find in ¹H spectra are shown in Figure 2.

Tip: Hydrogens in -OH groups are a special case when it comes to splitting. They are always singlets, and they don't affect the splitting patterns of neighbouring hydrogens.

Type of peak	Structure of peak	Number of hydrogens on adjacent carbon(s)
Singlet (not split)	∧	0
Doublet (split into two)	⋀	1
Triplet (split into three)	⋀	2
Quartet (split into four)	⋀	3

Figure 2: Splitting patterns in ¹H NMR.

Tip: For your exam, you don't need to know why ¹H NMR peaks split. It's all down to how the tiny magnetic fields of the hydrogen nuclei interact — it's pretty tricky stuff...

─ Example ─────────────────────────────

Here's the ¹H NMR spectrum for 1,1,2-trichloroethane:

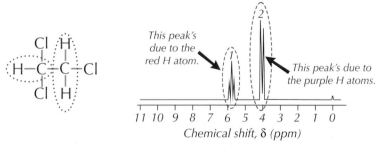

This peak's due to the red H atom.

This peak's due to the purple H atoms.

Chemical shift, δ (ppm)

The peak due to the purple hydrogens is split into two because there's one hydrogen on the adjacent carbon atom. The peak due to the red hydrogen is split into three because there are two hydrogens on the adjacent carbon atom. The numbers above the peaks confirm that the ratio of hydrogens in the red environment to those in the purple environment is 1 : 2.

──

Figure 3: ¹H NMR spectrum. In the ¹H NMR spectra of large organic molecules the splitting patterns can be very complicated. Thankfully you'll never have to deal with one like this in the exam.

¹H NMR spectra are usually more complicated than ¹³C NMR spectra because they have more, unclear split peaks to worry about.

Proton-free solvents

If a sample has to be dissolved, then a solvent is needed that doesn't contain any ^1H atoms — because these would show up on the spectrum and confuse things. **Deuterated solvents** are often used — their ^1H atoms have been replaced by deuterium (D or ^2H) (see Figure 4). Deuterium's an isotope of hydrogen that's got two nucleons (a proton and a neutron).

Unlike ^1H, deuterium don't interact with the external magnetic field, and don't produce peaks on the ^1H NMR spectrum. Here are some examples of deuterated solvents:

CCl_4 can also be used as a solvent — it doesn't contain any ^1H atoms either.

Figure 4: Atomic model of deuterium. Deuterium has one neutron and one proton in its nucleus, whereas ^1H has no neutrons. The atom also has one electron orbiting the nucleus.

Predicting structure from ^1H NMR spectra

^1H NMR spectra provide you with an awful lot of information to analyse. Here's a run down of the things to look out for:

- The number of peaks tells you how many different hydrogen environments there are in your compound.

- The ratio of the peak areas tells you about the relative number of hydrogens in each environment. Sometimes these ratios are written above the peaks on the spectrum for you, other times you may have to use the integration traces.

- You can use the chemical shift of each peak to work out what type of environment the hydrogen is in. You can use a table like the one in Figure 1 to help you.

- The splitting pattern of each peak tells you the number of hydrogens on the adjacent carbon. You can use the n+1 rule to work this out.

And here's one last example to help you on your way...

— Example —

Using the spectrum below, and the table of chemical shift data on page 261, predict the structure of the compound.

Chemical shift, δ (ppm)

- There are two peaks so there are two different hydrogen environments.

- From the area ratios, there's one proton in the environment at δ = 9.5 ppm for every three in the environment at δ = 2.5 ppm.

- Now using the chemical shift data, the peak at δ = 2.5 ppm is likely to be due to an R–COCH$_3$ group, and the peak at δ = 9.5 ppm is likely to be due to an R–CHO group. This fits nicely with the area ratio data.

- The peak at δ = 9.5 ppm is a quartet so this proton has got three neighbouring hydrogens. The peak at δ = 2.5 ppm is a doublet so these protons have got one neighbouring hydrogen. So, it's likely these two groups are next to each other.

You know the molecule has to contain these groups:

So all you have to do is fit them together so that each environment has the correct number of neighbouring hydrogens:

So this is the ^{1}H NMR spectrum for ethanal.

Exam Tip
Always go back and check to see if your structure matches the spectrum — you need to make sure you haven't overlooked an important piece of information.

Practice Questions — Application

Q1 The spectrum below is the ^{1}H NMR spectrum for propanoic acid.

propanoic acid

Assign the peaks **A** – **C** to the hydrogen environments found in propanoic acid.

Q2 Use the ^{1}H spectrum of compound **X** below, along with the chemical shift data on page 261 to work out the structure of compound **X**.
HINT: Compound **X** has the molecular formula C_4H_8O.

Tip: Remember to use all the different types of information that the spectrum gives you...

Practice Questions — Fact Recall

Q1 What does the number of peaks on the ^{1}H NMR spectrum of a compound correspond to?

Q2 What does the area under the peaks on an ^{1}H NMR spectrum of a compound correspond to?

Q3 What data about a peak in a ^{1}H NMR spectrum tells you about the functional group that hydrogen is in?

Q4 Suggest one solvent that could be used to dissolve a sample for analysis by ^{1}H NMR that wouldn't interfere with the spectrum.

5. Chromatography

Chromatography is used to separate and identify chemicals in mixtures.

The basics

Chromatography is used to separate stuff in a mixture — once it's separated out, you can often identify the components. There are quite a few different types of chromatography — but they all have the same basic set up:

- A **mobile phase** — where the molecules can move.
  This is always a liquid or a gas.
- A **stationary phase** — where the molecules can't move.
  This must be a solid, or a liquid on a solid support.

They also use the same basic principle. The mobile phase moves through or over the stationary phase. The distance each substance moves depends on its solubility in the mobile phase and its retention by the stationary phase — components that are more soluble in the mobile phase will travel further than components that are more strongly **adsorbed** (attracted) to the stationary phase. It's these differences in solubility and retention that separate out the different substances.

Thin-layer chromatography

REQUIRED PRACTICAL **12**

In **thin-layer chromatography** (TLC):

- The mobile phase is a liquid solvent, such as ethanol.
- The stationary phase is a thin layer of silica (silicon dioxide) or alumina (aluminium oxide) fixed to a glass or metal plate.

Here's how you separate a mixture using TLC:

1. Draw a line in pencil near the bottom of the TLC plate (the baseline) and put a very small drop of each mixture to be separated on the line.

2. Allow the spots on the plate to dry.

3. Place the plate in a beaker with a small volume of solvent (this is the mobile phase). The solvent level must be below the baseline, so it doesn't dissolve your samples away. Cover the top of the beaker with a watch glass.

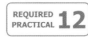

Figure 1: A thin-layer chromatography plate.

4. The solvent will start to move up the plate. As it moves, the solvent will carry the substances in the mixture with it — some chemicals will be carried faster than others and so travel further up the plate.

5. Leave the beaker until the solvent has moved almost to the top of the plate. Then remove the plate from the beaker. Before it's evaporated, use a pencil to mark how far the solvent travelled up the plate (this line is called the solvent front).

6. Place the plate in a fume cupboard and leave it to dry. The fume cupboard will prevent any toxic or flammable fumes from escaping into the room.

7. The result is called a chromatogram (see Figure 2). You can use the positions of the chemicals on the chromatogram to identify what the chemicals are.

Learning Objectives:

- Know that chromatography can be used to separate and identify the components in a mixture.
- Know that separation depends on the balance between solubility in the moving phase and retention by the stationary phase.
- Know that in thin-layer chromatography (TLC) a plate is coated with a solid and a solvent moves up the plate.
- Be able to separate species by thin-layer chromatography (Required practical 12).
- Know that R_f values are used to identify different substances.
- Be able to calculate R_f values from a chromatogram and compare them with standards to identify different substances.
- Know that in column chromatography (CC) a column is packed with a solid and a solvent moves down the column.

Specification Reference 3.3.16

Tip: Placing a watch glass over the top of the beaker stops the solvent from evaporating.

Tip: It's important that you carry out a risk assessment before beginning your experiment.

Figure 2: A TLC chromatogram.

Revealing colourless chemicals

If the chemicals in the mixture are coloured (such as the dyes that make up an ink) then you'll see them as a set of coloured dots at different heights on the TLC plate. But if there are colourless chemicals such as amino acids (see page 232-234) in the mixture, you need to find a way of making them visible.

Here are two ways:

- Many TLC plates have a special fluorescent dye added to the silica or alumina layer that glows when UV light shines on it. You can put the plate under a UV lamp and draw around the dark patches to show where the spots of chemical are.

- Expose the chromatogram to iodine vapour (leaving the plate in a sealed jar with a couple of iodine crystals does the trick). Iodine vapour is a locating agent — it sticks to the chemicals on the plate and they'll show up as purple spots.

R_f values

If you just want to know how many chemicals are present in a mixture, all you have to do is count the number of spots that form on the plate. But if you want to find out what each chemical is, you can calculate something called an R_f **value**. The formula for this is:

$$R_f \text{ value} = \frac{\text{distance travelled by spot}}{\text{distance travelled by solvent}}$$

When you're measuring how far a spot has travelled, you just measure from the base line (point of origin) to the vertical centre of the spot. When you're measuring how far the solvent has travelled, you measure from the base line to the solvent front (see Figure 3).

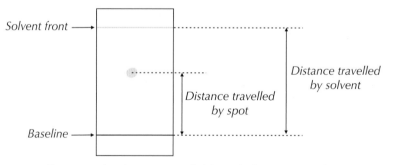

Figure 3: The distances needed for calculating an R_f value.

R_f values aren't dependent how big the plate is or how far the solvent travels — they're properties of the chemicals in the mixture and so can be used to identify those chemicals. This means you can look your R_f value up in a table of standard R_f values to identify what that substance is. But if the composition of the TLC plate, the solvent, or the temperature at which you carry out your chromatography experiment change even slightly, you'll get different R_f values. It's hard to keep the conditions at which you carry out your chromatography experiment identical. So, if you suspect that a mixture contains, say, chlorophyll, it's best to put a spot of chlorophyll on the baseline of the same plate as the mixture and run them both at the same time.

A sugar solution containing a mixture of three sugars is separated using TLC. The chromatogram is shown on the right.

Solvent → front

10.4 cm

2.5 cm

a) Calculate the R_f value of spot X.

To find the R_f value of spot X all you have to do is stick the numbers into the formula:

$$R_f \text{ value} = \frac{\text{distance travelled by spot}}{\text{distance travelled by solvent}}$$

$$= 2.5 \text{ cm} \div 10.4 \text{ cm} = \textbf{0.24}$$

Tip: R_f values are always between 0 and 1.

b) Figure 4 shows the R_f values of three sugars under the conditions used in the experiment. Use the table to suggest the sugar present in spot X.

Spot X has an R_f value of 0.24. Fructose also has an R_f value of 0.24. So the sugar present in spot X could be fructose.

Sugar	R_f value
Glucose	0.20
Fructose	0.24
Xylose	0.30

Figure 4: R_f values of sugars.

Column chromatography

Column chromatography (CC) is mostly used for purifying an organic product. This needs to be done to separate it from unreacted chemicals or side products. It involves packing a glass column with a solid, absorbent material such as aluminium oxide coated with water — this is called a slurry. This is the stationary phase. The mixture to be separated is added to the top of the column and allowed to drain down into the slurry. A solvent is then run slowly and continually through the column. This solvent is the mobile phase.

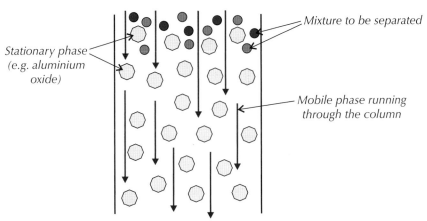

Stationary phase (e.g. aluminium oxide)

Mixture to be separated

Mobile phase running through the column

Figure 6: The initial set-up of a column for column chromatography.

Figure 5: Column chromatography equipment.

As the mixture is washed through the column, its components separate out according to how soluble they are in the mobile phase and how strongly they are adsorbed onto the stationary phase (**retention**). Each different component will spend some time adsorbed onto (stuck to) the stationary phase and some time dissolved in the mobile phase.

The longer a component spends dissolved in the mobile phase, the quicker it travels down the column. If a component spends a long time adsorbed onto the stationary phase, it will take a long time to travel down the column. So, the more soluble a component is in the mobile phase, the quicker it'll pass through the column (see Figure 7).

Tip: This chromatography stuff isn't as difficult as it first seems. You just have to remember that the mixture separates depending on how soluble components are in the mobile phase. Components that are most soluble will travel through the column, or up the plate, quickest.

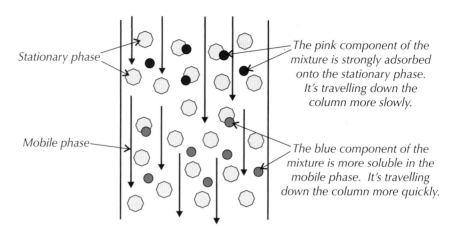

Stationary phase

The pink component of the mixture is strongly adsorbed onto the stationary phase. It's travelling down the column more slowly.

Mobile phase

The blue component of the mixture is more soluble in the mobile phase. It's travelling down the column more quickly.

Figure 7: *The passage of a two component mixture through a chromatography column.*

As a component of the mixture reaches the end of the column it is collected. It can then be identified using the time taken to pass through the column (**retention time**) or another technique (e.g. mass spectrometry, which you met in Year 1).

Amino acid	R_f value
Glycine	0.26
Alanine	0.39
Tyrosine	0.46
Valine	0.61
Leucine	0.74

Figure 8: R_f *values of amino acids.*

Practice Questions — Application

Q1 A student used thin-layer chromatography to separate out a mixture of three amino acids. The chromatogram that she produced is shown on the right.

a) Calculate the R_f values of the three spots, P, Q and R.

b) P, Q and R are each known to be one of the amino acids shown in Figure 8. Use the table in Figure 8 to identify the amino acid present in each spot.

Q2 A scientist is using column chromatography to purify an organic product. She knows that the pure product is more strongly adsorbed to the stationary phase than the impurities. Will the pure product leave the column before or after the impurities? Explain your answer.

Practice Questions — Fact Recall

Q1 What is chromatography used for?

Q2 Describe a method you could use to separate a mixture using thin-layer chromatography.

Q3 a) What are R_f values used for?

b) Give the formula for calculating R_f values.

Q4 Briefly explain why the components in a mixture separate out during column chromatography.

6. Gas Chromatography

Another type of chromatography you need to know about is gas chromatography. It's more high-tech than thin-layer chromatography, but the idea's just the same — a mobile phase, a stationary phase and things separating.

What is gas chromatography?

If you've got a mixture of volatile liquids (ones that turn into gases easily), then **gas chromatography** (GC) is the way to separate them out so that you can identify them. The stationary phase is a solid or a solid coated by a viscous liquid, such as an oil, packed into a long column. The column is coiled to save space, and built into an oven. The mobile phase is an unreactive carrier gas such as nitrogen. The sample is vaporised and passes through the oven as a gas.

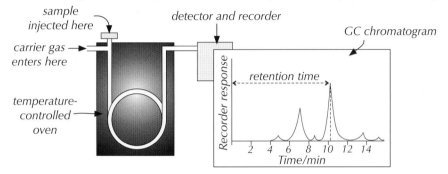

Figure 1: *GC equipment and chromatogram.*

Each component takes a different amount of time from being injected into the column to being recorded at the other end. This is the retention time. The retention times for the components in a mixture are shown on a chromatogram (see Figure 2). The retention time depends on how much time the component spends moving along with the carrier gas, and how much time it spends adsorbed to the viscous liquid. Under standard conditions, each separate substance will have a unique retention time — so you can use the retention time to identify the components of the mixture. (You have to run a known sample under the same conditions for comparison).

Tip: You can also use retention times to identify the components of a mixture in column chromatography.

Example

If you wanted to know if a mixture contained octane, you could run a sample of the mixture through the system, then run a sample of pure octane through, and see if there's a peak at the same retention time on both spectra.

The area under each peak tells you the relative amount of each component that's present in the mixture (see Figure 2).

Tip: You have to run the known sample under the same conditions as the unknown to ensure the variables of the experiment are kept the same.

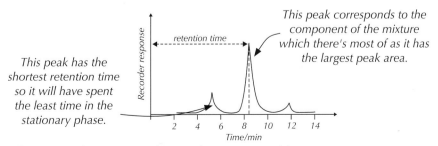

This peak has the shortest retention time so it will have spent the least time in the stationary phase.

This peak corresponds to the component of the mixture which there's most of as it has the largest peak area.

Figure 2: *A chromatogram showing the separation of three components in a mixture.*

GC can be used to find the level of alcohol in blood or urine — the results are accurate enough to be used as evidence in court. It's also used to find the proportions of various esters in oils used in paints — this lets picture restorers know exactly what paint was originally used.

Figure 3: *GC-MS being used in a police lab to analyse evidence found at a crime scene.*

GC-MS

Mass spectrometry is a technique used to identify substances from their mass/charge ratio. It's very good at identifying unknown compounds, but would give confusing results from a mixture of substances. Gas chromatography (see previous page), on the other hand, is very good at separating a mixture into its individual components, but not so good at identifying those components. If you put these two techniques together, you get an extremely useful analytical tool. Gas chromatography-mass spectrometry (or GC-MS for short) combines the benefits of gas chromatography and mass spectrometry to make a super analysis tool.

The sample is separated using gas chromatography, but instead of going to a detector, the separated components are fed into a mass spectrometer (see Figure 4). The spectrometer produces a mass spectrum for each component, which can be used to identify each one and show what the original sample consisted of. Computers can be used to match up the mass spectrum for each component of the mixture against a database, so the whole process can be automated.

Tip: Mass spectrometry was covered back in Year 1, so have a look back at those notes if you need a reminder on how it works, and the sort of spectra it produces.

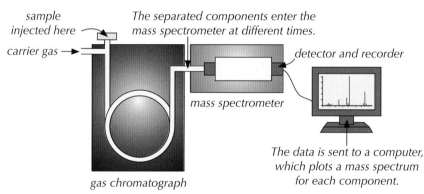

Figure 4: *GC-MS equipment.*

Tip: Combining different analytical techniques creates really powerful tools for working out the structures of unknown chemicals.

The advantage of this method over normal GC is that the components separated out by the chromatography can be positively identified, which can be impossible from a chromatogram alone (because compounds which are similar often have very similar retention times).

Practice Questions — Application

Q1 An environmental scientist ran a water sample through a GC-MS machine. He was looking for traces of the herbicide glyphosate.

a) What function does the gas chromatograph (GC) part of the scientist's GC-MS machine perform?

b) Explain how the scientist can confirm that the water is contaminated with glyphosate once he has the results from the GC-MS machine.

Q2 The GC chromatogram below shows the retention times of three components in a mixture.

a) State which peak corresponds to the component that spends the highest proportion of its time in the tube in the mobile phase.

b) One component of the mixture is hexene. When pure hexene is run through the machine it has a retention time of 8 minutes. Which of the components, A, B or C, is hexene?

Q3 A student runs an unknown mixture through gas chromatography machine. The GC chromatogram below shows the retention times of the two components in the mixture.

a) Estimate the retention time of component A.

b) Which component was present in the largest amount? Explain your answer.

c) The table in Figure 6 gives the standard retention times of some alcohols. Given that component A is an alcohol, use the table to suggest its identity.

d) How else could the student confirm that component A has been identified correctly?

Alcohol	Retention time (min)
2,3-dimethyl butan-2-ol	7.51
butan-1-ol	11.27
pentan-1-ol	21.62
hexan-1-ol	40.30

Figure 5: Retention times of alcohols.

Practice Questions — Fact Recall

Q1 Give an example of a mobile phase used in gas chromatography.

Q2 What is retention time?

Q3 Outline how GC-MS works.

Q4 Why is GC-MS a better technique for identifying compounds in a mixture than GC alone?

Section Summary

Make sure you know...

- That organic synthesis processes can involve several steps.
- That chemists aim to design organic synthesis processes that do not require solvents and that use non-hazardous starting materials to limit accidents and damage to the environment.
- That chemists aim to design organic synthesis processes with a minimal number of steps and a high atom economy to reduce waste.
- How to deduce the synthesis routes of organic compounds using the reactions covered in the Year 1 and Year 2 A Level Chemistry course.
- That you can combine data from different analytical methods to find the structure of an unknown molecule.
- That nuclear magnetic resonance (NMR) spectroscopy gives information about the position of ^{13}C or ^1H atoms in a molecule.
- That chemical shift (δ) depends on the molecular environment of a nucleus.
- Why tetramethylsilane (TMS) is used as a standard in NMR spectroscopy.
- How to use a ^{13}C NMR spectrum to work out the structure of a molecule.
- That integration traces can tell you the relative numbers of ^1H atoms in different environments.
- How to use peak splitting patterns on a ^1H NMR spectrum to work out how many hydrogens there are on neighbouring carbons (using the n+1 rule).
- That ^{13}C NMR gives a simpler spectrum that ^1H NMR.
- That ^1H NMR spectra are obtained using samples dissolved in deuterated solvents or CCl_4.
- How to use a ^1H NMR spectrum to work out the structure of a molecule.
- That chromatography is used to separate out mixtures of chemicals.
- That in chromatography you always have a mobile phase and a stationary phase, and that the mixture separates out because the different components spend different amounts of time in each phase.
- That how long a component spends in each phase depends on how soluble it is in the mobile phase and how strongly adsorbed it is to the stationary phase.
- That in thin-layer chromatography (TLC) the stationary phase is a plate coated with a solid, and the mobile phase is a solvent that moves up the plate.
- How to separate a mixture by thin-layer chromatography.
- What an R_f value is and how to calculate one using a TLC chromatogram.
- That you can compare R_f values with standard values to identify different substances.
- That in column chromatography (CC) the stationary phase is a column packed with a solid, and the mobile phase is a solvent that moves down the column.
- That in gas chromatography (GC) the stationary phase is a column packed with a solid or a solid coated by a liquid, and the mobile phase is a gas that passes through the column.
- What retention times are and how they can be used to identify different substances.
- How you can compare retention times to standards to identify different substances.
- That chromatography can be combined with mass spectrometry (GC-MS) to give a way of separating mixtures and identifying chemicals that works better than chromatography on its own.

Exam-style Questions

1 A scientist is trying to synthesise phenylethanone. The structure of phenylethanone is shown on the right.

1.1 Give a one step synthesis of this molecule from benzene.

(3 marks)

1.2 The scientist purifies his compound using column chromatography. Suggest a stationary phase that the scientist could use in the column.

(1 mark)

1.3 Briefly explain why the pure phenylethanone separates out from the impurities as the mixture passes through the column.

(2 marks)

1.4 The table below gives details of the δ values of the peaks seen on the ^{13}C NMR spectra of three different compounds. Which compound, **A**, **B** or **C**, is phenylethanone? Explain your answer.

Peak number	Spectrum A — δ / ppm	Spectrum B — δ / ppm	Spectrum C — δ / ppm
1	26.5	26.5	26.5
2	128.3	128.3	128.3
3	137.2	128.6	128.6
4	197.9	133.0	133.0
5		137.2	137.2
6			197.9

(2 marks)

2 The ^1H NMR spectrum of an alcohol is shown below.

chemical shift, δ (ppm)

2.1 Suggest a solvent that you could use to dissolve the sample for this spectrum.

(1 mark)

2.2 Use the chemical shift values and splitting patterns to identify the chemical. Explain your reasoning. You may use the table on page 261 to help with this question.

(6 marks)

3   A forensic scientist is analysing a sample of chemicals taken from the scene of a fire. The scientist uses GC-MS to identify the compounds in the mixture.

3.1   Explain how GC-MS is used to identify the different components in a mixture.

(2 marks)

3.2   The sample contains several short-chain alkanes.
Suggest why the scientist could not use gas chromatography alone to identify the components of the mixture.

(2 marks)

3.3   Several of the substances that the scientist finds in the mixture are common components of petrol. The structures of one of these molecules, methylbenzene, is shown below.

The scientist runs a sample of methylbenzene through an NMR spectrometer.
How many peaks will appear on the ^{13}C NMR spectrum of this molecule?

(1 mark)

4   A scientist has a sample of a fruit flavouring that is used in soft drinks.
He uses thin-layer chromatography to separate out the components of the mixture.
The thin-layer chromatogram that he produces is shown below.

4.1   Explain why the components of the mixture separate as they travel up the plate.

(2 marks)

4.2   Calculate the R_f value of spot X.

(1 mark)

4.3   Spot Y is made up of the ester methyl 2-methylpropanoate.
The structure of this ester is shown below, with its carbon atoms labelled.

The ^{1}H NMR spectrum of this ester has three peaks. Describe how the peaks will be split. State which hydrogen atoms are responsible for each splitting pattern.

(3 marks)

Maths skills for A-Level Chemistry

Maths crops up quite a lot in A-Level Chemistry so it's really important that you've mastered all the maths skills you'll need before sitting your exams. Maths skills are covered throughout this book but here's an extra little section, just on maths, to help you out.

1. Exam Technique

The way you answer calculation questions in the exams is important — you should always show your working, and remember all those pesky things like units and significant figures when giving your final answer.

Showing your working

When you're doing calculations the most important thing to remember is to show your working. You've probably heard it a million times before but it makes perfect sense. You won't get a mark for a wrong answer but you could get marks for the method you used to work out the answer.

Units

Make sure you always give the correct units for your answer (see pages 280-281 for more on units).

> ┌ **Example** — **Maths Skills**
>
> Here's an example of a question where you need to change the units so they match the answer the examiner wants.
>
> **1.1** Calculate the free energy change for the following reaction at 298 K, giving your answer in $kJ\ mol^{-1}$:
>
> $$MgCO_3 \rightarrow MgO + CO_2 \qquad \begin{aligned} \Delta H^{\ominus} &= 1.17 \times 10^5\ J\ mol^{-1} \\ \Delta S^{\ominus} &= 175\ J\ K^{-1}\ mol^{-1} \end{aligned}$$
>
> Here you use the equation: $\Delta G = \Delta H - T\Delta S$. Plugging the numbers in gives you an answer of $+64\ 900\ J\ mol^{-1}$ to three significant figures. But the question asks for the answer in $kJ\ mol^{-1}$, so you have to divide by 1000, giving an answer of $64.9\ kJ\ mol^{-1}$. If you left your answer as $+64\ 900\ J\ mol^{-1}$ you'd lose a mark.

Standard form

You might need to use numbers written in standard form in calculations. Standard form is used for writing very big or very small numbers in a more convenient way. Standard form must always look like this:

This number must always be between 1 and 10. → $A \times 10^n$ ← *This number is an integer and tells you the number of places and the direction in which the decimal point moves.*

You need to be able to convert between numbers written in ordinary form and standard form.

Tip: If you're converting a number from standard form back to ordinary form, you just move the decimal point the other way. If n is positive, that means the number you're converting is a large number, so you move the decimal point to the right (you need more digits in front of the decimal point). If n is negative then you're dealing with a very small number, so the decimal point needs to move to the left.

Examples — Maths Skills

Here's how to write 3 500 000 in standard form.

- First write all the digits up to the last non-zero digit. Put a decimal point after the first digit and a '$\times 10$' at the end:

$$3.5 \times 10$$

- Then count how many places the decimal point has moved to the left. This number sits to the top right of the 10, as a superscript.

$$3\,500\,000 = 3.5 \times 10^6$$

- Et voilà... that's 3 500 000 written in standard form.

Here are some more examples.

- You can write 450 000 as 4.5×10^5.

- The number 0.000056 is 5.6×10^{-5} in standard form — the n is negative because the decimal point has moved to the right instead of the left.

- You can write 0.003456 as 3.456×10^{-3}.

Significant figures

Use the number of significant figures given in the data as a guide for how many you need to give in your answer. Whether you're doing calculations with the results of an experiment or in an exam, the rule is the same — round your answer to the lowest number of significant figures in the data you're using.

> You should always write down the number of significant figures you've rounded to after your answer, so that other people can see what rounding you've done.

Tip: The fewer significant figures a measurement has, the less accurate it is. Your answer can only be as accurate as the least accurate measurement in the calculation — that's why you round your answer to the lowest number of significant figures in the data.

Examples — Maths Skills

In this question the data given to you is a good indication of how many significant figures you should give your answer to.

1.2 Calculate the free energy change of a reaction carried out at 298 K, given that $\Delta H = -2.43$ kJ mol^{-1} and $\Delta S = 94.5$ J mol^{-1} K^{-1}.

All the data values in the question are given to 3 s.f. so it makes sense to give your answer to 3 s.f. too. But sometimes it isn't as clear as that.

3.2 At 298 K, K_p for the following reaction is 1.15×10^{-1} kPa:
$N_2O_4 \rightleftharpoons 2NO_2$. Given that, at equilibrium, the partial pressure of N_2O_4 is 0.42 kPa, calculate the partial pressure of NO_2.

There are two types of data that you need to do the calculation in this question — K_p data and partial pressure data. K_p is given to 3 s.f. and the partial pressure data is given to 2 s.f. You should always give your answer to the lowest number of significant figures given — in this case that's to 2 s.f. The answer in full is 0.219772... kPa, so the answer rounded correctly would be 0.22 kPa (2 s.f.).

Exam Tip
You might get told in the question how many significant figures to give your answer to. If you are, make sure that you follow the instructions — you'll lose marks if you don't.

Tip: Even if the last significant figure is a zero, you still need to include it in your answer.

Remember that when you're converting between ordinary and standard form, you need to make sure the number you've converted to has the same number of significant figures as the number you've converted from.

2. Formulas and Equations

A big part of the maths you need to do in Chemistry involves using formulas.
Here are all of the ones you'll need for this course neatly summarised for you.

Amounts and identities of substances

First up is perhaps the most useful formula of all:

$$\text{Number of moles} = \frac{\text{Mass of substance}}{M_r} \qquad \text{also written as...} \quad n = \frac{m}{M_r}$$

Tip: M_r is relative molecular mass (or relative formula mass). You work it out by adding up the A_r (atomic mass) of each atom in the molecule or compound.

Then there's the one that uses the Avogadro constant (6.02×10^{23}):

$$\text{Number of particles} = \text{Number of moles} \times \text{the Avogadro constant}$$

You'll need these ones when you're dealing with solutions...

$$\text{Number of moles} = \frac{\text{Concentration (mol dm}^{-3}) \times \text{Volume (cm}^3)}{1000}$$

$$\text{Number of moles} = \text{Concentration (mol dm}^{-3}) \times \text{Volume (dm}^3)$$

Exam Tip
You don't need to learn the value of the Avogadro constant, or of the gas constant. They'll both be given to you if you need them in the exams.

Here's the ideal gas equation:

$$\begin{array}{c} \text{volume (m}^3) \searrow \quad \nwarrow \text{the gas constant } (= 8.31 \text{ J K}^{-1} \text{mol}^{-1}) \\ pV = nRT \\ \text{pressure (Pa)} \nearrow \quad \uparrow \quad \nwarrow \text{temperature (K)} \\ \text{number of moles} \end{array}$$

These two are handy when you're working out how much stuff you've made...

$$\% \text{ atom economy} = \frac{\text{Molecular mass of desired product}}{\text{Sum of molecular masses of reactants}} \times 100$$

$$\% \text{ yield} = \frac{\text{Actual yield}}{\text{Theoretical yield}} \times 100$$

R_f values let you identify unknown substances based on how far they travel up the plate in thin-layer chromatography. Here's how you calculate them:

$$R_f \text{ value} = \frac{\text{distance travelled by spot}}{\text{distance travelled by solvent}}$$

Exam Tip
All these formulas are really important — you have to learn them because they won't be given to you in the exam (with the exception of the Arrhenius equation — see next page).

Reaction rates

First up, here's a simple formula that you can use to find the average rate of a reaction over a set period of time from experimental data:

$$\text{rate of reaction} = \frac{\text{amount of reactant used or product formed}}{\text{time}}$$

The rate equation links the rate of a reaction to the concentration of the reactants, the orders of these reactants, and the rate constant:

rate of reaction (mol dm^{-3} s^{-1}) — reaction orders with respect to A and B (no units)

$$\text{rate} = k[A]^m[B]^n$$

rate constant (unit varies) — concentration of reactants A and B (mol dm^{-3})

You can find the rate constant, k, for a reaction using the Arrhenius equation:

Arrhenius constant (units vary) — activation energy (J mol^{-1})

$$k = Ae^{\frac{-E_a}{RT}}$$

rate constant (units vary) — temperature (K) — 8.31 (J K^{-1} mol^{-1})

This rearranges into a logarithmic form:

$$\ln k = \frac{-E_a}{RT} + \ln A$$

pH

You need to be able to convert between pH and the concentration of H$^+$ ions in a solution, and vice versa:

$$pH = -\log_{10}[H^+] \qquad [H^+] = 10^{-pH}$$

You also need to be able to convert between pK_a and K_a:

$$pK_a = -\log_{10} K_a \qquad K_a = 10^{-pK_a}$$

Equilibria

You need to be able to work out equilibrium constants for reactions. Here's the formula for the equilibrium constant (K_c).

For the general reaction aA + bB $\rightleftharpoons$ dD + eE : $\qquad K_c = \dfrac{[D]^d[E]^e}{[A]^a[B]^b} \qquad$ where [X] is the concentration of X (mol dm^{-3})

For acids, the equilibrium constant is called the acid dissociation constant, K_a, has units of mol dm^{-3} and is found using the formula:

$$K_a = \frac{[H^+][A^-]}{[HA]}$$

Water has a special dissociation constant — the ionic product of water, K_w. The units of K_w are mol^2 dm^{-6}, and it's found using the formula:

$$K_w = [H^+][OH^-]$$

Equilibrium reactions between gases have the equilibrium constant K_p.

For the general reaction aA + bB $\rightleftharpoons$ dD + eE : $\qquad K_p = \dfrac{p(D)^d p(E)^e}{p(A)^a p(B)^b} \qquad$ where p(X) is the partial pressure of X in Pa

You can work out the partial pressures and mole fractions of the gases in a mixture using the following formulas:

$$\text{partial pressure of a gas in a mixture (Pa)} = \text{mole fraction} \times \text{total pressure of the mixture (Pa)}$$

$$\text{mole fraction of a gas in a mixture} = \frac{\text{number of moles of gas}}{\text{total number of moles of all gases in the mixture}}$$

Tip: The mole fraction of a substance doesn't have any units.

Energy changes

Energy changes include enthalpy changes, entropy changes and free energy changes for reactions, as well as electrode potentials of electrochemical cells.

Here's the formula that you'll need for calculating the energy change of a reaction from experimental data:

mass (g) — *change in temperature (K or °C)*
$$q = mc\Delta T$$
heat lost or gained (J) — *specific heat capacity (J g^{-1} K^{-1})*

It doesn't matter whether the temperature is in K or °C — it's the <u>change</u> in temperature that goes into the formula, and that will be the same whether the units are K or °C.

To calculate the entropy change of a system, you use:

$$\Delta S = S_{\text{products}} - S_{\text{reactants}} \quad \text{where } \Delta S \text{ is the entropy change in J K}^{-1}\text{ mol}^{-1}$$

Exam Tip
Make sure you can rearrange all these formulas and give the units of each quantity as well.

If you know the enthalpy change, the entropy change and temperature of a reaction, you can calculate the free energy change (ΔG) using:

Free energy change (J mol^{-1}) — *Temperature (K)*
$$\Delta G = \Delta H - T\Delta S$$
Enthalpy change (J mol^{-1}) — *Entropy change (J K^{-1} mol^{-1})*

Here's the formula for calculating the cell potential of an electrochemical cell:

$$E^{\ominus}_{\text{cell}} = E^{\ominus}_{\text{reduced}} - E^{\ominus}_{\text{oxidised}}$$

Or, if you're given a cell diagram to work from, you can use this formula instead:

$$E^{\ominus}_{\text{cell}} = E^{\ominus}_{\text{right-hand side}} - E^{\ominus}_{\text{left-hand side}}$$

Tip: Electrode potentials are always measured in volts (V).

Finally, you need to know how to calculate the change in energy when a particle absorbs light of a certain frequency:

Planck's constant = 6.63 × 10^{-34} Js

energy absorbed (J)
$$\Delta E = h\nu = \frac{hc}{\lambda}$$
speed of light = 3.00 × 10^8 m s^{-1}

frequency of light absorbed (Hz) — *wavelength of light absorbed (m)*

3. Units

Units aren't the most exciting bit of chemistry but you need to be able to use them. Here's how to convert between units and work them out from scratch.

Converting between units

Volume

Volume can be measured in m^3, dm^3 and cm^3.

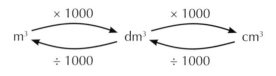

$$m^3 \xrightleftharpoons[\div 1000]{\times 1000} dm^3 \xrightleftharpoons[\div 1000]{\times 1000} cm^3$$

┌ **Example** — **Maths Skills** ────────────

Write 0.3 cm³ in dm³ and m³.

First, to convert 0.3 cm³ into dm³ you need to divide by 1000.
$$0.3 \div 1000 = 0.0003 \ dm^3 = 3 \times 10^{-4} \ dm^3$$
Then, to convert 0.0003 dm³ into m³ you need to divide by 1000.
$$0.0003 \div 1000 = 0.0000003 \ m^3 = 3 \times 10^{-7} \ m^3$$

Temperature

Temperature can be measured in K and °C.

$$K \xrightleftharpoons[+273]{-273} °C$$

┌ **Example** — **Maths Skills** ────────────

Write 25 °C in kelvins.

To convert 25 °C into K you need to add 273: $25 + 273 = 298 \ K$

Pressure

Pressure can be measured in Pa and kPa.

$$kPa \xrightleftharpoons[\div 1000]{\times 1000} Pa$$

┌ **Example** — **Maths Skills** ────────────

Write 3200 Pa in kPa.

To convert 3200 Pa into kPa you need to divide by 1000.
$$3200 \div 1000 = 3.2 \ kPa$$

Mass

Mass can be measured in kg and g.

$$kg \xrightleftharpoons[\div 1000]{\times 1000} g$$

┌ **Example** — **Maths Skills** ────────────

Write 5.2 kg in g.

To convert 5.2 kg into g you need to multiply by 1000.
$$5.2 \times 1000 = 5200 \ g$$

Figure 1: *Measuring cylinders like these measure volumes in cm³.*

Tip: Standard form (that's showing numbers as, for example, 3×10^{-7}) is covered on pages 275-276.

Exam Tip
Make sure you practise these conversions. It could save you valuable time in the exam if you can change between units confidently.

Tip: A kPa is bigger than a Pa, so you'd expect the number to get smaller when you convert from Pa to kPa — each unit is worth more so you'll have fewer of them.

Figure 2: *This balance measures mass in g.*

Energy

Energy can be measured in kJ and J.

kJ $\overset{\times 1000}{\underset{\div 1000}{\rightleftarrows}}$ J

Tip: If you're struggling with a unit conversion, try thinking about an example for that unit that you're certain of — e.g. if you know that 1 kJ is 1000 J, you know that to get from kJ to J you must have to multiply by 1000. Simple.

┌─ **Example** ── **Maths Skills** ─────────────

Write 78 kJ in J.

To convert 78 kJ into J you need to multiply by 1000.

$$78 \times 1000 = 78\,000\,J = 7.8 \times 10^4\,J$$

Life gets a bit confusing if you have to do lots of calculations one after the other — sometimes it can be difficult to keep track of your units. To avoid this, write down the units you're using with each line of the calculation. Then when you get to the end you know what units to give with your answer.

Calculating units

In chemistry, some quantities, like the equilibrium constant (K_c) and the rate constant (k), have variable units. This means you'll need to work the units out — you can't just learn them. To work out the units, you just follow these steps:

- Substitute the units that you know into the equation you're using.

- Cancel out units wherever possible — if the same unit is present on the top and the bottom of a fraction, you can cancel them out.

- Get rid of any fractions by using the rule $\frac{1}{a^n} = a^{-n}$ (see page 282) — any positive powers on the bottom of the fraction become negative and any negative powers become positive.

Figure 3: *When you're under pressure in an exam it's easy to make mistakes, so don't be afraid to use your calculator, even for simple calculations.*

┌─ **Example** ── **Maths Skills** ─────────────

The rate equation for the reaction $CH_3COCH_3 + I_2 \rightarrow CH_3COCH_2I + H^+ + I^-$ is Rate = $k[CH_3COCH_3][H^+]$. The rate of reaction is in mol dm^{-3} s^{-1} and the concentrations are in mol dm^{-3}. Find the units of k.

$$\text{Rate} = k[CH_3COCH_3][H^+] \qquad \text{so} \qquad k = \frac{\text{Rate}}{[CH_3COCH_3][H^+]}$$

First substitute in the units you know:

$$\text{units of } k = \frac{\text{mol dm}^{-3}\text{s}^{-1}}{(\text{mol dm}^{-3})(\text{mol dm}^{-3})}$$

Cancel out units where you can. In this case you can cancel a mol dm^{-3} from the top and the bottom of the fraction:

$$\text{units of } k = \frac{\cancel{\text{mol dm}^{-3}}\text{s}^{-1}}{(\cancel{\text{mol dm}^{-3}})(\text{mol dm}^{-3})} = \frac{\text{s}^{-1}}{\text{mol dm}^{-3}}$$

Then get rid of the fraction by using the rule $\frac{1}{a^n} = a^{-n}$:

$$\text{units of } k = \text{s}^{-1}\,\text{mol}^{-1}\,\text{dm}^3$$

Exam Tip
Always, always, give units with your answers. It's really important that the examiner knows what units you're working in — 10 g is very different from 10 kg. (Unless, of course, it's a quantity without units, for example pH.)

Tip: If you have more than one of a particular unit multiplied together, you add the powers together (see p.282), e.g. (mol dm^{-3})(mol dm^{-3}) is (mol^2 dm^{-6}).

Tip: Writing mol is the same as writing mol^1, so 1/mol = mol^{-1}.

4. Powers and Logarithms

A power is like an instruction that tells you how many times to multiply a number by itself. By contrast, a logarithm tells you how many times a number has been multiplied by itself in order to get to another number.

Powers

Tip: The small superscript number is sometimes called an exponent or an index.

When you see a term with a small number beside it, the small number is telling you what power the term has been raised to:

Powers can be positive or negative numbers.

A positive power tells you how many times to multiply the term by itself.

> **Examples** — Maths Skills
>
> $2^5 = 2 \times 2 \times 2 \times 2 \times 2 = \mathbf{32}$ $10^3 = 10 \times 10 \times 10 = \mathbf{1000}$

Tip: Powers are used a lot in rate equations. Have a look at page 50 to see them in action.

This is how to calculate a negative power: $a^{-n} = \dfrac{1}{a^n}$

> **Examples** — Maths Skills
>
> $4^{-2} = \dfrac{1}{4^2} = \dfrac{1}{4 \times 4} = \mathbf{0.0625}$ $5^{-3} = \dfrac{1}{5^3} = \dfrac{1}{5 \times 5 \times 5} = \mathbf{0.008}$

There are some rules for using powers in calculations that are useful to know:

- If you raise a number to the power 1, the result is just that number:
$$a^1 = a$$
- If you raise a number to the power 0, the result is always 1:
$$a^0 = 1$$
- If you multiply a number raised to a power by the same number raised to a power, the result is the same as the number raised to the sum of the two powers: $\quad a^n \times a^m = a^{(n+m)}$
- If you divide a number raised to a power by the same number raised to a power, the result is the same as the number raised to the value of the first power minus the value of the second power:
$$a^n \div a^m = a^{(n-m)}$$

Tip: These rules all apply to powers you find in units as well as in numerical equations.

- A number raised to a power in the denominator of a fraction is the same as that number raised to the negative of the power and then multiplied by the numerator: $\quad \dfrac{1}{a^n} = 1 \times a^{-n} = a^{-n}$

Tip: An irrational number is one that you <u>can't</u> write as a fraction. Irrational numbers have an infinite number of non-recurring decimal places (they go on forever and never repeat).

> **Examples** — Maths Skills
>
> $7^1 = \mathbf{7}$ $11^0 = \mathbf{1}$ $3^2 \times 3^4 = 3^6 = \mathbf{729}$
>
> $4^7 \div 4^5 = 4^2 = \mathbf{16}$ $\dfrac{1}{\text{mol}\,\text{dm}^{-3}} = \mathbf{mol^{-1}\,dm^3}$

The number 'e'

The number 'e' crops up occasionally in chemistry. Like 'π', it is a fixed, irrational number with an infinite number of decimal places.

$$e = 2.718281828459045235360...$$

In most of the calculations involving e that you will come across, it is raised to a power, so it looks like this: e^x. The function e^x is known as the 'exponential function'. To stop you having to type in a long string of numbers every time you carry out calculations involving exponentials, there should be a button on your calculator that looks a bit like this: .

Tip: The power rules on the previous page all apply to calculations involving e raised to a power.

┌─ **Examples** ── Maths Skills ├──────────────────
│
│ $e^9 = \mathbf{8103.1}$ $\qquad$ $e^{-4} = \mathbf{0.01832}$ $\qquad$ $e^0 = \mathbf{1}$
└

Logarithms

Logarithms tell you how many times a number (the **base**) has been multiplied by itself to get to another number. They are the opposite of powers.

$$\text{If } a^n = x \quad \text{then} \quad \log_a x = n$$

It's important to specify the base of your logarithm, but some numbers are so common they have their own symbols:

- You often want to know how many times the number 10 has been multiplied by itself. Sometimes $\log_{10} x$ is just written as $\log x$.
- The **natural logarithm** is the logarithm with a base of e. You write $\log_e x$ as $\ln x$.

These two functions are used so often that you'll probably have a button for each of them on your calculator — handy.

Tip: Your calculator may well have buttons that look like: $\log_{\blacksquare}\square$, log and ln .
The first button lets you specify your base. The second is $\log_{10}$ and the third is $\log_e$.

Tip: Logarithms tell you the order of magnitude a number is in, so they're really useful for comparing numbers that fall across a very large range.

┌─ **Examples** ── Maths Skills ├──────────────────
│
│ $\qquad$ $\log_2 16 = \mathbf{4}$ $\qquad$ $\log 100 = \mathbf{2}$ $\qquad$ $\ln 14 = \mathbf{2.6}$
└

Just like for powers, there are some rules for working with logarithms in calculations that are useful to know:

- The logarithm of two things multiplied together is the same as the sum of their individual logarithms:
$$\log_a (xy) = \log_a x + \log_a y$$

- The logarithm of the value of the base raised to a power is the value of the power:
$$\log_a a^x = x$$

Tip: The pH scale is a logarithmic scale in base 10. Have a look at page 99 to see more about it.

┌─ **Example** ── Maths Skills ├──────────────────
│
│ You can use these rules to rearrange the Arrhenius equation into its logarithmic form. Here's the ordinary version: $\qquad$ $k = Ae^{\frac{-E_a}{RT}}$
│
│ Taking the natural logarithm of both sides gives you:
│ $$\ln (k) = \ln (Ae^{\frac{-E_a}{RT}})$$
│
│ Using the first rule, you know that $\ln (xy) = \ln x + \ln y$, so:
│ $$\ln k = \ln (A) + \ln(e^{\frac{-E_a}{RT}})$$
│
│ Using the second rule, you know that $\ln e^x = \log_e (e^x) = x$, so:
│ $$\ln k = \ln A + \frac{-E_a}{RT}$$
│
│ This is the logarithmic form of the Arrhenius equation.
└

Tip: To make your calculations clear, always put brackets around the thing you're taking the log of. For example, $\log (a + b)$ and $\log(a) + b$ both clearly show what you're doing in a calculation. If you just write $\log a + b$, it's not obvious what's being done.

Tip: See pages 64-67 for lots more about the Arrhenius equation.

5. Graphs

Being able to interpret graphs can be a really important skill in Chemistry, so here's a recap of some of the trickier bits.

Straight line graphs

All straight line graphs have the general equation:

independent variable ↗ ← *y-intercept*

dependent variable ↘ $y = mx + c$ ← *gradient*

Tip: Straight line graphs you're likely to come across include rate-concentration graphs for first order reactions (page 60), Arrhenius plots (page 66) and free-energy graphs (page 35).

If you have an equation in this form and you plot a graph of the dependent variable against the independent variable, then the gradient of the graph will be equal to m, and the y-intercept will be equal to c.

Example ── **Maths Skills**

The logarithmic form of the Arrhenius equation is: $\ln k = \dfrac{-E_a}{RT} + \ln A$

This is an equation in the form $y = mx + c$ where:

$$\ln k = y, \qquad \frac{-E_a}{R} = m, \qquad \frac{1}{T} = x, \qquad \ln A = c$$

So if you plot a graph of $\ln k$ against $\dfrac{1}{T}$, it will have a gradient equal to $\dfrac{-E_a}{R}$ and a y-intercept of $\ln A$.

Finding the gradient of a straight line graph

The gradient of a graph tells you how much the y value changes as you change the x value — it's a measure of the steepness of your graph.

> gradient = change in y ÷ change in x

To measure the gradient of a straight line, start by picking two points on the line that are easy to read. Draw a vertical line down from one point and a horizontal line across from the other to make a triangle. The length of the vertical side of the triangle is the change in y and the length of the horizontal side is the change in x.

Example ── **Maths Skills**

First order reactions have the rate equation: Rate = k[A].

This is in the form $y = mx + c$, where Rate = y, $k = m$, [A] = x and 0 = c.

So a graph of rate against [A] will have a gradient equal to k.

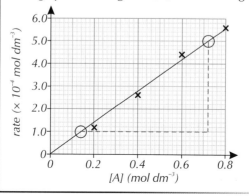

$\Delta x = 0.72 - 0.14 = 0.58$

$\Delta y = (5.0 \times 10^{-4}) - (1.0 \times 10^{-4})$
$\quad = 4.0 \times 10^{-4}$

Gradient = $(4.0 \times 10^{-4}) \div 0.58$
$\quad = 6.9 \times 10^{-4}$

$k = \mathbf{6.9 \times 10^{-4}\ s^{-1}}$

Tip: You might also see the gradient of a graph referred to as its 'slope'.

Tip: The change in y can be written as Δy, and the change in x can be written as Δx.

Tip: A line that slopes downwards from left to right has a negative gradient, because y decreases as x increases.

Exam Tip
Always check the labels of the axes. Here, the y axis units are 10^{-4} mol dm^{-3}, so each of the values on the y axis is multiplied by 10^{-4} to find its true value.

Finding the y-intercept of a graph

The y-intercept of a graph is the point at which the line of best fit crosses the y axis. You may have to extrapolate your line of best fit beyond your data points to find the y-intercept.

Example — **Maths Skills**

From the logarithmic form of the Arrhenius equation, $\ln k = \frac{-E_a}{RT} + \ln A$, you know that the y-intercept of a graph of $\ln k$ against $\frac{1}{T}$ is equal to $\ln A$.

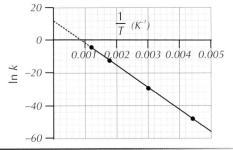

By extrapolating the line of best fit for this graph to the point where $x = 0$, you can see that $y = 12$.

So $\ln A = \textbf{12}$

Tip: Finding a value by extending your line of best fit beyond your data points is called extrapolation. Finding a value between two of your data points using a line of best fit is called interpolation.

Tip: You can't find the y-intercept from a graph if the axes have been contracted. Both axes need to run continuously from zero for it to work.

Finding the gradient of a curve

The gradient is different at different points along a curve. To find the gradient at a particular point, you first have to draw a tangent to the curve at that point, and then find the gradient of that.

Example — **Maths Skills**

The gradient of a graph of concentration against time at any point is equal to the rate of the reaction at that time.

For example, if you want to find the rate after 23 minutes, place a ruler at the point on the curve at 23 minutes so it's just touching the line. Position the ruler so that you can see the whole curve.

Adjust the ruler until the space between the ruler and the curve is equal on both sides of the point.

Tip: There's more about finding gradients on pages 47-48.

Now draw a line along the ruler to make the tangent.

Extend the line right across the graph — it'll help to make your gradient calculation easier as you'll have more points to choose from.

Finally, calculate the gradient of the tangent to find the rate:

- gradient = change in y ÷ change in x

  $= (1.05 - 0.80) \div (26.0 - 7.0) = 0.013...$ mol dm^{-3} min^{-1}

- So, the rate of reaction at 23 mins was **0.013 mol dm^{-3} min^{-1}**.

Exam Help

1. Exam Structure and Technique

Passing exams isn't all about revision — it really helps if you know how the exam is structured and have got your exam technique nailed so that you pick up every mark you can.

Figure 1: *The Room of Doom awaits you. But don't panic — prepare properly and there's no reason you can't ace the exam.*

Course structure

AQA A-Level Chemistry is split into three units:

Unit 1 — Physical chemistry

Unit 2 — Inorganic chemistry

Unit 3 — Organic chemistry

Exam structure

For AQA A-Level Chemistry you're going to have to sit three exams — Paper 1, Paper 2 and Paper 3.

- Paper 1 will test you on most of Physical chemistry and all of Inorganic chemistry.

- Paper 2 will test you on some of Physical chemistry and all of Organic chemistry.

- Paper 3 can test you on any of the material covered in the course.

All three papers could include questions on practical skills. If you want more detail on what could come up in each paper, look at the table below:

Exam Tip
Make sure you have a good read through of this exam structure. It might not seem important now but you don't want to get any nasty surprises just before an exam.

Tip: The exams will test you on material from both years of your A-Level course. This book only covers Year 2 material, so you'll need your Year 1 notes to revise from as well.

Exam Tip
Short answer questions are broken down into parts, but they can still be worth lots of marks overall.

Paper	Content Assessed	*Where the Year 2 content is covered in this book:*
1	▪ Unit 1: Physical chemistry. Specification references 3.1.1.1 to 3.1.4.4 (Year 1), 3.1.6.1 to 3.1.7 (Year 1), 3.1.8.1 to 3.1.8.2 (Year 2) and 3.1.10 to 3.1.12.6 (Year 2).	*← Unit 1 Sections 7 to 10*
	▪ Unit 2: Inorganic chemistry. Specification references 3.2.1.1 to 3.2.3.2 (Year 1) and 3.2.4 to 3.2.6 (Year 2).	*← Unit 2 Sections 3 and 4*
	▪ Relevant practical skills (see next page).	
2	▪ Unit 1: Physical chemistry. Specification references 3.1.2.1 to 3.1.6.2 (Year 1) and 3.1.9.1 to 3.1.9.2 (Year 2).	*← Unit 1 Section 8*
	▪ Unit 3: Organic chemistry. Specification references 3.3.1.1 to 3.3.6.3 (Year 1) and 3.3.7 to 3.3.16 (Year 2).	*← Unit 3 Sections 5 to 9*
	▪ Relevant practical skills (see next page).	
3	▪ Any content from Units 1, 2 and 3. ▪ Relevant practical skills (see next page).	

All the exams are 2 hours long. Papers 1 and 2 are both worth 105 marks, and are each worth 35% of your total mark. Paper 3 is worth 90 marks and is worth 30% of your total mark.

Paper 1 and Paper 2 are made up of short and long answer questions. Paper 3 will be made up of 40 marks on questions relating to practical techniques and data analysis, 20 marks on general questions from all parts of the specification, and 30 marks' worth of multiple choice questions.

Exam Tip
Make sure you know which units and sections will be assessed in each exam. That way, you can make sure that you're properly prepared when you actually come to sit the papers.

Relevant practical skills

At least 15% of the marks on your A-Level Chemistry exams will focus on practical skills. This means you will be given questions where you're asked to do things like comment on the design of experiments, make predictions, draw graphs, calculate means and percentage errors — basically, anything related to planning experiments or analysing results. Handily, the Practical Skills section of this book covers these skills, so make sure you've read through it.

Quality of written communication

Your A-Level Chemistry exam papers will have some extended response questions — in these questions you'll be tested on your ability to write clearly as well as on your chemistry knowledge. So for extended response questions, you need to make doubly sure that:

- your writing is legible.

- your spelling, punctuation and grammar are accurate.

- you organise your answer clearly and coherently — make sure everything you say is relevant and is in a logical order — it should be clear how your points are linked.

- you use specialist scientific vocabulary where it's appropriate.

Tip: Don't worry too much about extended response questions — they sound a bit scary, but as long as you write full and coherent answers whenever you tackle a long answer question, you'll be fine.

Time management

This is one of the most important exam skills to have. How long you spend on each question is really important in an exam — it could make all the difference to your grade. Some questions will require lots of work for only a few marks but other questions will be much quicker. Don't spend ages struggling with questions that are only worth a couple of marks — move on. You can come back to them later when you've bagged loads of other marks elsewhere.

Exam Tip
Don't forget to go back and do any questions that you left the first time round — you don't want to miss out on marks because you forgot to do the question.

─ Example ─

The questions below are both worth the same number of marks but require different amounts of work.

1.1 Define the term 'lattice enthalpy'.

(2 marks)

2.1 Draw the structures of the two monomers that react to form the condensation polymer shown above.

(2 marks)

Question 1.1 only requires you to write down a definition — if you can remember it this shouldn't take you too long.

Question 2.1 requires you to work out and draw the structures of two monomers used to make a condensation polymer — this may take longer than writing down a definition.

So, if you're running out of time it makes sense to do questions like 1.1 first and come back to 2.1 if you've got time at the end.

Exam Tip
It's a really good idea to do as many practice papers as you can before you actually sit the exams — that way you'll get a good feel for how to divide up your time. You could ask your teacher if they have any practice papers you can do, or look on the AQA website to see if there are any specimen papers or past papers for you to download.

It's worth keeping in mind that the multiple choice questions are only worth 1 mark each and some of them can be quite time-consuming to answer. If you're pressed for time, it's usually a good idea to focus on the written answer questions first, where there are more marks available, and then go back to the harder multiple choice questions later.

Command words

Command words are just the bit of the question that tell you what to do. You'll find answering exam questions much easier if you understand exactly what they mean, so here's a summary of the most common command words.

Command word	What to do
Give / State	Write a concise answer, from fact recall or from information that you've been given in the question.
Name	Give the correct technical term for a chemical or a process.
Identify	Say what something is.
Describe	Write about what something is like or how it happens.
Explain	Give reasons for.
Suggest / Predict	Use your scientific knowledge to work out what the answer might be.
Outline	Give a brief description of the main characteristics of a process or an issue.
Calculate	Work out the solution to a mathematical problem.
Estimate	Give an approximate answer.
Determine	Use the information given in the question to work something out.
Compare	Give the similarities and differences between two things.
Draw	Produce a diagram or graph.
Sketch	Draw something approximately — for example, draw a rough line graph to show the main trend of some data.
Justify	Give the case for or against, supported by evidence.

Not all of the questions will have a command word like this — instead they may just be a which / what / how type of question.

Exam data booklet

When you sit your exams, you'll be given a data booklet with the exam paper. In it you'll find some useful information to help you, including...

- the characteristic infrared absorptions, ^{13}C NMR shifts and ^{1}H NMR shifts of some common functional groups.
- the structures of some biologically important molecules, such as the DNA bases, some amino acids, common phosphates and sugars and Heme B.
- a copy of the periodic table.

You might have seen a few slightly different versions of the periodic table — in the exams you should use the information from the one in the data booklet, even if it's slightly different to something you've seen elsewhere. The examiners will use the information in the data booklet when they're marking.

2. Diagrams

When you're asked to draw diagrams or mechanisms in an exam it's important that you draw everything correctly and include all the details that are needed.

Organic reaction mechanisms

Organic reaction mechanisms are used to show what happens during a chemical reaction. One of the most common mistakes people make when drawing these is to get the curly arrows wrong.

--- **Example** ---

When you're drawing organic reaction mechanisms the curly arrows must come from either a lone pair of electrons or from a bond, like this:

The examples below are incorrect — you wouldn't get marks for them:

 You won't get marks if the curly arrows come from atoms, like this... *...or if they come from a charge or from thin air like these.*

Tip: It's important that the curly arrows come from a lone pair or a bond because curly arrows show the movement of electrons and that's where the electrons are found.

Exam Tip
Make sure you draw full charges (+ and –) or dipoles (partial charges shown using $\delta+$ and $\delta-$) clearly — you could lose marks if it's not clear which type of charge you mean.

Displayed and skeletal formulas

Displayed formulas show how all the atoms are connected in a molecule.

--- **Examples** ---

If a question asks you for a displayed formula you have to show all of the bonds and all of the atoms in the molecule. That means you have to draw displayed formulas like this:

And not like this:

 Some of the bonds between the carbon atoms and the hydrogen atoms haven't been shown, so it's not a displayed formula and you wouldn't get the marks.

If you're not asked specifically for a displayed formula then either of the diagrams above will do. Just make sure that the bonds are always drawn between the right atoms. For example, ethanol should be drawn like this:

 And not like this: *It's the oxygen that's bonded to the carbon, not the hydrogen, so drawing it like this is wrong.*

Skeletal formulas are handy when you're drawing large organic molecules. You might have to either draw or interpret skeletal formulas in your exam, so make sure that you're happy drawing and using them. Remember — bonds between carbon atoms are shown by a line and carbon atoms are found at each end. Atoms that aren't carbon or hydrogen have to be drawn on:

Tip: If you're not totally comfortable drawing skeletal formulas, it might help to draw the displayed formula first. That will help you to see what atoms need to be drawn in the skeletal formula.

┌─ **Example** ─────────────────────

1,5-difluoropentane (FCH$_2$CH$_2$CH$_2$CH$_2$CH$_2$F)

The carbon-carbon bonds are shown by lines.

Each junction represents one carbon atom.

You still have to show the atoms that aren't carbon or hydrogen.

You don't draw any carbon or hydrogen atoms from the main carbon chain when you're drawing a skeletal formula, so both of the diagrams below are wrong.

You don't show the carbon atoms or the hydrogen atoms.

Hydrogen bonds

Drawing a diagram showing hydrogen bonding is a fairly common exam question. You need to know how to draw hydrogen bonds properly to pick up all the marks you can.

Exam Tip
Make sure you include everything the question asks for in your answer. For example, if the question asks you to show lone pairs and dipoles in a diagram, don't forget to add them.

┌─ **Example** ─────────────────────

The hydrogen bond needs to come from a lone pair of electrons.

(The electrons are shown as crosses here, but dots would be fine too.)

Hydrogen bond

Make sure you label the hydrogen bond and put all the partial charges on the atoms.

Hydrogen bonds have to go to a hydrogen atom — duh.

General advice on diagrams

These pages cover some of the types of diagram that are likely to come up in your exams. But you could be asked to draw other diagrams. Whatever diagram you're drawing, make sure it's really clear. A small scribble in the bottom corner of a page isn't going to show enough detail to get you the marks. Draw the diagrams nice and big, but make sure that you stay within the space given for that answer. It may also help to add clear, concise labels to your diagram, particularly for things like drawings of the apparatus needed for an experiment.

If you've drawn a diagram incorrectly don't scribble part of it out and try to fix it — it'll look messy and be hard for the examiner to figure out what you're trying to show. Cross the whole thing out and start again. And always double check that you've included all the things that you should have done.

3. The Periodic Table — Facts and Trends

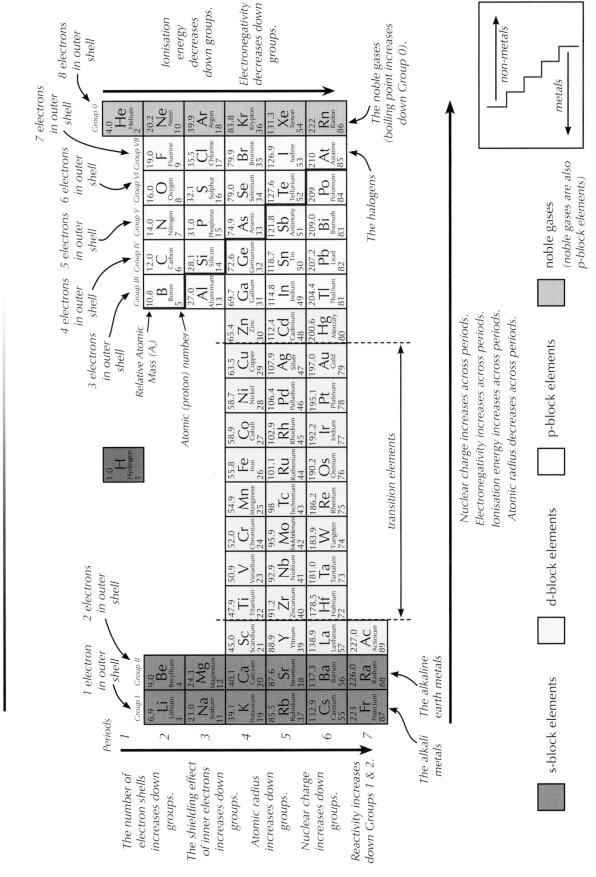

Unit 1

Section 7 — Thermodynamics

1. Enthalpy Changes
Page 22 — Fact Recall Questions
Q1 Enthalpy change is the heat energy transferred in a reaction at constant pressure.
Q2 ΔH
Q3 Lattice formation enthalpy is the enthalpy change when 1 mole of a solid ionic compound is formed from its gaseous ions.
Lattice dissociation enthalpy is the enthalpy change when 1 mole of a solid ionic compound is completely dissociated into its gaseous ions.
Q4 a) Enthalpy change of formation is the enthalpy change when 1 mole of a compound is formed from its elements in their standard states under standard conditions.
b) Second electron affinity is the enthalpy change when 1 mole of gaseous 2– ions is made from 1 mole of gaseous 1– ions.
c) The enthalpy change of hydration is the enthalpy change when 1 mole of aqueous ions is formed from gaseous ions.
Q5 a) Enthalpy change of atomisation of an element.
b) The first ionisation energy.
Q6 a) ΔH_{hyd}
b) ΔH_{diss}

2. Born-Haber Cycles
Pages 26-27 — Application Questions
Q1

Q2 a)

b) $\Delta H1 = \Delta H2 + \Delta H3 + \Delta H4 + \Delta H5 + \Delta H6$
$= (+122) + (+159) + (+520) + (-349) + (-861)$
$= \textbf{–409 kJ mol}^{-1}$

Q3 a)

b) $\Delta H6 = -\Delta H5 - \Delta H4 - \Delta H3 - \Delta H2 + \Delta H1$
$= -(-328) - (+419) - (+89) - (+79) + (-563)$
$= \textbf{–822 kJ mol}^{-1}$
c) The purely ionic model of a lattice, which theoretical lattice enthalpies are based on, assumes that all the ions are spherical, and have their charge evenly distributed around them. But the experimental lattice enthalpy from the Born-Haber cycle is usually different. This is because ionic compounds usually have some covalent character. The positive and negative ions in a lattice aren't usually exactly spherical. Positive ions polarise neighbouring negative ions to different extents, and the more polarisation there is, the more covalent the bonding will be.

3. Enthalpies of Solution
Page 29 — Application Questions
Q1 $\Delta H3 = \Delta H1 + \Delta H2 = +826 + (-520 + -364) = \textbf{–58 kJ mol}^{-1}$

Q2 a)

b) $\Delta H3 = \Delta H1 + \Delta H2 = +747 + (-406 + -336)$
$= \textbf{+5 kJ mol}^{-1}$

Page 29 — Fact Recall Question

Q1 a) The bonds between the ions break (the ions dissociate), and bonds between the ions and water are made (the ions become hydrated).

b) Dissociation is endothermic, and hydration is exothermic.

4. Entropy
Page 32 — Application Questions

Q1 The entropy will increase when the solid sodium hydroxide dissolves in the aqueous hydrogen chloride. The entropy of the water will increase when it turns to a gas and the entropy of the sodium chloride will decrease when it turns to a solid.

Q2 $\Delta S = S_{products} - S_{reactants}$
$= (214 + (2 \times 69.9)) - (186 + (2 \times 205))$
$= \textbf{-242.2 J K}^{-1}\textbf{mol}^{-1}$

Q3 $\Delta S = S_{products} - S_{reactants}$
$= ((3 \times 31.6) + (2 \times 69.9)) - (248 + (2 \times 206))$
$= \textbf{-425.4 J K}^{-1}\textbf{mol}^{-1}$

Page 32 — Fact Recall Questions

Q1 a) It is a measure of the amount of disorder in a system (e.g. the number of ways that particles can be arranged and the number of ways that the energy can be shared out between particles).

b) ΔS

Q2 a) The entropy increases because particles move around more in gases than in liquids and their arrangement is more disordered.

b) The entropy increases because particles move around more in solution than in solids and their arrangement is more disordered.

c) The entropy increases because the more gaseous particles you've got, the more ways they and their energy can be arranged.

5. Free-Energy Change
Page 36 — Application Questions

Q1 a) $\Delta S = S_{products} - S_{reactants}$
$= ((2 \times 28.3) + (3 \times 27.0)) - (51.0 + (3 \times 32.5))$
$= \textbf{-10.9 J K}^{-1}\textbf{mol}^{-1}$

b) $\Delta H^{\ominus} = -130$ kJ mol^{-1} $= -130 \times 10^3$ J mol^{-1}
$\Delta G = \Delta H - T\Delta S$
$= -130 \times 10^3 - (298 \times -10.9)$
$= \textbf{-127 000 J mol}^{-1}$ (3 s.f.)

c) The reaction is feasible at 298 K because ΔG is negative.

Q2 $\Delta H^{\ominus} = 178.0$ kJ mol^{-1} $= 178.0 \times 10^3$ J mol^{-1}
$T = \Delta H \div \Delta S = 178.0 \times 10^3 \div 165.0 = \textbf{1079 K}$

Q3 a) $\Delta H = -20\ 000$ J mol^{-1} $= \textbf{-20 kJ mol}^{-1}$
The enthalpy change is the y-intercept of the straight line.

b) $\Delta S = -$gradient
$= -(\Delta y \div \Delta x) = -((30\ 000 - (-20\ 000)) \div (600 - 0))$
$= -(50\ 000 \div 600) = \textbf{-83.3 J K}^{-1}\textbf{mol}^{-1}$

c) The reaction is not feasible at 400 K. From the graph, ΔG is positive at 400 K.

Page 36 — Fact Recall Questions

Q1 a) Free-energy change is a measure used to predict whether a reaction is feasible. It is 0 or negative for a feasible reaction and positive for a non-feasible reaction.

b) ΔG

c) J mol^{-1} OR kJ mol^{-1}

Q2 $\Delta G = \Delta H - T\Delta S$

Q3 no

Q4 $T = \Delta H \div \Delta S$

Exam-style Questions — pages 38-41

1 D *(1 mark)*.
The equation $\Delta G = \Delta H - T\Delta S$ is the equation of a straight line, $y = mx + c$. So the enthalpy change is the y-intercept, which is negative. The gradient is equal to the entropy change with the opposite sign. So, since the gradient is positive, entropy change must be negative.

2.1

(1 mark for a complete correct cycle,
1 mark for correctly labelled arrows)

2.2 Enthalpy change of solution (SrF$_{2(s)}$)
$=$ lattice dissociation enthalpy (SrF$_{2(s)}$)
$+$ enthalpy of hydration (Sr$_2{}^+{}_{(g)}$)
$+$ [2 $\times$ enthalpy of hydration (F$^-{}_{(g)}$)] *(1 mark)*
$= 2492 + (-1480) + (2 \times -506) = \textbf{0 kJ mol}^{-1}$ *(1 mark)*
You have to double the enthalpy of hydration for F$^-$ because there are two in SrF$_2$.

3.1 It is the enthalpy change when 1 mole of gaseous atoms is formed from an element in its standard state *(1 mark)*.

3.2

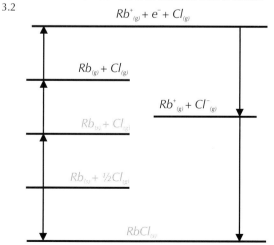

(1 mark for each correct label).

3.3 $\Delta H6 = -\Delta H5 - \Delta H4 - \Delta H3 - \Delta H2 + \Delta H1$
$= -(-349) - (+403) - (+81) - (+122) + (-435)$
$= \mathbf{-692\ kJ\ mol^{-1}}$
(3 marks for correct answer, otherwise 1 mark for correct equation, 1 mark for correct substitution)

3.4 When experimental and theoretical lattice enthalpies are very similar, it shows that a compound has very little covalent character *(1 mark)*. This means that rubidium chloride fits the purely ionic model very well and has almost 100% ionic character. *(1 mark)*.

3.5 $+692\ kJ\ mol^{-1}$ *(1 mark)*

3.6 Enthalpy change of solution *(1 mark)*.

3.7 $\Delta H3 = \Delta H1 + \Delta H2 = +692 + (-296 + -364)$
$= \mathbf{+32\ kJ\ mol^{-1}}$ *(1 mark)*
If you used the value of +300 kJ mol⁻¹ for the enthalpy change of dissociation you'll get an answer of −360 kJ mol⁻¹. If you got this answer, give yourself the mark.

4.1 Increase. Every 5 molecules of reactants produces 6 molecules of products *(1 mark)* so the products will have higher entropy because there are more ways of arranging 6 molecules than 5 *(1 mark)*.
You generally don't get marks for 50:50 guesses at Year 2 — so you won't get any marks just for saying it increases. The marks come for the explanation.

4.2 It would decrease. Particles move around less in liquids than in gases and their arrangement is less disordered, so liquids have lower entropy *(1 mark)*.

4.3 $\Delta S = S_{products} - S_{reactants}$
$= ((2 \times 198) + (4 \times 189)) - ((2 \times 186) + (3 \times 205))$
$= \mathbf{+165\ J\ K^{-1}\ mol^{-1}}$
(3 marks for correct answer, otherwise 1 mark for correct equation, 1 mark for correct substitution).

4.4 $\Delta G = \Delta H - T\Delta S$ *(1 mark)*.

4.5 ΔH is negative and ΔS_{system} is positive *(1 mark)*. This means that the value of ΔG will always be negative irrespective of the temperature *(1 mark)*.

5.1 $\Delta S = S_{products} - S_{reactants}$
$= (32.0 + 214) - (53.0 + 5.70)$
$= +187.3\ J\ K^{-1}\ mol^{-1}$ *(1 mark)*.
$\Delta H^\circ = +127\ kJ\ mol^{-1} = +127 \times 10^3\ J\ mol^{-1}$
$\Delta G = \Delta H - T\Delta S$ *(1 mark)*.
$= (+127 \times 10^3) - (1473 \times 187.3)$ *(1 mark)*.
$= \mathbf{-149000\ J\ mol^{-1}}$ or $\mathbf{-149\ kJ\ mol^{-1}}$ (3 s.f.) *(1 mark)*.

5.2 If the free-energy change is negative or equal to zero the reaction is feasible *(1 mark)*.

5.3 $T = \Delta H \div \Delta S$ *(1 mark)*.

5.4 $T = (+127 \times 10^3) \div 187.3$
$= 678\ K$
(1 mark for correct substitution, 1 mark for correct answer).
Don't forget, reactions become feasible when ΔG is 0.

5.5 The standard enthalpy change of formation is the enthalpy change when 1 mole of a compound is formed from its elements in their standard states and under standard conditions *(1 mark)*.

5.6 The formation of manganese(IV) oxide would be exothermic *(1 mark)*.
It's an exothermic reaction because ΔH is negative.

Section 8 — Rate Equations and K_p

1. Monitoring Reactions

Page 46 — Application Questions

Q1 a) E.g. use colorimetry to measure the change in absorbance, measure the change in pH.
b) E.g. measure the loss of mass, measure the volume of gas produced, measure the change in pH.
c) E.g. use colorimetry to measure the change in absorbance, measure the loss of mass, measure the volume of gas produced.

Q2 The calculated rate would be less than the true rate. Not all of the gas produced would be collected, as some would escape from the system. This means that the reaction would appear to have produced less gas than it really had, and so the rate would appear lower.

Q3 Initial number of moles HCl = conc × vol
$= 1.5 \times (250 \div 1000) = 0.375$

Time / seconds	Mass lost / g	Concentration of HCl / mol dm⁻³
0	0.00	**1.50**
10	0.60	**1.36**
20	1.18	**1.22**
30	1.77	**1.08**
40	2.37	**0.944**
50	2.94	**0.810**
60	3.51	**0.677**

See page 45 for a full method for this type of question.

Q4 $Na_2CO_3 + H_2SO_4 \rightarrow Na_2SO_4 + H_2O + CO_2$
Initial number of moles H_2SO_4 = conc × vol
$= 1.00 \times (100 \div 1000)$
$= 0.100$

Time / seconds	Concentration of H_2SO_4 / mol dm⁻³
0	**1.00**
15	**0.999**
30	**0.997**
45	**0.996**
60	**0.995**
75	**0.994**

See page 43 for a full method for this type of question.

Page 46 — Fact Recall Questions

Q1 Continuous monitoring is a method for following the progress of a reaction. It involves taking measurements at regular intervals, over the course of a reaction, to measure the loss of a reactant or the formation of a product.

Q2

Bung
Delivery tube
Gas syringe
Reaction vessel
Reactants

Q3 Colorimeters measure the absorbance of a solution.

Q4 E.g. you could measure the loss of mass, at regular intervals, as a gaseous product forms and escapes. By carrying out the reaction on a balance, you can follow how the mass changes throughout the experiment. / You could collect the gas in a gas syringe and record the volume of gas produced, at regular intervals, over the course of the reaction.

2. Reaction Rates and Graphs
Page 49 — Application Questions
Q1 a)

E.g. gradient = change in y ÷ change in x
$$= 1.3 ÷ 2.1 = \textbf{0.62 mol dm}^{-3}\textbf{ min}^{-1}\textbf{ (2 s.f.)}$$
In questions where you have to find a gradient, it's okay if you get a slightly different answer — your rate will vary if you use a slightly different line of best fit, tangent or pair of points to calculate the gradient from.
b) The rate of reaction is the same throughout the 4 minutes.
Q2 a)

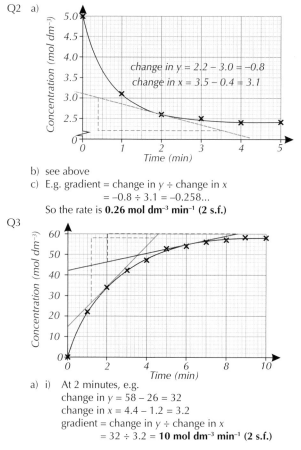

b) see above
c) E.g. gradient = change in y ÷ change in x
$$= -0.8 ÷ 3.1 = -0.258...$$
So the rate is **0.26 mol dm^{-3} min^{-1} (2 s.f.)**
Q3

a) i) At 2 minutes, e.g.
change in y = 58 − 26 = 32
change in x = 4.4 − 1.2 = 3.2
gradient = change in y ÷ change in x
$$= 32 ÷ 3.2 = \textbf{10 mol dm}^{-3}\textbf{ min}^{-1}\textbf{ (2 s.f.)}$$

ii) At 6 minutes, e.g.
change in y = 60 − 46 = 14
change in x = 8.6 − 2 = 6.6
gradient = change in y ÷ change in x
$$= 14 ÷ 6.6 = \textbf{2.1 mol dm}^{-3}\textbf{ min}^{-1}\textbf{ (2 s.f.)}$$
b) E.g. when the reaction is complete (after about 9 minutes), the student is correct in their statement. However, the rate of the reaction changes/decreases throughout the reaction so, before this point, the student is incorrect.

3. Rate Equations
Page 53 — Application Questions
Q1 a) No. You can't predict the orders of reactions, and therefore the rate equation, by looking at the balanced chemical equation. You can only work out reaction orders and the rate equation by carrying out experiments.
b) The student's rate equation shows that the reaction is second order with respect to iodide ions. Therefore, halving the concentration of iodide would cause the rate of reaction to be 4 times slower.
Q2 a) Rate = $k[H_2][NO]^2$
b) 3
c) If the concentration of NO were doubled the rate of the reaction would be four times faster.
d) Rate = $221 × (1.54 × 10^{-3}) × (1.54 × 10^{-3})^2$
$$= \textbf{8.07 × 10}^{-7}\textbf{ mol dm}^{-3}\textbf{ s}^{-1}\textbf{ (3 s.f.)}$$
Q3 a) Rate = $k[NO]^2[Cl_2]$
b) $5.85 × 10^{-6} = k(0.400)^2(0.400)$ so
$$k = \frac{5.85 × 10^{-6}}{[0.400]^2[0.400]} = 9.14 × 10^{-5}$$
units of $k = \dfrac{\text{mol dm}^{-3}\,\text{s}^{-1}}{(\text{mol dm}^{-3})^2(\text{mol dm}^{-3})} = \text{mol}^{-2}\,\text{dm}^6\,\text{s}^{-1}$

$k = \textbf{9.14 × 10}^{-5}\textbf{ mol}^{-2}\textbf{ dm}^6\textbf{ s}^{-1}$
When calculating k in exams, don't forget to work out the units as well.
c) If the temperature was increased the value of k would increase.
d) Rate = $k[NO]^2[Cl_2]$
Rate = $(9.14 × 10^{-5}) × 0.500^2 × 0.200$
$$= \textbf{4.57 × 10}^{-6}\textbf{ mol dm}^{-3}\textbf{ s}^{-1}$$

Page 53 — Fact Recall Questions
Q1 The rate equation tells you how the rate of a reaction is affected by the concentration of the reactants.
Q2 Rate = $k[A]^m[B]^n$
Q3 a) The rate constant.
b) The concentration of reactant Y.
c) The order of the reaction with respect to X.
Q4 Input all of the units for the different values into the rate equation. Cancel down as much as possible.

4. The Initial Rates Method
Page 57 — Application Questions
Q1 E.g.

Gradient = change in y ÷ change in x
$$= -0.44 \div 1.5 = -0.293...$$
So the rate is **0.29 mol dm⁻³ min⁻¹ (2 s.f.)**

Q2 Start by calculating the 1/reaction time for each trial number.

Trial no.	[I₂] / mol dm⁻³	[S₂O₃²⁻] / mol dm⁻³	Reaction time / s	1/time / s⁻¹
1	0.040	0.040	312	3.21×10^{-3}
2	0.080	0.040	156	6.41×10^{-3}
3	0.040	0.020	624	1.60×10^{-3}

$1/t$ can be used as a measure of the rate, so from the $1/t$ values, you can see that if the concentration of I_2 is doubled, the rate also doubles. If the concentration of $S_2O_3^{2-}$ is halved, then the rate also halves. Therefore the reaction must be first order with respect to both reactants.
Rate = $k[I_2][S_2O_3^{2-}]$

Q3 a) Looking at experiments 1 and 2: doubling [B] quadruples the rate so the reaction is order 2 with respect to [B]. Looking at experiments 2 and 3: tripling [C] triples the rate so the reaction is order 1 with respect to [C]. Looking at experiments 2 and 4: halving [A] halves the rate so the reaction is order 1 with respect to [A].
So, Rate = $k[A][B]^2[C]$
b) Rate = $k[A][B]^2[C]$ so k = rate ÷ $[A][B]^2[C]$
For experiment 1:
$k = 0.25 \div [(1.2) \times (1.2)^2 \times (1.2)] = 0.12$
units of k = mol dm⁻³ s⁻¹ ÷ [(mol dm⁻³) × (mol dm⁻³)² × (mol dm⁻³)]
$k = $ **0.12 mol⁻³ dm⁹ s⁻¹**

Page 57 — Fact Recall Questions
Q1 Take the gradient of the tangent to the curve, right at the start of the reaction/at time = 0.
Q2 E.g. set up a reaction where you are monitoring the loss of a reactant or the production of a product at the start of a reaction. Use this data to draw a concentration-time graph and calculate the initial rate of the reaction by working out the gradient at time = 0. Then, repeat the same experiment multiple times, but altering the concentration of one of the reactants each time. After each reaction, draw a concentration-time graph. Continue this until you have varied the concentration of each reactant in isolation. Compare the initial rates from each of your reactions to obtain information on how the initial rate varies with the concentration with respect to each reactant.
Q3 In a clock reaction, you measure the time take for a given amount of product to form. The shorter the time, the faster the initial rate.

5. Clock Reactions
Page 59 — Fact Recall Questions
Q1 In a clock reaction, you measure how the time taken for a set amount of product to form changes as you vary the concentration of one of the reactants.
Q2 You have to assume that the concentration of each reactant doesn't change significantly over the time period of your clock reaction, the temperature stays constant and that when the endpoint is seen, the reaction has not proceeded too far.
Q3 The solution turns from colourless to blue-black.

6. Rate-concentration Graphs
Page 61 — Application Questions
Q1 a) A = first order
B = zero order
C = second order
b) (i) If [A] was halved the rate of reaction would also halve.
(ii) If [B] was tripled the rate of reaction would stay the same.
(iii) If [C] was doubled, the reaction rate would increase by a factor of four (quadruple).
Q2 a)

If you're asked to draw or sketch a graph in your exam, make sure you label the axes — if you don't your graph could be showing anything and you won't get the marks.
b) If the concentration of O_2 was doubled the reaction rate would also double.

Pages 61 — Fact Recall Questions
Q1 Find the gradient at various points along the concentration-time graph. Plot rate of reaction against concentration to produce a rate-concentration graph.
Q2 0
Q3

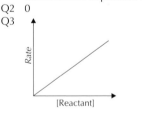

7. The Rate-determining Step
Page 63 — Application Questions
Q1 a) Step 1. The rate equation shows that the rate-determining step involves two molecules of NO_2, and there are two NO_2 molecules in step 1.
Don't forget — if it's in the rate equation it must be involved in the rate-determining step.
b) If the reaction had a one-step mechanism, that step would have to involve CO. CO is not in the rate equation so can't be involved in the rate-determining step. So a one-step mechanism isn't possible.
Q2 Rate = $k[A]^2[B][C]$

Page 63 — Fact Recall Questions

Q1 The rate-determining step is the slowest step in a reaction mechanism, so it's the step which determines the overall rate of the reaction.

Q2 2

8. The Arrhenius Equation
Page 68 — Application Questions

Q1 a) The rate constant of the uncatalysed reaction would be greater than that of the uncatalysed reaction. This is because introducing a catalyst decreases the activation energy of a reaction. Since the rate constant is proportional to $e^{-E_a/RT}$, decreasing the value of E_a makes the number that the exponent is raised to less negative. This increases the value of the exponent, and therefore increases the value of the rate constant.

b) Decreasing the temperature would decrease the rate constant of the reaction. Since the rate constant is proportional to $e^{-E_a/RT}$, decreasing the value of T makes the number that the exponent is raised to more negative. This decreases the value of the exponent, and therefore decreases the value of the rate constant.

Q2 a) $k = Ae^{\frac{-E_a}{RT}}$

$A = k \div e^{-E_a/RT}$
$= 1.10 \times 10^{-5} \div e^{-180\,000/(8.31 \times 600)}$
$= 1.10 \times 10^{-5} \div 2.09... \times 10^{-16}$
$= \mathbf{5.25 \times 10^{10}\ mol^{-1}\ dm^3\ s^{-1}\ (3\ s.f.)}$

b) $k = Ae^{\frac{-E_a}{RT}}$

$\ln(k) = \ln(A) - E_a/RT$
$\ln(k) - \ln(A) = -E_a/RT$
$E_a = (\ln(A) - \ln(k)) \times RT$
$E_a = (\ln(5.25 \times 10^{10}) - \ln(2.02 \times 10^{-5})) \times (8.31 \times 600)$
$= 176\,972...\ J\ mol^{-1} = \mathbf{177\ kJ\ mol^{-1}\ (3\ s.f.)}$

Q3 a)

$1/T$ / K^{-1}	$\ln k$
0.00180	−14.9
0.00159	−10.4
0.00150	−8.42
0.00143	−6.77
0.00127	−3.23

Plotting these values on a graph of $1/T$ vs $\ln k$ gives:

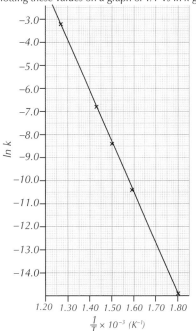

b) E.g. gradient $= -E_a/R$
gradient = change in y ÷ change in x
gradient $= [-14.5 - (-3.5)] \div$
$\qquad (1.78 \times 10^{-3} - 1.28 \times 10^{-3})$
gradient $= -11 \div (5.0 \times 10^{-4}) = -22\,000$
$-E_a/R = -22\,000$
$E_a = 22000 \times 8.31 = 182820\ J\ mol^{-1} = \mathbf{183\ kJ\ mol^{-1}}$

c) E.g. by substituting E_a and a data point for T and k into the equation $k = Ae^{-E_a/RT}$.
when $k = 3.50 \times 10^{-7}$ and $T = 555$,
$3.50 \times 10^{-7} = Ae^{(-182\,820 \div (8.31 \times 555))}$
$A = \mathbf{5.7 \times 10^{10}}$

Page 68 — Fact Recall Questions

Q1 $k = Ae^{\frac{-E_a}{RT}}$, where k = the rate constant, A = the Arrhenius constant, E_a = the activation energy, R = the gas constant and T = the temperature.

Q2 When the temperature of a reaction is increased, the rate increases.

Q3 $\ln k = -E_a/RT + \ln A$

Q4 $1/T$ and $\ln k$

9. Gas Equilibria
Page 72 — Application Questions

Q1 a) $2NH_{3\,(g)} + 1\tfrac{1}{2}O_{2(g)} \rightleftharpoons N_{2\,(g)} + 3H_2O_{(g)}$

b) total pressure $= p_{NH_3} + p_{O_2} + p_{N_2} + p_{H_2O}$

c) total pressure $= 42 + 85 + 21 + 12 = \mathbf{160\ kPa}$

d) partial pressure of a gas in a mixture
= mole fraction of gas × total pressure of the mixture
So mole fraction of $H_2O = 12 \div 160 = \mathbf{0.075}$

Q2 No. moles of He $= 4.00 \div 4 = 1.00$
No. moles of $O_2 = 2.81 \div (16 \times 2) = 0.0878...$
Total moles of gas $= 1.00 + 0.0878... = 1.0878...$
Mole fraction of $O_2 = 0.0878... \div 1.0878... = 0.0807...$
So partial pressure of $O_2 = 0.0807... \times 8.12$
$= \mathbf{0.655\ kPa\ (3\ s.f.)}$

Q3 a) $K_p = \dfrac{p_{C_6H_{12}}}{p_{C_6H_6} \times (p_{H_2})^3}$

b) Since the partial pressures of all three gases are equal,
$p_{C_6H_{12}} = p_{C_6H_6} = p_{H_2} = x$
$4.80 \times 10^{-13} = \dfrac{x}{x \times (x)^3} = 1/x^3$
$x^3 = 1 \div 4.80 \times 10^{-13}$
$x = \sqrt[3]{2.08... \times 10^{12}}$
$x = \textbf{12 800 kPa}$

Q4 a) $2HF \rightleftharpoons H_2 + F_2$
Equal amounts of H_2 and F_2 are produced, so if there are 9.34 mol of F_2 present at equilibrium, there are also 9.34 mol of H_2.
There are the same number of moles of gas on each side of the equation, so the total number of moles of gas at equilibrium must still be 24.32.
mole fraction of H_2 = 9.34 ÷ 24.32 = 0.384...
partial pressure of H_2 = 0.384... × 2313 = **888.3 kPa**

b) partial pressure of H_2 = partial pressure of F_2, so partial pressure of F_2 = 888.3 kPa.
$p_{HF} = 2313 - 888.3 - 888.3 = 536.4$ kPa
$K_p = \dfrac{p_{H_2} \times p_{F_2}}{(p_{HF})^2} = 888.3 \times 888.3 \div (536.4)^2 = \textbf{2.742}$ (no units)

Page 72 — Fact Recall Questions

Q1 The partial pressure of a gas is the pressure that an individual gas in a mixture exerts on a system.

Q2 mole fraction of a gas = number of moles of that gas ÷ total number of moles of gas in the mixture

Q3 $K_p = \dfrac{(p_D)^d (p_E)^e}{(p_A)^a (p_B)^b}$

10. Changing Gas Equilibria
Page 74 — Application Questions

Q1 The student is incorrect. Because there are the same number of moles of gas on both sides of the equation, this particular reaction would not be affected by changes in pressure.

Q2 a) There are two moles of reactants, and only one mole of product. Decreasing pressure would shift equilibrium to the side of the reaction where there are more moles of gas. Therefore, equilibrium would move to the left.

b) Since the forward reaction is exothermic, a decrease in temperature would favour the forward reaction. This would increase the moles of product present at equilibrium, and there would be comparatively fewer moles of reactant. This would increase the value of K_p.

Page 74 — Fact Recall Questions

Q1 Le Chatelier's principle states that if a reversible reaction at equilibrium is subjected to a change in temperature, pressure or concentration, then the equilibrium will shift to try and counteract the change.

Q2 Increasing the temperature of a reaction that is exothermic in the forward direction would shift equilibrium to the left. The endothermic reaction is favoured as it can absorb some of the extra heat.

Q3 K_p is not affected by changes in pressure.

Q4 Catalysts do not affect the position of equilibrium or K_p.

Exam-style Questions — pages 76-78

1 B *(1 mark)*

2 B *(1 mark)*

3 C *(1 mark)*

4 D *(1 mark)*

5.1 E.g. measure the change in pH / measure the volume of gas produced using a gas syringe *(1 mark)*.

5.2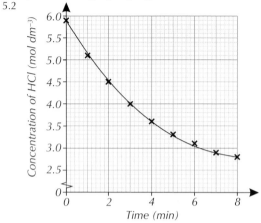

(4 marks in total — 1 mark for appropriate scale chosen on each axis, 1 mark for axes correctly labelled, 1 mark for points correctly plotted, 1 mark for correctly drawn line of best fit.)

5.3 At $t = 0$: E.g. gradient = change in y ÷ change in x
= (2.7 − 6.0) ÷ (3.6 − 0.0) *(1 mark)*
= −3.3 ÷ 3.6 = 0.916...
So rate is **0.92 mol dm⁻³ min⁻¹** *(1 mark)*

6.1 $k = Ae^{\frac{-E_a}{RT}}$
$\ln k = -E_a/RT + \ln A$
$\ln k = \ln A - E_a/RT$
$RT \times (\ln A - \ln k) = E_a$ *(1 mark)*
$(8.31 \times 600) \times (\ln (2.21) - \ln (1.28 \times 10^{-5})) = E_a$
$E_a = 60\ 126.46...$ J mol⁻¹ = **60.1 kJ mol⁻¹** *(1 mark)*

6.2 A catalyst decreases the activation energy of a reaction *(1 mark)*. The Arrhenius equation shows that the rate of reaction is proportional to e^{-E_a}, so as E_a decrease, the value of the exponential increases, therefore the rate constant increases *(1 mark)*.

6.3 First, you need to convert your values of T and k into $1/T$ and $\ln k$ values.

$1/T$ / K⁻¹	$\ln k$
3.50×10^{-3}	−9.50
3.40×10^{-3}	−8.50
3.34×10^{-3}	−7.90
3.19×10^{-3}	−6.50
3.11×10^{-3}	−5.65
2.99×10^{-3}	−4.50

(2 marks — 1 mark for correct values of 1/T, 1 mark for correct values of ln k)

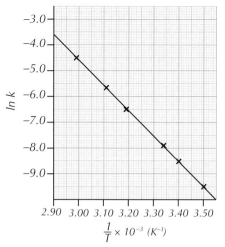

$\frac{1}{T} \times 10^{-3}\ (K^{-1})$

(2 marks — 1 mark for correct plot, 1 mark for correctly drawn line of best fit.)

e.g. gradient = $-E_a/R$ *(1 mark)*

gradient = change in y ÷ change in x

gradient = $[-8.5 - (-4.0)] \div (3.40 \times 10^{-3} - 2.94 \times 10^{-3})$

gradient = $-4.5 \div (4.6 \times 10^{-4})$

$-E_a/R = 9782.60...$

$E_a = 81\ 293.47...$ J mol^{-1} = **81.3 kJ mol^{-1}** *(1 mark)*

By substituting E_a and a data point for T and k into the Arrhenius equation, $k = Ae^{-E_a/RT}$.

When $k = 7.49 \times 10^{-5}$ and $T = 286$,

$7.49 \times 10^{-5} = Ae^{(-81\ 293.47... \div (8.31 \times 286)}$ *(1 mark)*

$A = $ **5.36 × 10^{10} mol dm^{-3} s^{-1}** *(1 mark)*

Remember, the units of A are the same as the units of k.

7.1 $K_p = (p_{NH_3})^2 \div [p_{N_2} \times (p_{H_2})^3]$ *(1 mark)*

$p_{N_2} = (p_{NH_3})^2 \div [K_p \times (p_{H_2})^3]$

$= 8920^2 \div (52.7 \times 19^3)$

$= $ **220 kPa** *(1 mark)*

7.2 The introduction of a catalyst would have no effect on K_p *(1 mark)*.

7.3 Increasing the temperature would shift the equilibrium position over to the left to favour the endothermic, reverse reaction and absorb the extra heat *(1 mark)*. This would decrease the value of K_p *(1 mark)* (as there would be more reactants and less product present in the reaction container).

8.1 The reaction is first order with respect to H_2 *(1 mark)* and second order with respect to NO *(1 mark)*.

Finding the reaction order with respect to NO is tricky. You know the reaction is first order with respect to H_2 from experiments 1 and 2, so if only $[H_2]$ changed from experiment 2 to 3 you would expect the rate of reaction to halve. But the rate of reaction is four times greater than this, so the reaction must be second order with respect to NO.

8.2 rate = $k[H_2][NO]^2$ *(1 mark)*

8.3 rate = $k[H_2][NO]^2$ so $k = $ rate ÷ $[H_2][NO]^2$

E.g. Using experiment 1:

$k = (4.5 \times 10^{-3}) \div (6 \times 10^{-3})(3 \times 10^{-3})^2 = 8.3 \times 10^4$

$k = $ mol dm^{-3} s^{-1} ÷ (mol dm^{-3})(mol dm^{-3})^2 = mol^{-2} dm^6 s^{-1}

$k = $ **8.3 × 10^4 mol^{-2} dm^6 s^{-1}**

(3 marks for correct answer, otherwise 1 mark for correct method and 1 mark for correct units.)

8.4 rate = $k[H_2][NO]^2$

$= (8.3 \times 10^4) \times (2.5 \times 10^{-3}) \times (4.5 \times 10^{-3})^2$

$= $ **4.2 × 10^{-3} mol dm^{-3} s^{-1}**

(1 mark for correct value, 1 mark for correct units — full marks if the method is correct but error carried forward from (c).)

8.5 The rate equation shows that the rate-determining step involves 2 molecules of NO and 1 molecule of H_2 *(1 mark)*. There are 2 molecules of H_2 in the overall equation so there must be another step involving another molecule of H_2 *(1 mark)*.

8.6 A possible mechanism for this reaction would be:

Step 1: $2NO + H_2 \rightarrow N_2O + H_2O$

Step 2: $N_2O + H_2 \rightarrow H_2O + N_2$

(1 mark for the left-hand side of step 1, 1 mark for rest of step 1 and step 2)

Other mechanisms are possible and will gain credit as long as:

The reactants in the first equation are 2NO and H_2.

The steps add together to give the overall reaction.

Both equations are balanced.

Section 9 — Electrode Potentials and Cells

1. Electrode Potentials

Page 83 — Application Questions

Q1 a) (i) $Ag^+_{(aq)} + e^- \rightarrow Ag_{(s)}$

(ii) $Ca_{(s)} \rightarrow Ca^{2+}_{(aq)} + 2e^-$

b) $Ca_{(s)} \mid Ca^{2+}_{(aq)} \parallel Ag^+_{(aq)} \mid Ag_{(s)}$

c) $E_{cell} = E_{RHS} - E_{LHS} = 0.80 - (-2.87) = $ **+3.67 V**

Q2 a) At the positive electrode: $Tl^{3+}_{(aq)} + 2e^- \rightarrow Tl^+_{(aq)}$

At the negative electrode: $Fe^{2+}_{(aq)} \rightarrow Fe^{3+}_{(aq)} + e^-$

b) $E_{RHS} = E_{cell} + E_{LHS} = 0.48 + 0.77 = $ **+1.25 V**

Q3 a) The Mg^{2+}/Mg half-cell.

b) $Mg_{(s)} \mid Mg^{2+}_{(aq)} \parallel Fe^{3+}_{(aq)}, Fe^{2+}_{(aq)} \mid Pt$

Page 83 — Fact Recall Questions

Q1 a) platinum

b) Platinum is inert, so it won't react with the solution, but it's a solid that conducts electricity.

Q2 reduction

Q3 Any two from, e.g.: the half-cell with the more negative potential goes on the left / the oxidised forms go in the centre of the cell diagram / the reduced forms go at the edge of the cell diagram / double vertical lines are used to show a salt bridge / things in different phases are separated by a vertical line / things in the same phase are separated by a comma.

Any two facts about how to draw a cell diagram will do here — just flick back to page 81 if you need a quick reminder.

2. Standard Electrode Potentials

Page 85 — Application Question

Q1 a) $Pt \mid H_{2(g)} \mid H^+_{(aq)} \parallel Pb^{2+}_{(aq)} \mid Pb_{(s)}$

b) −0.13 V

c) oxidation

The electrode potential of the standard hydrogen electrode is 0.00 V, so the Pb^{2+}/Pb half-cell has the more negative electrode potential and oxidation occurs in this half-cell.

Page 85 — Fact Recall Questions

Q1 E.g. temperature, pressure and concentrations of reactants.

Q2 Hydrogen gas is bubbled into a solution of aqueous H^+ ions. The electrode is made of platinum. The standard conditions used are a temperature of 298 K (25 °C), a pressure of 100 kPa and all solutions of ions have a concentration of 1.00 mol dm^{-3}.

Q3 a) 0.00 V
   b) It's zero by definition (scientists decided it would have that value).

Q4 The voltage measured under standard conditions when a half-cell is connected to a standard hydrogen electrode.

3. Electrochemical Series

Page 89 — Application Questions

Q1 a) Aluminium — they are both metals and aluminium has the more negative standard electrode potential.
   b) Chlorine — they are both non-metals and chlorine has the more positive standard electrode potential.
   c) Copper — they are both metals and copper has the more negative (least positive) standard electrode potential.
   Although the electrode potential for copper is positive, it is still more negative than that for silver, so copper is more reactive.

Q2 a) $E^{\ominus}_{cell} = E^{\ominus}_{reduced} - E^{\ominus}_{oxidised} = 0.80 - (-1.66) = $ **+2.46 V**
   b) $E^{\ominus}_{cell} = E^{\ominus}_{reduced} - E^{\ominus}_{oxidised} = 1.36 - 0.34 = $ **+1.02 V**

Q3 a) $Mg^{2+}_{(aq)} + 2e^- \rightarrow Mg_{(s)}$ $E^{\ominus} = -2.38$ V
   $Ni^{2+}_{(aq)} + 2e^- \rightarrow Ni_{(s)}$ $E^{\ominus} = -0.25$ V
   The electrode potential of the magnesium half-cell is more negative than the nickel half-cell, so $Mg_{(s)}$ will be oxidised by $Ni^{2+}_{(aq)}$.
   So the full reaction is: $Mg_{(s)} + Ni^{2+}_{(aq)} \rightarrow Mg^{2+}_{(aq)} + Ni_{(s)}$

   b) $Fe^{3+}_{(aq)} + e^- \rightarrow Fe^{2+}_{(aq)}$ $E^{\ominus} = +0.77$ V
   $Br_{2(aq)} + 2e^- \rightarrow 2Br^-_{(aq)}$ $E^{\ominus} = +1.07$ V
   The electrode potential of the iron half-cell is more negative than the bromine half-cell, so $Br_{2(aq)}$ will be oxidised by $Fe^{2+}_{(aq)}$.
   So the full reaction is: $2Fe^{2+}_{(aq)} + Br_{2(aq)} \rightarrow 2Fe^{3+}_{(aq)} + 2Br^-_{(aq)}$
   Don't forget to balance the charges when you combine redox equations — that's why you need 2Fe^{2+} ions here.

Q4 a) $Sn^{4+}_{(aq)} + 2e^- \rightarrow Sn^{2+}_{(aq)}$ $E^{\ominus} = +0.15$ V
   $Cu^{2+}_{(aq)} + 2e^- \rightarrow Cu_{(s)}$ $E^{\ominus} = +0.34$ V
   So if Cu^{2+} is reduced by Sn^{2+},
   $E^{\ominus}_{cell} = E^{\ominus}_{reduced} - E^{\ominus}_{oxidised} = 0.34 - 0.15 = +0.19$ V
   $E^{\ominus}_{cell}$ is positive, so the reaction is feasible.

   b) $Sn^{4+}_{(aq)} + 2e^- \rightarrow Sn^{2+}_{(aq)}$ $E^{\ominus} = +0.15$ V
   $Zn^{2+}_{(aq)} + 2e^- \rightarrow Zn_{(s)}$ $E^{\ominus} = -0.76$ V
   So if Zn^{2+} is reduced by Sn^{2+},
   $E^{\ominus}_{cell} = E^{\ominus}_{reduced} - E^{\ominus}_{oxidised} = -0.76 - 0.15 = -0.91$ V
   $E^{\ominus}_{cell}$ is negative, so the reaction is not feasible.

Q5 The proposed reaction is $Sn^{2+}_{(aq)} + 2Ag^+_{(aq)} \rightarrow Sn^{4+}_{(aq)} + 2Ag_{(s)}$
   $Sn^{4+}_{(aq)} + 2e^- \rightarrow Sn^{2+}_{(aq)}$ $E^{\ominus} = +0.15$
   $Ag^+_{(aq)} + e^- \rightarrow Ag_{(s)}$ $E^{\ominus} = +0.80$
   So if Ag^+ is reduced by Sn^{2+},
   $E^{\ominus}_{cell} = E^{\ominus}_{reduced} - E^{\ominus}_{oxidised} = 0.80 - 0.15 = +0.65$ V
   $E^{\ominus}_{cell}$ is positive, so the reaction is feasible, so Sn^{2+} ions will react with Ag^+ ions in solution.

Page 89 — Fact Recall Questions

Q1 A list of electrode potentials for different electrochemical half-cells, written in order from the most negative to the most positive.

Q2 In the direction of reduction.

Q3 reduction

Q4 a) Very negative.
   b) Very positive.

4. Electrochemical Cells

Page 92 — Application Questions

Q1 a) $E^{\ominus}_{cell} = (E^{\ominus}_{R.H.S.} - E^{\ominus}_{L.H.S}) = 0.52 - (-0.88) = $ **+1.40 V**
   b) $2NiO(OH)_{(s)} + Cd_{(s)} + 2H_2O_{(l)} \rightarrow 2Ni(OH)_{2(s)} + Cd(OH)_{2(s)}$
   Don't forget, you need to cancel out the OH$^-$ ions.

Q2 a) $2H_{2(g)} + O_{2(g)} \rightarrow 2H_2O_{(l)}$
   b) $Pt \mid H_{2(g)} \mid OH^-_{(aq)}, H_2O_{(l)} \parallel O_{2(g)} \mid H_2O_{(l)}, OH^-_{(aq)} \mid Pt$

Page 92 — Fact Recall Questions

Q1 You can recharge a rechargeable battery because the reaction that occurs within it can be reversed if a current is supplied to force the electrons to flow in the opposite direction around the circuit.

Q2 There are two platinum electrodes separated by anion exchange membranes. Oxygen is fed into the negative electrode, where it reacts with water and electrons to produce OH$^-$ anions. The OH$^-$ anions can cross the anion exchange membrane and travel through the electrolyte to the positive electrode. Hydrogen is fed into the positive electrode where it reacts with the OH$^-$ anions to produce water and electrons. The electrons travel round the external circuit, towards the negative electrode, generating electricity.

Q3 You need energy to produce the supply of hydrogen. This is normally generated by burning fossil fuels.

Q4 Advantages: E.g. they don't need electrically recharging / the only waste product is water / they don't produce CO_2 emissions / they are more efficient than the internal combustion engine.
   Disadvantages: E.g. they are not usually carbon neutral / hydrogen is highly flammable so needs to be handled carefully.

Exam-style Questions — pages 94-96

1.1 Oxidation: $Mg_{(s)} \rightarrow Mg^{2+}_{(aq)} + 2e^-$ *(1 mark)*
   Reduction: $Fe^{3+}_{(aq)} + e^- \rightarrow Fe^{2+}_{(aq)}$ *(1 mark)*

1.2 $Mg_{(s)} \mid Mg^{2+}_{(aq)} \parallel Fe^{3+}_{(aq)}, Fe^{2+}_{(aq)} \mid Pt$
   (1 mark for left-hand side correct,
   1 mark for right-hand side correct)
   Don't forget to include the platinum electrode...

1.3 $E_{cell} = E_{RHS} - E_{LHS} = 0.77 - (-2.38) = $ **+3.15 V** *(1 mark)*

1.4 $E^{\ominus}$ for Sn^{4+}/Sn^{2+} is more negative than $E^{\ominus}$ for VO_2^+/VO^{2+}, so Sn^{2+} ions will reduce VO_2^+ ions *(1 mark)*
   $2VO_2^+_{(aq)} + Sn^{2+}_{(aq)} + 4H^+_{(aq)} \rightarrow 2VO^{2+}_{(aq)} + Sn^{4+}_{(aq)} + 2H_2O_{(l)}$
   (1 mark)
   $E^{\ominus}$ for Sn^{4+}/Sn^{2+} is more negative than $E^{\ominus}$ for VO^{2+}/V^{3+}, so Sn^{2+} ions will reduce VO^{2+} ions created in the previous reaction *(1 mark)*.
   $2VO^{2+}_{(aq)} + Sn^{2+}_{(aq)} + 4H^+_{(aq)} \rightarrow 2V^{3+}_{(aq)} + Sn^{4+}_{(aq)} + 2H_2O_{(l)}$
   (1 mark)
   The V^{3+} ions made in this reaction don't react with the Sn^{2+} ions because the electrode potential for V^{3+}/V^{2+} is more negative than that for Sn^{4+}/Sn^{2+}.

1.5 A temperature of 298 K. A pressure of 100 kPa. Any solutions of ions have a concentration of 1.00 mol dm^{-3} **(1 mark)**.

1.6 It is zero by definition/scientists decided it would be that value **(1 mark)**.

1.7 Platinum conducts electricity and is inert (so it doesn't react with the ions formed) **(1 mark)**.

1.8 +0.80 V **(1 mark)**

1.9 Silver is less reactive than vanadium **(1 mark)** because it has a less negative electrode potential **(1 mark)**.

2.1 $CoO_{2(s)} + Li_{(s)} \rightleftharpoons Li^+[CoO_2]^-_{(s)}$ **(1 mark)**

2.2 The reactions that occur within them can be reversed if a current is supplied to force the electrons to flow in the opposite direction around the circuit **(1 mark)**.

2.3 It is cheaper **(1 mark)** and it provides a larger surface area so the reaction goes faster **(1 mark)**.

2.4 Any two from, e.g.: they're more efficient / they don't need to be electrically recharged / the only waste product is water / they don't produce CO_2 emissions **(1 mark for each, up to a maximum of 2 marks)**.

3 B **(1 mark)**
Aluminium is above zinc in the electrochemical series so the Al^{3+}/Al half-reaction has a more negative electrode potential than Zn^{2+}/Zn half-reaction. So $Al^{3+}_{(aq)}$ cannot oxidise $Zn_{(s)}$.

4.1 $Tl^{3+}_{(aq)} + 3e^- \rightleftharpoons Tl_{(s)}$ **(1 mark)**

4.2 $E_{RHS} = E_{LHS} + E_{cell} = 0.15 + 0.57 = $ **+0.72 V (1 mark)**

4.3 $Pt \mid H_{2(g)} \mid H^+_{(aq)} \parallel Tl^{3+}_{(aq)} \mid Tl_{(s)}$ **(1 mark)**

Section 10 — Acids, Bases and pH

1. Acids, Bases and K_w
Page 98 — Fact Recall Questions
Q1 a) Brønsted-Lowry acids are proton donors.
   b) Brønsted-Lowry bases are proton acceptors.
Q2 a) $HA_{(aq)} + H_2O_{(l)} \rightarrow H_3O^+_{(aq)} + A^-_{(aq)}$
   (or $HA_{(aq)} \rightarrow H^+_{(aq)} + A^-_{(aq)}$)
   b) $B_{(aq)} + H_2O_{(l)} \rightarrow BH^+_{(aq)} + OH^-_{(aq)}$
   c) $HA_{(aq)} + B_{(aq)} \rightleftharpoons BH^+_{(aq)} + A^-_{(aq)}$
   When you're writing equations for reversible reactions don't forget to use the funky double arrows. If you just draw a normal arrow it won't be correct.
Q3 $H_2O_{(l)} \rightleftharpoons H^+_{(aq)} + OH^-_{(aq)}$
Q4 a) K_w is a constant called the ionic product of water.
   b) $K_w = [H^+][OH^-]$
   c) mol^2 dm^{-6}
   d) In pure water there is always one H^+ ion per OH^- ion so $[H^+]=[OH^-]$ and $[H^+][OH^-]$ is the same as $[H^+]^2$.

2. pH Calculations
Page 99 — Application Questions
Q1 pH = $-\log[H^+] = -\log[0.050] = $ **1.30**
Q2 $[H^+] = 10^{-pH} = 10^{-2.86} = $ **1.4 × 10^{-3} mol dm^{-3}**
Q3 pH = $-\log[H^+] = -\log[0.020] = $ **1.70**

Page 101 — Application Questions
Q1 HCl is monoprotic so $[H^+] = [HCl] = 0.080$ mol dm^{-3}
   pH = $-\log[H^+] = -\log[0.080] = $ **1.1**
Q2 H_2SO_4 is diprotic so $[H^+] = 2[H_2SO_4] = 2 \times 0.025$
   $= 0.050$ mol dm^{-3}
   pH= $-\log[H^+] = -\log[0.050] = $ **1.3**

Q3 KOH is a strong base so $[OH^-] = [KOH] = 0.200$ mol dm^{-3}
   $K_w = [H^+][OH^-]$ so $[H^+] = K_w \div [OH^-]$
   $= (5.48 \times 10^{-14}) \div 0.200 = 2.74 \times 10^{-13}$
   pH = $-\log[H^+] = -\log[2.74 \times 10^{-13}] = $ **12.562**

Page 101 — Fact Recall Questions
Q1 pH = $-\log_{10}[H^+]$
Q2 Monoprotic means that each molecule of acid releases one proton. Diprotic means that each molecule of acid releases two protons.

3. The Acid Dissociation Constant
Page 105 — Application Questions
Q1 a) $K_a = [H^+][CN^-] \div [HCN]$
   You can use $[H^+]^2$ in your calculations, but not as the expression for K_a — this isn't correct, so you wouldn't get the marks for it.
   b) $K_a = [H^+]^2 \div [HCN]$ so $[H^+]^2 = K_a \times [HCN]$
   $= (4.9 \times 10^{-10}) \times 2.0 = 9.8 \times 10^{-10}$
   $[H^+] = \sqrt{9.8 \times 10^{-10}} = 3.13 \times 10^{-5}$ mol dm^{-3}
   pH = $-\log[H^+] = -\log[3.13 \times 10^{-5}] = $ **4.504**
Q2 $[H^+] = 10^{-pH} = 10^{-3.8} = 1.584... \times 10^{-4}$ mol dm^{-3}
   $K_a = [H^+]^2 \div [HNO_2]$ so $[HNO_2] = [H^+]^2 \div K_a$
   $= (1.584... \times 10^{-4})^2 \div 4.0 \times 10^{-4} = $ **6.28 × 10^{-5} mol dm^{-3}**
Q3 $K_a = [H^+]^2 \div [HA]$ so $[H^+]^2 = K_a \times [HA]$
   $= (1.38 \times 10^{-4}) \times 0.48 = 6.624 \times 10^{-5}$
   $[H^+] = \sqrt{6.624 \times 10^{-5}} = 8.14 \times 10^{-3}$ mol dm^{-3}
   pH = $-\log[8.14 \times 10^{-3}] = $ **2.09**
Q4 $[H^+] = 10^{-pH} = 10^{-4.11} = 7.76 \times 10^{-5}$ mol dm^{-3}
   $K_a = [H^+]^2 \div [HA] = (7.76 \times 10^{-5})^2 \div 0.28$
   $= $ **2.15 × 10^{-8} mol dm^{-3}**
Q5 $[H^+] = 10^{-pH} = 10^{-3.67} = 2.14 \times 10^{-4}$ mol dm^{-3}
   $K_a = [H^+]^2 \div [HCOOH]$ so $[HCOOH] = [H^+]^2 \div K_a$
   $= (2.14 \times 10^{-4})^2 \div (1.8 \times 10^{-4}) = $ **2.54 × 10^{-4} mol dm^{-3}**
Q6 a) $K_a = 10^{-pK_a} = 10^{-4.78} = $ **1.7 × 10^{-5} mol dm^{-3}**
   b) $K_a = [H^+]^2 \div [CH_3COOH]$ so
   $[H^+]^2 = K_a \times [CH_3COOH] = (1.7 \times 10^{-5}) \times 0.25$
   $= 4.25 \times 10^{-6}$ mol^2 dm^{-6}
   $[H^+] = \sqrt{4.25 \times 10^{-6}} = 2.06 \times 10^{-3}$ mol dm^{-3}
   pH = $-\log[H^+] = -\log[2.06 \times 10^{-3}] = $ **2.69**
Q7 $[H^+] = 10^{-pH} = 10^{-4.5} = 3.16 \times 10^{-5}$ mol dm^{-3}
   $K_a = [H^+]^2 \div [HA] = (3.16 \times 10^{-5})^2 \div 0.154$
   $= 6.49 \times 10^{-9}$ mol dm^{-3}
   $pK_a = -\log(K_a) = -\log(6.49 \times 10^{-9}) = $ **8.188**
Q8 $K_a = 10^{-pK_a} = 10^{-3.14} = 7.24 \times 10^{-4}$ mol dm^{-3}
   $[H^+] = 10^{-pH} = 10^{-3.2} = 6.31 \times 10^{-4}$ mol dm^{-3}
   $K_a = [H^+]^2 \div [HF]$ so $[HF] = [H^+]^2 \div K_a$
   $= (6.31 \times 10^{-4})^2 \div 7.24 \times 10^{-4} = $ **5.50 × 10^{-4} mol dm^{-3}**
Q9 $K_a = 10^{-pK_a} = 10^{-4.5} = 3.16 \times 10^{-5}$ mol dm^{-3}
   $K_a = [H^+]^2 \div [HX]$ so $[H^+]^2 = K_a \times [HX]$
   $= (3.16 \times 10^{-5}) \times 0.6 = 1.90 \times 10^{-5}$ mol^2 dm^{-6}
   so $[H^+] = \sqrt{1.9 \times 10^{-5}} = 4.36 \times 10^{-3}$ mol dm^{-3}
   pH = $-\log[H^+] = -\log[4.36 \times 10^{-3}] = $ **2.36**

Page 105 — Fact Recall Questions
Q1 mol dm^{-3}
Q2 a) $K_a = [H^+][A^-] \div [HA]$
   b) $K_a = [H^+]^2 \div [HA]$
   c) $[HA] = [H^+]^2 \div K_a$
Q3 E.g. Calculating the pH of a weak acid and calculating the concentration of a weak acid.

Q4 a) $pK_a = -\log_{10}(K_a)$

    b) $K_a = 10^{-pK_a}$

4. Titrations and pH Curves
Page 109 — Application Questions
Q1 a) Strong base/weak acid, phenolphthalein
    b) Strong acid/weak base, methyl orange
    c) Strong acid/strong base, phenolphthalein/cresol purple/ litmus
    d) Weak base/strong acid, methyl orange

Q2 Any curve with the vertical section covering pH 6.8 and pH 8.0. E.g.

You could also have drawn a curve showing an acid being added to a base.

Page 109 — Fact Recall Questions
Q1 a)

If the question says that a strong acid neutralises a strong base, the base is being neutralised so it's the acid that's added.

Q2 a) In most titrations, at the end point a tiny amount of acid/ base causes a sudden big change in pH and the base/ acid is just neutralised. But in weak acid/weak base titrations, the change in pH is more gradual, and the end point is when the base/acid is just neutralised.
    b) The pH indicator changes colour/the pH meter shows a sudden big change/the pH meter shows a reading of 7.
    c) In most titrations, the pH curve becomes close to vertical. In weak acid/weak base titrations, the end point is at the point on pH curve where pH = 7.

Q3 For an indicator to be suitable it must change colour over a narrow pH range that lies entirely within the vertical part of the pH curve for the titration.

5. Titration Calculations
Pages 112-113 — Application Questions
Q1 Moles HCl = (conc. × volume) ÷ 1000
= (1.5 × 13.8) ÷ 1000 = 0.0207 moles.
HCl + NaOH → NaCl + H_2O so 1 mole of HCl neutralises 1 mole of NaOH and 0.0207 moles of HCl must neutralise 0.0207 moles of NaOH.
Conc. NaOH = (moles × 1000) ÷ volume
= (0.0207 × 1000) ÷ 20 = **1.04 mol dm^{-3}**

Q2 Moles NaOH = (conc. × volume) ÷ 1000
= (0.25 × 30) ÷ 1000 = 7.5 × 10^{-3} moles.
HNO_3 + NaOH → $NaNO_3$ + H_2O so 1 mole of NaOH neutralises 1 mole of HCl and 7.5 ×10^{-3} moles of NaOH must neutralise 7.5 × 10^{-3} moles of HCl.
Conc. HNO_3 = (moles × 1000) ÷ volume
= (7.5 × 10^{-3} × 1000) ÷ 17.8 = **0.421 mol dm^{-3}**

Q3 a) average = (22.4 + 22.5 + 22.4) ÷ 3
= 67.3 ÷ 3 = **22.4 cm^3**
    b) Moles KOH = (conc. × volume) ÷ 1000
= (0.25 × 22.4) ÷ 1000 = 5.6 × 10^{-3} moles.
HCl + KOH → KCl + H_2O so 1 mole of KOH neutralises 1 mole of HCl and 5.6 × 10^{-3} moles of KOH must neutralise 5.6 × 10^{-3} moles of HCl.
Conc. HCl = (moles × 1000) ÷ volume
= (5.6 × 10^{-3} × 1000) ÷ 24 = **0.233 mol dm^{-3}**

Q4 From the graph, the volume of HCl required to neutralise the NaOH solution was 27.5 cm^3
Allow any answer between 27 cm^3 and 28 cm^3. This is the volume of HCl at the equivalence point.
Moles HCl = (conc. × volume) ÷ 1000
= (0.85 × 27.5) ÷ 1000 = 0.0234 moles.
HCl + NaOH → NaCl + H_2O so 1 mole of HCl neutralises 1 mole of NaOH and 0.0234 moles of HCl must neutralise 0.0234 moles of NaOH.
Conc. NaOH = (moles × 1000) ÷ volume
= (0.0234 × 1000) ÷ 30 = **0.780 mol dm^{-3}**
Allow any answer between 0.77 mol dm^{-3} and 0.79 mol dm^{-3}, depending on the value from reading the graph.

Q5 Moles H_2SO_4 = (conc. × volume) ÷ 1000
= (0.4 × 18) ÷ 1000 = 7.2 × 10^{-3} moles.
H_2SO_4 + 2KOH → K_2SO_4 + $2H_2O$ so 1 mole of H_2SO_4 neutralises 2 moles of KOH and 7.2 × 10^{-3} moles of H_2SO_4 must neutralise (7.2 × 10^{-3}) × 2 = 0.0144 moles of KOH.
Conc. KOH = (moles × 1000) ÷ volume
= (0.0144 × 1000) ÷ 32 = **0.450 mol dm^{-3}**

Q6 Moles KOH = (conc. × volume) ÷ 1000
= (1.2 × 26.2) ÷ 1000 = 0.0314 moles.
H_2CO_3 + 2KOH → K_2CO_3 + $2H_2O$ so 2 moles of KOH neutralises 1 mole of H_2CO_3 and 0.03144 moles of KOH must neutralise 0.03144 ÷ 2 = 0.01572 moles of H_2CO_3.
Conc. H_2CO_3 = (moles × 1000) ÷ volume
= (0.01572 × 1000) ÷ 20 = **0.786 mol dm^{-3}**

Page 113 — Fact Recall Questions
Q1 moles = (concentration × volume) ÷ 1000 if the units are cm^3 or moles = concentration × volume if the units are dm^3.

Q2

Q3   Diprotic acids release two protons when they react with a base. So, the pH curve for a diprotic acid has two equivalence points (one corresponding to the loss of the first proton and one corresponding to the loss of the second proton). Monoprotic acids only release one proton so pH curves for monoprotic acids only have one equivalence point.

Q4   0.5 moles

6. Buffer Action
Page 116 — Fact Recall Questions

Q1   A buffer is a solution that resists changes in pH when small amounts of acid or alkali are added.

Q2   Acidic buffers contain a weak acid with one of its salts.

Q3   a) When acid is added $[H^+]$ increases. Most of the extra H^+ ions combine with A^- ions to form HA. This shifts the equilibrium to the left so $[H^+]$ is reduced to close to its original value and the pH doesn't change much.

     b) When a base is added $[OH^-]$ increases. Most of the extra OH^- ions react with H^+ ions to form water. This removes H^+ ions from the solution so the equilibrium shifts to the right to compensate by more HA dissociating. So more H^+ ions are formed and the pH doesn't change much.

Q4   Basic buffers contain a weak base with one of its salts.

Q5   a) When acid is added the H^+ concentration increases. These H^+ ions react with OH^- ions so $[OH^-]$ goes down. The equilibrium then shifts to the right to replace the lost OH^- ions, so the pH doesn't change much.

     b) When a base is added, the OH^- concentration increases. These OH^- ions react with the salt to form more base and H_2O. So, the equilibrium shifts to the left to remove the excess OH^- ions in the solution and the pH doesn't change much.

Q6   Any two from, e.g. in shampoo/in biological washing powders/in biological systems (such as blood).

7. Calculating the pH of Buffers
Page 119 — Application Questions

Q1   a) $CH_3CH_2COOH \rightleftharpoons H^+ + CH_3CH_2COO^-$ so
$$K_a = \frac{[H^+][CH_3CH_2COO^-]}{[CH_3CH_2COOH]}$$

     b) $K_a = [H^+][CH_3CH_2COO^-] \div [CH_3CH_2COOH]$ so
$[H^+] = (K_a \times [CH_3CH_2COOH]) \div [CH_3CH_2COO^-]$
$= ((1.35 \times 10^{-5}) \times 0.2) \div 0.35 = \mathbf{7.7 \times 10^{-6} \ mol \ dm^{-3}}$

     c) $pH = -\log[H^+] = -\log(7.7 \times 10^{-6}) = \mathbf{5.11}$

Q2 $CH_3COOH \rightleftharpoons H^+ + CH_3COO^-$ so
$K_a = [H^+][CH_3COO^-] \div [CH_3COOH]$ so
$[H^+] = (K_a \times [CH_3COOH]) \div [CH_3COO^-]$
$= ((1.74 \times 10^{-5}) \times 0.15) \div 0.25 = 1.04 \times 10^{-5} \ mol \ dm^{-3}$
$pH = -\log[H^+] = -\log(1.04 \times 10^{-5}) = \mathbf{4.98}$

Q3   a) $CH_3CH_2COOH + KOH \rightarrow$
$CH_3CH_2COO^-K^+ + H_2O$

     b) initial moles CH_3CH_2COOH = (conc. × vol.) ÷ 1000
$= (0.500 \times 30) \div 1000 = \mathbf{0.0150 \ moles}$.
initial moles KOH = (conc. × vol.) ÷ 1000
$= (0.250 \times 20) \div 1000 = \mathbf{5.00 \times 10^{-3} \ moles}$.

     c) From the equation, moles salt = moles base = 5.00×10^{-3} moles. Also, 1 mole of base neutralises 1 mole of acid so 5.00×10^{-3} moles of base neutralises 5.00×10^{-3} moles of acid. So $0.0150 - (0.500 \times 10^{-3}) = 0.0100$ moles of acid remain.
Total volume = 30.0 + 20.0 = 50.0 cm³
conc. acid in buffer = (moles × 1000) ÷ vol.
$= (0.0100 \times 1000) \div 50.0 = \mathbf{0.200 \ mol \ dm^{-3}}$
conc. salt in buffer = (moles × 1000) ÷ vol.
$= ((5.00 \times 10^{-3}) \times 1000) \div 50.0 = \mathbf{0.100 \ mol \ dm^{-3}}$

     d) $K_a = [H^+][CH_3CH_2COO^-] \div [CH_3CH_2COOH]$ so
$[H^+] = (K_a \times [CH_3CH_2COOH]) \div [CH_3CH_2COO^-]$
$= ((1.35 \times 10^{-5}) \times 0.200) \div 0.100$
$= \mathbf{2.70 \times 10^{-5} \ mol \ dm^{-3}}$

     e) $pH = -\log[H^+] = -\log(2.70 \times 10^{-5}) = \mathbf{4.569}$

Q4   initial moles HCOOH = (conc. × vol.) ÷ 1000
$= (0.2 \times 25) \div 1000 = 5 \times 10^{-3}$ moles.
initial moles NaOH = (conc. × vol.) ÷ 1000
$= (0.1 \times 15) \div 1000 = 1.5 \times 10^{-3}$ moles.
$HCOOH + NaOH \rightarrow HCOO^-Na^+ + H_2O$ so moles salt = moles base = 1.5×10^{-3} moles. Also, 1 mole of base neutralises 1 mole of acid and 1.5×10^{-3} moles of base neutralises 1.5×10^{-3} moles of acid.
So $(5 \times 10^{-3}) - (1.5 \times 10^{-3}) = 3.5 \times 10^{-3}$ moles of acid remain.
Total volume = 15 + 25 = 40 cm³
final conc. acid = (moles × 1000) ÷ vol.
$= ((3.5 \times 10^{-3}) \times 1000) \div 40 = 0.0875 \ mol \ dm^{-3}$
final conc. salt = (moles × 1000) ÷ vol.
$= ((1.5 \times 10^{-3}) \times 1000) \div 40 = 0.0375 \ mol \ dm^{-3}$
$K_a = [H^+][HCOO^-] \div [HCOOH]$ so
$[H^+] = (K_a \times [HCOOH]) \div [HCOO^-]$
$= ((1.6 \times 10^{-4}) \times 0.0875) \div 0.0375$
$= 3.73 \times 10^{-4} \ mol \ dm^{-3}$
$pH = -\log[H^+] = -\log(3.73 \times 10^{-4}) = \mathbf{3.43}$

Pages 121-123 — Exam-style Questions

1   A *(1 mark)*
$K_w = [H^+][OH^-]$, so $[H^+] = K_w \div [OH^-] = 1.00 \times 10^{-14} \div 0.20$
$= 5.0 \times 10^{-14}$.
$pH = -\log[H^+] = -\log(5.0 \times 10^{-14}) = 13.30$.

2   A *(1 mark)*
Ammonia is a weak base, so the graph starts off at around pH 9. It gets titrated with nitric acid, a strong acid, so it has a steep curve that ends at around pH 1.

3   C *(1 mark)*
A titration of a diprotic acid would benefit from using an indicator with two colour changes. The only option that's diprotic is ethanedioic acid.

4.1 $K_w = [H^+][OH^-]$ *(1 mark)*

4.2 $pH = -\log[H^+]$ *(1 mark)*

4.3   NaOH is a strong base so
$[OH^-] = [NaOH] = 0.15 \ mol \ dm^{-3}$
$K_w = [H^+][OH^-]$ so $[H^+] = K_w \div [OH^-]$
$= 1 \times 10^{-14} \div 0.15 = 6.67 \times 10^{-14} \ mol \ dm^{-3}$
$pH = -\log[H^+] = -\log[6.67 \times 10^{-14}] = \mathbf{13.18}$
(3 marks for correct answer, otherwise 1 mark for $[OH^-]$ = 0.15 and 1 mark for $[H^+]$ = 6.67×10^{-4}.)

4.4   B *(1 mark)*
This titration was a strong acid against a strong base so the curve should start at around pH 14 and fall to around pH 1.

4.5 Moles NaOH = (conc. × volume) ÷ 1000
= (0.15 × 25) ÷ 1000 = 3.75 × 10^{-3} moles.
HCl + NaOH → NaCl + H$_2$O so 1 mole of NaOH
neutralises 1 mole of HCl and
3.75 × 10^{-3} moles of NaOH must neutralise 3.75 × 10^{-3}
moles of HCl.
Conc. HCl = (moles × 1000) ÷ volume
= ((3.75 × 10^{-3}) × 1000) ÷ 18.5 = **0.20 mol dm^{-3}**
(3 marks for correct answer, otherwise
1 mark for moles NaOH = 3.75 × 10^{-3} and
1 mark for moles HCl = 3.75 × 10^{-3}.)

4.6 HCl is a strong acid and fully dissociates so
[H$^+$] = [HCl] = 0.20 mol dm^{-3}
pH = −log[H$^+$] = −log(0.2) = **0.70**
(2 marks for correct answer, otherwise 1 mark for [H$^+$] =
0.20 mol dm^{-3}.)

4.7 Any weak acid (e.g. methanoic acid/ethanoic acid/hydrogen
cyanide) *(1 mark)*. Any strong base (e.g. potassium
hydroxide/sodium hydroxide) *(1 mark)*.

4.8 Phenolphthalein *(1 mark)*

5.1 HCOOH ⇌ H$^+$ + HCOO$^-$ *(1 mark)*

5.2 K_a = [H$^+$][HCOO$^-$] ÷ [HCOOH] *(1 mark)*

5.3 [H$^+$] = 10^{-pH} = 10$^{-2.2}$ = 6.31 × 10^{-3}
K_a = [H$^+$]^2 ÷ [HCOOH] = (6.31 × 10^{-3})^2 ÷ 0.24
= 1.66 × 10^{-4} mol dm^{-3}
pK_a = −log(K_a) = −log(1.66 × 10^{-4}) = **3.78**
(3 marks for correct answer, otherwise 1 mark for [H$^+$] =
6.31 × 10^{-3} and 1 mark for K_a = 1.66 × 10^{-4}.)

5.4 initial moles HCOOH = (conc. × vol.) ÷ 1000
= (0.24 × 30) ÷ 1000 = 7.2 × 10^{-3} moles *(1 mark)*
initial moles NaOH = (conc. × vol.) ÷ 1000
= (0.15 × 20) ÷ 1000 = 3.0 × 10^{-3} moles *(1 mark)*
moles salt = moles base = 3.0 × 10^{-3} moles *(1 mark)*
HCOOH + NaOH → HCOO$^-$Na$^+$ + H$_2$O so 1 mole of base
neutralises 1 mole of acid and 3.0 × 10^{-3} moles of base
neutralise 3.0 × 10^{-3} moles of acid. So (7.2 × 10^{-3}) − (3.0 ×
10^{-3}) = 4.2 × 10^{-3} moles of acid remain *(1 mark)*.
Total volume = 20 + 30 = 50
final conc. acid = (moles × 1000) ÷ vol.
= ((4.2 × 10^{-3}) × 1000) ÷ 50 = 0.084 mol dm^{-3}
final conc. salt = (moles × 1000) ÷ vol.
= ((3.0 × 10^{-3}) × 1000) ÷ 50 = 0.06 mol dm^{-3}
HCOOH ⇌ H$^+$ + HCOO$^-$
K_a = [H$^+$][HCOO$^-$] ÷ [HCOOH] so
[H$^+$] = (K_a × [HCOOH]) ÷ [HCOO$^-$]
= ((1.66 × 10^{-4}) × 0.084) ÷ (0.06)
= 2.32 × 10^{-4} mol dm^{-3} *(1 mark)*
pH = −log[H$^+$] = −log(2.32 × 10^{-4}) = **3.63**
(1 mark) (Maximum of 6 marks for correct answer.)
You calculated K_a for this acid in the previous part of the
question.

5.5 HCOOH ⇌ H$^+$ + HCOO$^-$. Adding an acid increases [H$^+$]
(1 mark) so the equilibrium shifts to the left to remove the
excess H$^+$ *(1 mark)*. The excess H$^+$ combines with HCOO$^-$
to form HCOOH *(1 mark)*.

5.6 E.g. biological washing powder/shampoo/human blood
(1 mark for each correct answer, maximum of 3 marks).

Unit 2

Section 3 — Period 3 Elements

1. Period 3 Elements

Page 125 — Application Question

Q1 a) A is sodium, B is magnesium, C is sulfur.
b) A: 2Na$_{(s)}$ + ½O$_{2(g)}$ → Na$_2$O$_{(s)}$
B: Mg$_{(s)}$ + ½O$_{2(g)}$ → MgO$_{(s)}$
C: S$_{(s)}$ + O$_{2(g)}$ → SO$_{2(g)}$

Page 125 — Fact Recall Questions

Q1 a) (i) 2Na$_{(s)}$ + 2H$_2$O$_{(l)}$ → 2NaOH$_{(aq)}$ + H$_{2(g)}$
(ii) Mg$_{(s)}$ + 2H$_2$O$_{(l)}$ → Mg(OH)$_{2(aq)}$ + H$_{2(g)}$
b) Sodium reacts more vigorously. Sodium is in Group
1 and magnesium is in Group 2. So when they react
sodium loses one electron and magnesium loses two.
It takes less energy to lose one electron than it does to
lose two, so sodium is more reactive.

Q2 a) 2Al$_{(s)}$ + 1½O$_{2(g)}$ → Al$_2$O$_{3(s)}$
b) P$_{4(s)}$ + 5O$_{2(g)}$ → P$_4$O$_{10(s)}$

2. Period 3 Oxides

Page 128 — Application Question

Q1 a) E.g. A is magnesium oxide (MgO), B is aluminium oxide
(Al$_2$O$_3$), C is silicon dioxide (SiO$_2$).
b) Magnesium oxide has a higher melting point than
aluminium oxide because the Al^{3+} ions in aluminium
oxide distort the oxygen's electron cloud, making the
bonds partially covalent. This makes them weaker than
the ionic bonds in magnesium oxide. So more heat
energy is required to break the bonds in magnesium
oxide and melt it.

Page 128 — Fact Recall Questions

Q1 a) (i) MgO forms a giant ionic lattice with strong ionic
bonds between the ions.
(ii) Al$_2$O$_3$ forms a giant ionic lattice. Bonding is ionic
with partial covalent character because the Al^{3+} ions
distort the oxygen electron clouds.
(iii) SiO$_2$ has a giant macromolecular structure with
strong covalent bonds between the atoms.
(iv) P$_4$O$_{10}$ has a simple molecular structure with weak
intermolecular forces (e.g. dipole-dipole/van der
Waals) between the molecules.
b) MgO$_{(s)}$ + H$_2$O$_{(l)}$ → Mg(OH)$_{2(aq)}$
P$_4$O$_{10(s)}$ + 6H$_2$O$_{(l)}$ → 4H$_3$PO$_{4(aq)}$
c) (i) Basic
(ii) Amphoteric
(iii) Acidic
(iv) Acidic

Q2 a) MgO$_{(s)}$ + 2HCl$_{(aq)}$ → MgCl$_{2(aq)}$ + H$_2$O$_{(l)}$
b) SO$_{2(g)}$ + 2NaOH$_{(aq)}$ → Na$_2$SO$_{3(aq)}$ + H$_2$O$_{(l)}$

Exam-style Questions — page 129

1.1 Mg$_{(s)}$ + 2H$_2$O$_{(l)}$ → Mg(OH)$_{2(aq)}$ + H$_{2(g)}$ *(1 mark)*.
1.2 Magnesium loses two electrons to form an Mg^{2+} ion but
sodium only loses one electron to form an Na$^+$ ion *(1 mark)*.
It takes less energy for sodium to lose one electron than it
does for magnesium to lose two, so more energy is needed
for magnesium to react *(1 mark)*.
1.3 2Na$_{(s)}$ + ½O$_{2(g)}$ → Na$_2$O$_{(s)}$ *(1 mark)*
1.4 Yellow *(1 mark)*

1.5 Both form giant ionic lattices *(1 mark)*, with strong ionic bonds between each ion *(1 mark)*.

1.6 MgO has the higher melting temperature *(1 mark)*. Magnesium forms Mg^{2+} ions, which attract O^{2-} ions more strongly than the Na^+ ions in Na_2O, so the ionic bonds in MgO are stronger and more heat energy is required to break the bonds *(1 mark)*.

1.7 Sulfur dioxide has a simple molecular structure *(1 mark)*. Only weak intermolecular forces (e.g. dipole-dipole/van der Waals) hold the molecules together so little heat energy is needed to overcome these forces *(1 mark)*.

1.8 Silicon dioxide has a giant macromolecular structure *(1 mark)*, with strong covalent bonds holding the molecules together, so lots of energy is required to break these bonds *(1 mark)*.

2.1 $MgO_{(s)} + H_2O_{(l)} \rightarrow Mg(OH)_{2(aq)}$ *(1 mark)*
pH 9-10 *(1 mark)*
$SO_{2(g)} + H_2O_{(l)} \rightarrow H_2SO_{3(aq)}$ *(1 mark)*
pH 0-1 *(1 mark)*

2.2 Aluminium oxide/silicon dioxide *(1 mark)*.

2.3 Aluminium oxide *(1 mark)*.

2.4 $Al_2O_{3(s)} + 3H_2SO_{4(aq)} \rightarrow Al_2(SO_4)_{3(aq)} + 3H_2O_{(l)}$ *(1 mark)*
$Al_2O_{3(s)} + 2NaOH_{(aq)} + 3H_2O_{(l)} \rightarrow 2NaAl(OH)_{4(aq)}$ *(1 mark)*

Section 4 — Transition Metals

1. Transition Metals — The Basics

Page 133 — Application Questions

Q1 a) $[Ar]3d^34s^2$
b) $[Ar]3d^74s^2$
c) $[Ar]3d^54s^2$
d) $[Ar]3d^84s^2$
For these questions you don't have to write [Ar]. Writing out the whole electron configuration starting from $1s^2$ is fine too.

Q2 a) $[Ar]3d^2$
b) $[Ar]3d^7$
c) $[Ar]3d^5$
d) $[Ar]3d^8$
Don't forget, the s electrons are always removed first, then the d electrons.

Q3 Zinc has the electron configuration $1s^22s^22p^63s^23p^63d^{10}4s^2$. It can only form Zn^{2+} ions which have an electron configuration of $1s^22s^22p^63s^23p^63d^{10}$. This ion has a full d sub-level, so zinc cannot form a stable ion with an incomplete d sub-level and it therefore can't be a transition metal.

Page 133 — Fact Recall Questions

Q1 In the d block.
Q2 A transition metal is a metal that can form one or more stable ions with an incomplete d sub-level.
Q3 10
Q4 Electrons fill up the lowest energy sub-levels first and electrons fill orbitals singly before they start sharing.
Q5 a) Chromium prefers to have one electron in each orbital of the 3d sub-level and just one in the 4s sub-level because this gives it more stability.
b) Copper prefers to have a full 3d sub-level and one electron in the 4s sub-level because it's more stable that way.
Q6 They can form complex ions, form coloured ions, act as catalysts and exist in variable oxidation states.
Q7 Their incomplete d sub-level.

2. Complex Ions

Page 137 — Application Questions

Q1 a) 6
b) 2
c) 4

Q2 a) Overall charge of $[CuF_6]^{4-}$ is –4. Each F^- ion has a charge of –1 so the oxidation state of copper must be $-4 - (6 \times -1) = $ **+2**.
b) Overall charge of $[Ag(S_2O_3)_2]^{3-}$ is –3. Each $S_2O_3^{2-}$ ion has charge of –2 so the oxidation state of silver must be $-3 - (2 \times -2) = $ **+1**.
c) Overall charge of $[CuCl_4]^{2-}$ is –2. Each Cl^- ion has a charge of –1 so the oxidation state of copper must be $-2 - (4 \times -1) = $ **+2**

Q3 a) Octahedral:

When you're drawing the shapes of ions and molecules make sure you include the dashed arrows and the wedged arrows to show that it's 3-D.

b) Linear:

c) Tetrahedral:

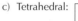

Q4 a)

b) 3
Oxygen atoms are small so six of them will fit around a Cu^{2+} ion and form co-ordinate bonds with it. This means that three molecules of $C_2O_4^{2-}$ will each form two co-ordinate bonds with the ion.

Q5 Square planar:

Page 137 — Fact Recall Questions

Q1 a) A metal ion surrounded by co-ordinately bonded ligands.
b) A covalent bond where both of the electrons in the shared pair come from the same atom.
c) An atom, ion or molecule that donates a pair of electrons to a central metal ion.

Q2 a) Monodentate means that a ligand can form one co-ordinate bond, bidentate means that a ligand can form two co-ordinate bonds and multidentate means that a ligand can form two or more co-ordinate bonds.
b) monodentate: e.g. H_2O/NH_3/Cl^-
bidentate: e.g. $NH_2CH_2CH_2NH_2$/$C_2O_4^{2-}$
multidentate: e.g. $EDTA^{4-}$

Q3 The number of co-ordinate bonds that are formed with the central metal ion in a complex ion.

3. Isomerism in Complex Ions
Page 139 — Application Questions
Q1 a) *cis-trans* isomerism
    b) optical isomerism
    c) *cis-trans* isomerism
Q2 *cis*:   *trans*:

Page 139 — Fact Recall Questions
Q1 optical isomerism and *cis-trans* isomerism
Q2

4. Formation of Coloured Ions
Page 143 — Application Questions
Q1 The change in the ligand.
Q2 The change in the oxidation state of iron.
Q3 $\Delta E = hc/\lambda$
    $= (6.63 \times 10^{-34} \times 3.00 \times 10^8) \div 580 \times 10^{-9}$
    $= \mathbf{3.43 \times 10^{-19}}$ **J**

Page 143 — Fact Recall Questions
Q1 They split into two different energy levels.
Q2 a) Light energy.
    b) $\Delta E = h\nu = hc/\lambda$
Q3 Transition metal ions have incomplete 3d sub-levels. When visible light hits transition metal ions, some of the frequencies are absorbed by electrons which jump up to the higher energy orbitals. The frequencies that remain are reflected and these make up the colour you see.
Q4 A change in oxidation state, a change in co-ordination number and a change in ligand.
Q5 a) White light is shone through a filter, which is chosen to only let the colour of light through that is absorbed by the sample. The light then passes through the sample to a colorimeter, which measures how much light is absorbed by the sample.
    b) Measure the absorbances of known concentrations of solutions and plot the results on a graph with absorbance on the *y*-axis and concentration on the *x*-axis.

5. Ligand Substitution Reactions
Page 148 — Application Questions
Q1 a) octahedral
    b) tetrahedral
Q2 $[Mn(H_2O)_6]^{2+}_{(aq)} + 4Cl^-_{(aq)} \rightleftharpoons [MnCl_4]^{2-}_{(aq)} + 6H_2O_{(l)}$
Q3 a) $[Cu(H_2O)_6]^{2+}_{(aq)} + 4NH_{3(aq)} \rightarrow [Cu(NH_3)_4(H_2O)_2]^{2+}_{(aq)} + 4H_2O_{(l)}$
    b) (elongated) octahedral
Q4 a) $[Cr(NH_3)_6]^{3+}_{(aq)} + 3NH_2CH_2CH_2NH_{2\,(aq)} \rightarrow [Cr(NH_2CH_2CH_2NH_2)_3]^{3+}_{(aq)} + 6NH_{3\,(aq)}$

b) The enthalpy change (ΔH) for this reaction will be very small because six Cr–N bonds are broken and six Cr–N bonds are formed. The entropy change (ΔS) will be positive and large because the number of particles increases during the reaction.

Page 148 — Fact Recall Questions
Q1 a) There will be no change in co-ordination number or shape but the colour may change.
    b) There will be a change in co-ordination number and shape and the colour may change.
Q2 a) It helps transport oxygen around the body.
    b) Four come from nitrogen atoms in the porphyrin ring, one comes from a nitrogen atom in a globin protein and one comes from either water or oxygen.
Q3 a) In the lungs, the concentration of oxygen is high. So water ligands that were bound to the haemoglobin are substituted for oxygen ligands, forming oxyhaemoglobin.
    b) At sites where oxygen is needed the concentration of oxygen is low. So oxygen ligands that were bound to haemoglobin are substituted for water ligands, forming deoxyhaemoglobin.
Q4 Carbon monoxide is a very strong ligand for haemoglobin. When it is inhaled, it binds to the central Fe^{2+} ion and prevents it from binding to oxygen. As a result, oxygen can no longer be transported around the body.
Q5 When monodentate ligands are substituted with bidentate or multidentate ligands, the number of particles and the entropy increases. The enthalpy change (ΔH) for these reaction will be very small because six metal-ligand bonds are broken and six metal-ligand bonds are formed. Reactions that result in an large increase in entropy and a small change in enthalpy are more likely to occur and so multidentate ligands form much more stable complexes than monodentate ligands. This is the chelate effect.

6. Variable Oxidation States
Page 151 — Application Question
Q1 The manganate(VII) ion has a higher redox potential so it is more unstable than the iron(III) ion and therefore, more easily reduced.

Page 151 — Fact Recall Questions
Q1 $2V^{3+}_{(aq)} + Zn_{(s)} \rightarrow 2V^{2+}_{(aq)} + Zn^{2+}_{(aq)}$
Q2 E.g. type of ligand and pH.
Q3 a) A silver mirror would form on the inside of the test tube.
    b) No change.
Q4 $[Ag(NH_3)_2]^+$

7. Transition Metal Titrations
Page 154 — Application Questions
Q1 $MnO_4^-_{(aq)} + 8H^+_{(aq)} + 5Fe^{2+}_{(aq)} \rightarrow Mn^{2+}_{(aq)} + 4H_2O_{(l)} + 5Fe^{3+}_{(aq)}$
    Moles Fe^{2+} = (conc. × volume) ÷ 1000
    $= (0.0500 \times 28.3) \div 1000 = 1.415 \times 10^{-3}$ moles.
    5 moles of Fe^{2+} reacts with 1 mole of MnO_4^- so 1.415×10^{-3} moles of Fe^{2+} must react with $(1.415 \times 10^{-3}) \div 5 = 2.83 \times 10^{-4}$ moles of MnO_4^-.
    Conc. MnO_4^- = (moles × 1000) ÷ volume
    $= ((2.83 \times 10^{-4}) \times 1000) \div 30.0 = \mathbf{0.00943\ mol\ dm^{-3}}$

Q2 $2MnO_4^-{}_{(aq)} + 16H^+{}_{(aq)} + 5C_2O_4^{2-}{}_{(aq)} \rightarrow$
$2Mn^{2+}{}_{(aq)} + 8H_2O_{(l)} + 10CO_{2(g)}$
Moles $C_2O_4^{2-}$ = (conc. × volume) ÷ 1000
= (0.600 × 28.0) ÷ 1000 = 0.0168 moles.
5 moles of $C_2O_4^{2-}$ reacts with 2 moles of MnO_4^- so
0.0168 moles of $C_2O_4^{2-}$ must react with
(0.0168 ÷ 5) × 2 = 6.72 × 10^{-3} moles of MnO_4^-.
Volume MnO_4^- = (moles × 1000) ÷ conc.
= ((6.72 × 10^{-3}) × 1000) ÷ 0.0750 = **89.6 cm³**

Q3 $MnO_4^-{}_{(aq)} + 8H^+{}_{(aq)} + 5Fe^{2+}{}_{(aq)} \rightarrow Mn^{2+}{}_{(aq)} + 4H_2O_{(l)} + 5Fe^{3+}{}_{(aq)}$
Moles MnO_4^- = (conc. × volume) ÷ 1000
= (0.0550 × 24.0) ÷ 1000 = 1.32 × 10^{-3} moles.
1 mole of MnO_4^- reacts with 5 moles of Fe^{2+} so
1.32 × 10^{-3} moles of MnO_4^- must react with
(1.32 × 10^{-3}) × 5 = 6.60 × 10^{-3} moles of Fe^{2+}.
Volume Fe^{2+} = (moles × 1000) ÷ conc.
= ((6.60 × 10^{-3}) × 1000) ÷ 0.450 = **14.7 cm³**

Page 154 — Fact Recall Questions
Q1 Acid is added to make sure there are plenty of H^+ ions to allow all the oxidising agent to be reduced.
Q2 a) e.g. manganate(VII) ions (MnO_4^-).
b) e.g. colourless to purple.

8. Transition Metal Catalysts
Page 158 — Application Question
Q1 a) A heterogenous catalyst.
b) Mn is a transition metal. Transition metals have incomplete d sub-levels so can have multiple oxidation states. This means they can transfer electrons to speed up reactions.

Page 158 — Fact Recall Questions
Q1 A heterogenous catalyst is a catalyst in a different phase from the reactants and a homogenous catalyst is a catalyst in the same phase as the reactants.
Q2 E.g. the Haber Process. Iron is the catalyst. It catalyses the reaction $N_{2(g)} + 3H_{2(g)} \rightarrow 2NH_{3(g)}$.
The Contact Process. Vanadium(V) oxide (V_2O_5) is the catalyst. It catalyses the reaction $SO_{2(g)} + \frac{1}{2}O_{2(g)} \rightarrow SO_{3(g)}$.
Q3 The reaction happens on the surface of the heterogenous catalyst. So increasing the surface area of the catalyst increases the rate of reaction. Using a support medium maximises the surface area for minimal extra cost.
Q4 Catalytic poisoning is when impurities bind to the surface of the catalyst and block reactants from being adsorbed. It can be reduced by purifying the reactants to remove as many impurities as possible.
Q5 The reaction between $S_2O_8^{2-}$ and I^- is very slow because both ions are negatively charged and repel each other. When Fe^{2+} ions are added, the reaction can proceed in two stages, both involving a positive and a negative ion, so there's no repulsion and the reaction happens a lot faster.
Q6 Autocatalysis is when one of the products of a reaction also catalyses it. E.g. the catalysis of the reaction between $C_2O_4^{2-}$ and MnO_4^- by Mn^{2+}.

9. Metal-Aqua Ions
Page 164 — Application Question
Q1 copper 2+/Cu^{2+}

Page 164 — Fact Recall Questions
Q1 co-ordinate/dative covalent bonds
Q2 Metal 3+ ions have a high charge density (charge/size ratio). The metal 2+ ions have a much lower charge density. This makes the 3+ ions much more polarising than the 2+ ions. More polarising power means that they attract electrons from the oxygen atoms of the co-ordinated water molecules more strongly, weakening the O–H bond. So it's more likely that a hydrogen ion will be released. And more hydrogen ions means a more acidic solution. This means that metal-aqua 3+ ions are more acidic than metal-aqua 2+ ions.
Q3 $[Fe(H_2O)_6]^{3+}{}_{(aq)} + H_2O_{(l)} \rightleftharpoons [Fe(OH)(H_2O)_5]^{2+}{}_{(aq)} + H_3O^+{}_{(aq)}$
$[Fe(OH)(H_2O)_5]^{2+}{}_{(aq)} + H_2O_{(l)} \rightleftharpoons [Fe(OH)_2(H_2O)_4]^+{}_{(aq)} + H_3O^+{}_{(aq)}$
$[Fe(OH)_2(H_2O)_4]^+{}_{(aq)} + H_2O_{(l)} \rightleftharpoons Fe(OH)_3(H_2O)_{3(s)} + H_3O^+{}_{(aq)}$
You could also write these equations using $OH^-{}_{(aq)}$ *instead of* $H_2O_{(l)}$ *and replacing* $H_3O^+{}_{(aq)}$ *with* $H_2O_{(l)}$. *For example:*
$[Fe(H_2O)_6]^{3+}{}_{(aq)} + OH^-{}_{(aq)} \rightleftharpoons [Fe(OH)(H_2O)_5]^{2+}{}_{(aq)} + H_2O_{(l)}$
Q4 A white precipitate would form in the colourless solution.
Q5 The solution would turn from blue to deep blue.

Exam-style Questions — pages 166-169
1 C *(1 mark)*.
The electron configuration of manganese is
$1s^2\ 2s^2\ 2p^6\ 3s^2\ 3p^6\ 3d^5\ 4s^2$.
2 A *(1 mark)*.
When chloride ions are added to $[Cu(H_2O)_6]^{2+}{}_{(aq)}$, $[CuCl_4]^{2-}$ *is formed, which is tetrahedral.*
3 B *(1 mark)*.
Test 1 rules out Al(III) as its precipitate dissolves in excess $NaOH_{(aq)}$. *Test 2 rules out Cu(II) as its precipitate dissolves in excess* $NH_{3(aq)}$. *Test 3 rules out Fe(III) as +3 ions produce carbon dioxide gas after reacting with sodium carbonate.*
4.1 blue *(1 mark)*
4.2 Cu: $1s^2 2s^2 2p^6 3s^2 3p^6 3d^{10} 4s^1$ *(1 mark)*
Cu^{2+}: $1s^2 2s^2 2p^6 3s^2 3p^6 3d^9$ *(1 mark)*
4.3 Cu^{2+} has the characteristic chemical properties of transition element ions because it has an incomplete d sub-level *(1 mark)*.
4.4

Don't forget to include the charge on the complex ion when you're drawing its structure.
The shape of $[Cu(H_2O)_6]^{2+}$ is octahedral *(1 mark)*.
4.5 6 *(1 mark)*
4.6 When visible light hits a transition metal ion, some frequencies are absorbed but others are reflected *(1 mark)*. The reflected frequencies combine to make the complement of the colour of the absorbed frequencies and this is the colour you see *(1 mark)*.
4.7 Change in oxidation state *(1 mark)*, ligand *(1 mark)* or co-ordination number *(1 mark)*.
5.1 square planar *(1 mark)*
5.2 *cis-trans* isomerism *(1 mark)*

5.3

(1 mark for each correctly drawn isomer)

5.4 optical isomerism **(1 mark)**

5.5 The oxygen atoms have lone pairs of electrons **(1 mark)** which they can donate to the chromium(III) ion to form co-ordinate bonds **(1 mark)**.

5.6

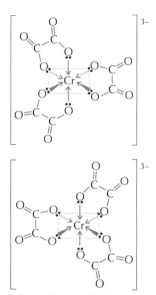

(1 mark for each correctly drawn isomer. The structures must be shown as 3-D, i.e. with wedged and dotted bonds)

These are fiendishly difficult isomers to draw so don't worry if you've messed up your first few attempts — you can always simplify the structure of the ligands to make the whole thing a bit easier. Make sure you get lots of practice at drawing them before the exam and you'll be fine.

6.1 Transition metals exist in variable oxidation states **(1 mark)** so they can transfer electrons to speed up reactions **(1 mark)**.

6.2 A heterogenous catalyst **(1 mark)**.
It's a heterogenous catalyst because it's in a different physical state than the reactants.

6.3 The reaction happens on the surface of the heterogenous catalyst **(1 mark)**. Using a ceramic lattice increases the surface area, making it more effective **(1 mark)** and reduces the cost because only a thin layer of catalyst is needed **(1 mark)**.

6.4 Catalytic poisoning is when impurities bind to the surface of a catalyst **(1 mark)** and block reactants from being adsorbed **(1 mark)**. This reduces the surface area of the catalyst available to the reactants, slowing down the reaction **(1 mark)**.

6.5 The reacting ions are both negatively charged **(1 mark)** so they will repel each other and are unlikely to collide **(1 mark)**.

6.6 $S_2O_8^{2-}{}_{(aq)} + 2Fe^{2+}{}_{(aq)} \rightarrow 2Fe^{3+}{}_{(aq)} + 2SO_4^{2-}{}_{(aq)}$ **(1 mark)**.
$2Fe^{3+}{}_{(aq)} + 2I^-{}_{(aq)} \rightarrow I_{2(aq)} + 2Fe^{2+}{}_{(aq)}$ **(1 mark)**.

7.1 Water molecules form co-ordinate/dative covalent bonds with the central metal ion **(1 mark)**. Each water molecule donates a pair of electrons to the central metal ion **(1 mark)**.

7.2 $[Fe(H_2O)_6]^{2+}{}_{(aq)}$ **(1 mark)**

7.3 $[Fe(H_2O)_6]^{2+}{}_{(aq)} + H_2O_{(l)} \rightleftharpoons [Fe(OH)(H_2O)_5]^+{}_{(aq)} + H_3O^+{}_{(aq)}$ **(1 mark)**

7.4 Al^{3+} has a higher charge density (charge/size ratio) than Fe^{2+} **(1 mark)**. This makes the Al^{3+} ions much more polarising than the Fe^{2+} ions **(1 mark)**. More polarising power means that they attract electrons from the oxygen atoms of the co-ordinated water molecules more strongly, weakening the O–H bond **(1 mark)**. So it's more likely that a hydrogen ion will be released. And more hydrogen ions means a more acidic solution **(1 mark)**.

7.5 The solution will remain green but a green precipitate will form in it **(1 mark)**.

7.6 $[Fe(H_2O)_6]^{3+}{}_{(aq)}$ **(1 mark)**

7.7 $2[Fe(H_2O)_6]^{3+}{}_{(aq)} + 3CO_3^{2-}{}_{(aq)}$
$\rightleftharpoons 2Fe(OH)_3(H_2O)_{3(s)} + 3CO_{2(g)} + 3H_2O_{(l)}$ **(1 mark)**

7.8 A brown precipitate would form **(1 mark)** and bubbles of CO_2 gas would be given off **(1 mark)**.

7.9 $[Al(H_2O)_6]^{3+}{}_{(aq)} + 3NH_2CH_2CH_2NH_{2(aq)} \rightarrow$
$[Al(NH_2CH_2CH_2NH_2)_3]^{3+}{}_{(aq)} + 6H_2O_{(l)}$ **(1 mark)**

7.10 The products have a lot more entropy than the reactants while the enthalpy change in both directions is small **(1 mark)** so the forward reaction happens easily while the reverse reaction doesn't **(1 mark)**.

8.1 An amphoteric species can act as both a base and an acid **(1 mark)**.

8.2 white precipitate **(1 mark)**

8.3 $Al(OH)_3(H_2O)_{3(s)} + OH^-{}_{(aq)} \rightleftharpoons [Al(OH)_4(H_2O)_2]^-{}_{(aq)} + H_2O_{(l)}$
(2 marks, 1 mark for correct products, 1 mark for correct charge on product ion)

8.4 It is acting as a Brønsted-Lowry acid **(1 mark)** because it's donating H^+ ions in the reaction **(1 mark)**.

9.1 The complex ion present is $[Ag(NH_3)_2]^+$ **(1 mark)**.

$$\left[H_3N\!:\longrightarrow Ag\longleftarrow:NH_3\right]^+$$ **(1 mark)**.

The shape of the molecule is linear **(1 mark)**.

9.2 Tollens' reagent is used to distinguish between aldehydes and ketones **(1 mark)**. It reacts with aldehydes to form a silver mirror **(1 mark)**. It does not react with ketones **(1 mark)**.

9.3 $MnO_4^-{}_{(aq)} + 8H^+{}_{(aq)} + 5Fe^{2+}{}_{(aq)}$
$\rightarrow Mn^{2+}{}_{(aq)} + 4H_2O_{(l)} + 5Fe^{3+}{}_{(aq)}$ **(1 mark)**
Moles Fe^{2+} = (conc. × volume) ÷ 1000
= $(0.150 \times 30.0) \div 1000 = 4.50 \times 10^{-3}$ moles **(1 mark)**.
5 moles of Fe^{2+} reacts with 1 mole of MnO_4^- so
4.50×10^{-3} moles of Fe^{2+} must react with
$(4.50 \times 10^{-3}) \div 5 = 9.00 \times 10^{-4}$ moles of MnO_4^- **(1 mark)**.
Conc. MnO_4^- = (moles × 1000) ÷ volume
= $((9.00 \times 10^{-4}) \times 1000) \div 15.8 = \mathbf{0.0570\ mol\ dm^{-3}}$ **(1 mark)**

9.4 The solution will be purple at the end point **(1 mark)**.

Unit 3

Section 5 — Isomerism and Carbonyl Compounds

1. Optical Isomerism

Page 173 — Application Questions

Q1 a)

b)

c)

d)

Q2 a)

b)

Q3

Page 173 — Fact Recall Questions

Q1 Optical isomerism is a type of stereoisomerism. In optical isomers four groups are arranged in two different ways around a central carbon atom so that two different molecules are made — these molecules are non-superimposable mirror images of each other and are called enantiomers or optical isomers. Optical isomers differ by their effect on plane polarised light.

Q2 A chiral carbon atom is a carbon atom that has four different groups attached to it.

Q3 Optically active molecules will rotate plane polarised light.

Q4 Racemic mixtures contain equal quantities of two enantiomers. The two enantiomers cancel each other's light-rotating effect so the mixture doesn't show any optical activity.

2. Aldehydes and Ketones

Page 177 — Application Questions

Q1 a) butanal
   b) hexan-2-one
   c) pentan-3-one
   d) 2-ethyl-3-methylbutanal

Q2 a)

b)

c)

d)

Q3 $CH_3COCH_2CH_2CH_3 + 2[H] \rightarrow CH_3CHOHCH_2CH_2CH_3$

Page 177 — Fact Recall Questions

Q1 Aldehydes have a carbonyl group at the end of the carbon chain, ketones have a carbonyl group in the middle of the carbon chain.

Q2 A carboxylic acid.

Q3 The carbonyl group is in the middle of the carbon chain so to oxidise it, a carbon-carbon bond would have to be broken. This requires a lot of energy, so ketones are not easily oxidised.

Q4 a) In the presence of an aldehyde a silver mirror is produced. In the presence of a ketone there is no change.

b) In the presence of an aldehyde a brick-red precipitate is formed. In the presence of a ketone there is no change.

Q5 e.g. $NaBH_4$

3. Hydroxynitriles

Page 180 — Application Questions

Q1 a)

b)

Q2 a) 2-hydroxy-2-methylbutanenitrile

b)

c) butanone

d)

Q3 a)

b) The C=O bond is planar, so nucleophilic attack of the δ+ carbon can occur from above or below the C=O bond. Depending on which side the nucleophile attacks from, a different optical isomer/enantiomer will form.

Page 180 — Fact Recall Questions

Q1 A hydroxynitrile is a molecule with a nitrile (CN) group and a hydroxyl (OH) group.

Q2 nucleophilic addition

Q3 a) KCN is toxic.

b) E.g. Any reaction involving KCN should be done in a fume cupboard If heating KCN, this should be done using a water bath or electric mantle, rather than an open flame.

4. Carboxylic Acids and Esters

Page 183 — Application Questions

Q1 a) (i) methanoic acid

(ii) 2-ethyl-4-hydroxypentanoic acid

b) $2HCOOH_{(aq)} + Na_2CO_{3(s)} \rightarrow 2HCOONa_{(aq)} + H_2O_{(l)} + CO_{2(g)}$

Q2 a) (i) propyl methanoate

(ii) ethyl benzoate

b) (i) propan-1-ol and methanoic acid

(ii) ethanol and benzoic acid

Q3 a)

b) $HCOOH + CH_3CH(OH)CH_3 \rightarrow$ $HCOOCH(CH_3)CH_3 + H_2O$

Page 183 — Fact Recall Questions

Q1 A salt, water and carbon dioxide.

Q2 a) Esterification reaction / condensation reaction.

b) A strong acid catalyst.

E.g. $H_2SO_4/HCl/H_3PO_4$.

5. Reactions and Uses of Esters

Page 187 — Application Questions

Q1 a) $CH_3CH_2COOCH_3 + H_2O \rightarrow CH_3CH_2COOH + CH_3OH$

b) $CH_3CH_2COOCH_3 + OH^- \rightarrow CH_3CH_2COO^- + CH_3OH$

Q2 a)

b)

We've had to write the equation vertically here so it'll fit on the page. In the exam, write the equation horizontally like normal.

c) Mix the sodium salt produced with a strong acid such as HCl.

Q3 a)
$CH_2OOC(CH_2)_{14}CH_3$
$CH_2OOC(CH_2)_{14}CH_3$ + 3CH$_3$OH
$CH_2OOC(CH_2)_{14}CH_3$

↓

H–C–OH
H–C–OH + 3 $CH_3(CH_2)_{14}$–C(=O)O–CH$_3$
H–C–OH
H

b) E.g. KOH/potassium hydroxide or NaOH/sodium hydroxide.

Page 187 — Fact Recall Questions

Q1 Any three from: e.g. in perfumes / as food flavourings / as solvents (e.g. in glue/printing ink) / as plasticisers / to produce methyl esters for biofuels.

Q2 a) A carboxylic acid and an alcohol.
   b) A carboxylate ion/carboxylate salt and an alcohol.

Q3 Glycerol (propane-1,2,3-triol) and long chain carboxylic acids (fatty acids).

Q4 Fats contain mostly saturated hydrocarbon chains which fit neatly together, which increases the strong van der Waals forces. As a result a higher temperature is needed to melt them and they are solid at room temperature.
Oils contain mostly unsaturated hydrocarbon chains which don't fit together very closely, which decreases the effect of the van der Waals forces. As a result a lower temperature is needed to melt them and they are liquid at room temperature.

Q5 Glycerol and a sodium salt of a fatty acid (soap).

Q6 By reacting rapeseed/vegetable oils with methanol in the presence of a strong alkali catalyst (e.g. KOH or NaOH) to form methyl esters. Biodiesel is a mixture of methyl esters.

Q7 Biodiesel isn't always 100% carbon neutral because energy is used to make the fertilizer to grow the crop and is used in planting, harvesting and converting the plants to oil. This energy often comes from burning fossil fuels, which produces CO_2, so the process isn't carbon neutral overall.

6. Acyl Chlorides
Page 190 — Application Questions

Q1 a) methanoyl chloride
   b) propanoyl chloride
   c) 2-methylpropanoyl chloride
   d) 4-hydroxy-2-methylbutanoyl chloride

Q2 a)

b)

c)

d)

Page 190 — Fact Recall Questions

Q1 $C_nH_{2n-1}OCl$

Q2 a) A carboxylic acid and HCl.
   b) An ester and HCl.
   c) An amide and HCl.
   d) An N-substituted amide and HCl.

Q3 nucleophilic addition-elimination

7. Acid Anhydrides
Page 192 — Application Questions

Q1 a)

b)

c)

Q2 a)

Unless you're asked for it, you don't have to draw out the full displayed formula for the molecule in the exam. You could just have written this equation as $CH_3CH_2COOCOCH_2CH_3 + H_2O \rightarrow 2CH_3CH_2COOH$. Either way of writing the equation will get you the marks.

b)

c)

Q3

The equations in Q2 and Q3 are written vertically for space. In the exam, write them horizontally.

Page 192 — Fact Recall Questions

Q1 Propanyl propanoate and propanoic acid.

Q2 Ethanoic anhydride is cheaper than ethanoyl chloride. Ethanoic anhydride is safer than ethanoyl chloride because it's less corrosive, reacts more slowly with water and doesn't produce dangerous HCl fumes.

8. Purifying Organic Compounds

Page 196 — Application Questions

Q1 E.g. Redistill the mixture as hexane will distil out of the mixture at a lower temperature than ethanol, so the two liquids can be collected separately. / Use separation to separate hexane (insoluble in water) from ethanol (soluble in water). You'll be left will an organic layer containing hexane and an aqueous layer containing water and ethanol. The ethanol can be separated from the water by redistillation (as ethanol has a lower boiling point than water) or can be dried using an anhydrous salt, e.g. $MgSO_4$ or $CaCl_2$, which can then be removed by filtration.

Q2 The student could carry out the reaction in distillation apparatus, as the product would distil out of the reaction mixture as it formed, and so it wouldn't be over-oxidised.

Page 196 — Fact Recall Questions

Q1 E.g. anhydrous magnesium sulfate ($MgSO_4$) and anhydrous calcium chloride ($CaCl_2$).

Q2

Q3 The different boiling points of the compounds.
Q4 A narrow range.

Exam-style Questions — pages 198-201

1   A *(1 mark)*
2   D *(1 mark)*
3   B *(1 mark)*
4.1 A — propanal *(1 mark)*
     B — propanone *(1 mark)*
4.2 E.g. Tollens' reagent *(1 mark)* produces a silver mirror with
     A but not with B *(1 mark)*/Fehling's solution or Benedict's
     solution *(1 mark)* produces a brick-red precipitate with A
     but not with B *(1 mark)*.
4.3 $NaBH_4$/sodium borohydride/sodium tetrahydridoborate(III)
     (1 mark).
4.4

     *(1 mark for each correct curly arrow, 1 mark for correct
     structures.)*
     To get a mark for your curly arrow the end of the arrow must
     start at a lone pair of electrons or a bond and the point of the
     arrow must point to wherever the electrons are heading.
4.5 nucleophilic addition *(1 mark)*

     *(1 mark for each correct curly arrow, 1 mark for correct
     structures.)*
4.6 2-hydroxy-2-methylpropanenitrile *(1 mark)*

4.7 The reaction of acidified KCN and compound A involves
     nucleophilic attack at the carbonyl carbon. The C=O bond
     is planar, and nucleophilic attack can occur from above
     or below the plane of the bond *(1 mark)*. Depending on
     which direction the nucleophile attacks from, a different
     enantiomer will be formed. There is an equal chance that
     the nucleophilic attack will occur from each side of the
     bond, so the two enantiomers form in a racemate/racemic
     mixture *(1 mark)*.
     A racemate/racemic mixture has no effect on plane
     polarised light, as the two enantiomers cancel out each
     other's light-rotating effect *(1 mark)*.
5.1

     (1 mark)
5.2

     *(1 mark for correct chiral centre marked, 1 mark for
     correctly drawn enantiomers.)*
5.3 $2C_2H_5CH(CH_3)COOH + Na_2CO_3 \rightarrow$
     $2C_2H_5CH(CH_3)COONa + H_2O + CO_2$
     *(1 mark for correct chemical formulas, 1 mark for
     balancing the equation)*.
5.4

     (1 mark)
5.5 methyl 2-methylbutanoate *(1 mark)*
5.6 Any strong acid (e.g. $HCl/H_2SO_4/H_3PO_4$) *(1 mark)*.
5.7

     ↓ reflux

     *(1 mark for correct equation, 1 mark for
     correct structure of products)*.
5.8 E.g. food flavouring / perfume / plasticisers / solvent /
     biodiesel production / soap production *(1 mark)*.
6.1 Fats contain mainly saturated hydrocarbon chains, whereas
     oils contain mainly unsaturated hydrocarbon chains
     (1 mark). Saturated hydrocarbon chains fit neatly together
     increasing the van der Waals forces between them, whereas
     unsaturated hydrocarbon chains are bent and don't pack
     well decreasing the van der Waals forces between them
     (1 mark). Stronger van der Waals forces mean a higher
     melting temperature so fats are solid at room temperature,
     whereas weaker van der Waals forces mean a lower melting
     temperature so oils are liquid at room temperature *(1 mark)*.

6.2

$$CH_2OOC(CH_2)_{16}CH_3$$
$$CH_2OOC(CH_2)_{16}CH_3 \quad + 3NaOH$$
$$CH_2OOC(CH_2)_{16}CH_3$$

$$\downarrow$$

H–C–OH
H–C–OH + 3CH$_3$(CH$_2$)$_{16}$COO$^-$Na$^+$
H–C–OH
   H

(1 mark for glycerol, 1 mark for correct sodium salt, 1 mark for balancing the equation).

6.3 soap *(1 mark)*

6.4 Biodiesel is a mixture of methyl esters that can be used as a fuel *(1 mark)*.

6.5

$$CH_2OOC(CH_2)_{16}CH_3$$
$$CH_2OOC(CH_2)_{16}CH_3 \quad + 3CH_3OH$$
$$CH_2OOC(CH_2)_{16}CH_3$$

$$\downarrow$$

H–C–OH
H–C–OH + 3CH$_3$(CH$_2$)$_{16}$COOCH$_3$
H–C–OH
   H

(1 mark for methanol, 1 mark for correct methyl ester, 1 mark for balancing the equation).
These equations are written vertically for space. In the exam, write them horizontally.

6.6 KOH acts as a catalyst *(1 mark)*.

7.1

(1 mark for each correct product, maximum 2 marks).
This equation could also have been written as:
CH$_3$CH(CH$_3$)CH(CH$_3$)COCl + NH$_3$ →
CH$_3$CH(CH$_3$)CH(CH$_3$)CONH$_2$ + HCl

7.2 nucleophilic addition-elimination *(1 mark)*

+ HCl

(1 mark for each correct curly arrow, maximum 5 marks)
Examiners often ask you to name and outline mechanisms. Don't forget to name it — it's easy to get carried away with the mechanism and lose a mark just for forgetting to put the name of the mechanism.

7.3

CH$_3$–C
CH$_3$–C

(1 mark)

7.4 CH$_3$COOCOCH$_3$ + H$_2$O → 2CH$_3$COOH
(1 mark for correct product, 1 mark for balancing the equation.)

7.5

(1 mark for correct reactants, 1 mark for correct products.)

7.6 Ethanoic anhydride *(1 mark)*. Any two from, e.g. ethanoic anhydride is cheaper / less corrosive / reacts less vigorously / doesn't produce toxic HCl fumes *(1 mark for each)*.

7.7 E.g. you could use recrystallisation. To do this, first add just enough hot solvent to the impure aspirin so that it completely dissolves *(1 mark)*. Then, leave the saturated solution of the impure product to cool slowly, allowing solid crystals of pure aspirin to form *(1 mark)*. The aspirin crystals can be removed using filtration, washed with ice-cold solvent and left to dry *(1 mark)*.

Section 6 — Aromatic Compounds and Amines

1. Aromatic Compounds
Page 204 — Application Question
Q1 The $\Delta H_{hydrogenation}$ for cyclohexene is -120 kJmol^{-1}. So if benzene had three double bonds, as in the theoretical molecule cyclohexa-1,3,5-triene, you would expect it to have a $\Delta H_{hydrogenation}$ of -360 kJmol^{-1}. But, $\Delta H_{hydrogenation}$ for benzene is only -208 kJmol^{-1}. This is 152 kJ mol^{-1} less exothermic than expected so benzene must be more stable than cyclohexa-1,3,5-triene would be, so must have a different structure.

Page 205 — Application Questions
Q1 a) 1,2-dinitrobenzene
   b) 4-methylphenol
   c) 2,4,6-trichlorophenylamine

Page 205 — Fact Recall Questions
Q1 Aromatic compounds are compounds that contain a benzene ring.
Q2 Benzene has a planar cyclic structure. Each carbon atom forms single covalent bonds to the carbons on either side of it and to one hydrogen atom. The final unpaired electron on each carbon atom is located in a p-orbital that sticks out above and below the plane of the ring. The p-orbitals on each carbon atom combine to form a ring of delocalised electrons. All the bonds in the ring are the same, so they are the same length which lies between the length of a single C–C bond and a double C=C bond.

2. Reactions of Aromatics
Page 208 — Application Questions
Q1 a) AlCl$_3$
   b)

   c) Electrophilic substitution.

Page 208 — Application Questions
Q2 a) $HNO_3 + H_2SO_4 \rightarrow HSO_4^- + NO_2^+ + H_2O$

Don't forget that the formation of the nitronium ion is part of the mechanism too.
   b) A concentrated H_2SO_4 catalyst and a temperature below 55 °C.

Page 208 — Fact Recall Questions
Q1 Aromatic compounds contain a benzene ring, which is a region of high electron density. Electrophiles are electron deficient so are attracted to these regions of high electron density.
Q2 E.g. nitro compounds can be reduced to form aromatic amines which are used to manufacture dyes and pharmaceuticals / nitro compounds decompose violently when heated so can be used as explosives (e.g. TNT).
Q3 AlCl$_3$ is a halogen carrier. It accepts a lone pair of electrons from the acyl chloride, forming a carbocation. This carbocation is a much stronger electrophile than the acyl chloride and is strong enough to react with the benzene ring.

3. Amines and Amides
Page 212 — Application Questions
Q1 a) ethylamine
   b) dipropylamine
   c) ethyldimethylamine
Q2 a) Ethylamine is the strongest base. The alkyl group on this amine pushes electrons away from itself so the electron density on the nitrogen atom increases. This makes the lone pair more available to form a co-ordinate bond with a hydrogen ion.
   b) Phenylamine is the weakest base. The benzene ring draws electrons towards itself so the nitrogen's lone pair of electrons is partially delocalised onto the ring and the electron density on the nitrogen decreases. This makes the lone pair less available to bond with a hydrogen ion.
Q3 a) propanamide
   b) N-propylmethanamide

Page 212 — Fact Recall Questions
Q1 A quaternary ammonium ion is a positively charged ion that consists of a nitrogen atom with four alkyl groups attached.
Q2 a) A quaternary ammonium salt with at least one long hydrocarbon chain.
   b) E.g. in fabric softener / in hair conditioner / in detergent.
Q3 The availability of the lone pair of electrons on the nitrogen/ the electron density around the nitrogen.

4. Reactions of Amines

Page 216 — Application Questions

Q1 a) $CH_3Cl + 2NH_3 \rightarrow CH_3NH_2 + NH_4Cl$

b) nucleophilic substitution

Q2 a) $CH_3CH_2CN + 2H_2 \rightarrow CH_3CH_2CH_2NH_2$

b) E.g. a platinum/nickel catalyst and high temperature and pressure.

Q3

Page 217 — Fact Recall Questions

Q1 a) Heat the halogenoalkane with an excess of ethanolic ammonia.

b) The amine that is formed still has a lone pair of electrons on the nitrogen so it can still act as a nucleophile. This means that further substitutions can take place, and a mixture of primary, secondary and tertiary amines and quaternary ammonium salts can be produced.

Q2 a) E.g. by reducing the nitrile with $LiAlH_4$ and adding dilute acid. By catalytic hydrogenation (using e.g. a platinum/nickel catalyst and a high temperature and pressure).

b) Catalytic hydrogenation. $LiAlH_4$ is too expensive for industrial use.

Q3 a) primary, secondary and tertiary amines and quaternary ammonium salts

b) an amide

c) an amide and a carboxylic acid

Q4 Take a nitro compound (e.g. nitrobenzene). Heat the nitro compound with tin metal and concentrated HCl under reflux to form a salt. Mix the salt with an alkali (e.g. NaOH) to produce an aromatic amine.

Exam-style Questions — Pages 218-219

1 A **(1 mark)**

2.1

(1 mark for AlCl₃ and reflux, 1 mark for correct products).

2.2 $AlCl_3$ accepts a lone pair of electrons from the propanoyl chloride **(1 mark)**. The resulting carbocation is a strong enough nucleophile to react with benzene **(1 mark)**.

2.3 $CH_3CH_2COCl + AlCl_3 \rightarrow CH_3CH_2CO^+ + AlCl_4^-$
(1 mark, this mark is also awarded if the mechanism for this part of the reaction is correctly shown with curly arrows).

(1 mark for each correct curly arrow, 1 mark for correct structure of intermediate, maximum 3 marks).

2.4 $HNO_3 + H_2SO_4 \rightarrow HSO_4^- + NO_2^+ + H_2O$ *(1 mark)*
E.g.

(1 mark for each correct curly arrow, 1 mark for correct structure of intermediate).

2.5

(1 mark for correct reactants and products, 1 mark for balanced equation).
The conditions are: reflux **(1 mark)** with tin (Sn) and concentrated HCl **(1 mark)**, then add NaOH **(1 mark)**.

3 B **(1 mark)**

4.1 X is 2-methylpropylamine **(1 mark)**.
Y is 2,3-dimethylphenylamine **(1 mark)**.

4.2 $2NH_3 + CH_3CH(CH_3)CH_2Br \rightarrow$
$CH_3CH(CH_3)CH_2NH_2 + NH_4^+Br^-$
(1 mark for correct reactants and products, 1 mark for balanced equation).
It's a nucleophilic substitution reaction *(1 mark)*.

(1 mark for each correct curly arrow, 1 mark for correct structure of intermediate, maximum 4 marks).

4.3 More than one of the hydrogens attached to the nitrogen may be substituted *(1 mark)*.
E.g.

$$CH_2CH(CH_3)CH_3$$

$$H \quad CH_2CH(CH_3)CH_3$$

Triamine and quaternary ammonium salt also acceptable *(1 mark)*.

If you're asked to draw a structure like this and you're given a choice, always just draw the easiest one. You won't get any extra marks for giving harder answers and you're more likely to get it wrong. For example, if you drew the quaternary ammonium salt for this answer and forgot to give it a positive charge you wouldn't get the mark.

4.4 E.g. increase the concentration of ammonia *(1 mark)*.
4.5 E.g. $CH_3CH(CH_3)CN + 4[H] \rightarrow CH_3CH(CH_3)CH_2NH_2$ *(1 mark)*.
Further substitutions aren't possible, so amine X is the only possible product *(1 mark)*.
4.6 There is a lone pair of electrons on the nitrogen which can be donated to form a co-ordinate bond with an H^+ ion *(1 mark)*.
Amine X is the stronger base *(1 mark)*. In amine X the alkyl group pushes electrons away from itself/in amine Y the benzene ring draws electrons towards itself *(1 mark)*. This increases electron density on the nitrogen in amine X/this decreases electron density on the nitrogen in amine Y *(1 mark)*. So the lone pair of electrons is more available to form a bond with hydrogen in amine X/so the lone pair of electrons is less available to form a bond with hydrogen in amine Y *(1 mark)*.

Section 7 — Polymers

1. Condensation Polymerisation
Page 223 — Fact Recall Questions
Q1 a) e.g dicarboxylic acids and diamines / amino acids
    b) dicarboxylic acids and diols
Q2 condensation reactions
Q3 a) E.g.

b) E.g.

c) E.g.
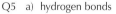

Q4 a) a dicarboxylic acid and a diamine
    b) a dicarboxylic acid and a diol
Q5 a) hydrogen bonds

b) E.g.

hydrogen bonds

2. Monomers & Repeating Units
Pages 227 — Application Questions
Q1 a) polyamide

b) polyester

c) polyamide

d) polyamide

Q2 a)

b)

c)

d)

3. Disposing of Polymers

Page 230 — Application Question

Q1   Polymer A is biodegradable. It's a polyamide, so it can be broken down by hydrolysis. (Polymer B is a polyalkene, so it's chemically inert and non-biodegradable.)

Page 230 — Fact Recall Questions

Q1 a) The bonds in addition polymers are non-polar so they are not susceptible to attack by nucleophiles and won't react easily.

    b) It means they don't react with things and degrade when they are being used.

    c) It means that addition polymers are non-biodegradable.

Q2 a) biodegradable

    b) The bonds in condensation polymers are polar. This means they are susceptible to attack by nucleophiles and can be broken by hydrolysis. This means the polymer will break down naturally. Addition polymers have non-polar bonds which can't be hydrolysed so won't break down naturally.

Q3   E.g. it requires areas of land / as the waste decomposes it releases methane (a greenhouse gas) / leaks from landfill sites can contaminate water supplies.

Q4   By passing the waste gases through scrubbers which can neutralise toxic gases by allowing them to react with a base.

Q5 a) E.g. by melting and remoulding / by cracking into monomers which can be used to make more plastic or other chemicals.

    b) Plastic products are marked with numbers which show what type of plastic they are made from.

    c) Advantages: any two from: e.g. it reduces the amount of waste going into landfill / it saves raw materials / the cost is lower than making plastics from scratch / it produces less CO_2 emissions than burning plastic.
Disadvantages: any two from: e.g. it is technically difficult / it is more expensive than burning/landfill / the product isn't usually suitable for its original purpose / the plastic can be easily contaminated.

Exam-style Questions — Page 231

1   A *(1 mark)*

2.1

(1 mark for each, maximum 2 marks).

2.2 Condensation polymerisation *(1 mark)*

2.3 An amide / peptide link *(1 mark)*

3.1 A polyamide *(1 mark)*.

3.2

$$-\overset{\displaystyle O}{\overset{\|}{C}}-(CH_2)_4-\overset{\displaystyle O}{\overset{\|}{C}}-\underset{\underset{\displaystyle H}{|}}{N}-(CH_2)_6-\underset{\underset{\displaystyle H}{|}}{N}-$$

(1 mark).

When drawing repeating units make sure you include the trailing bonds which join the repeating units together. You'll lose a mark if you don't.

3.3 Biodegradable *(1 mark)*. The amide bonds in nylon 6,6 are polar *(1 mark)*, so they are susceptible to attack by nucleophiles *(1 mark)* and can be hydrolysed *(1 mark)*.

3.4 Advantages: e.g. it reduces the amount of waste going into landfill / it saves raw materials / the cost is lower than making plastics from scratch / it produces less CO_2 emissions than burning the nylon *(1 mark for each, maximum 2 marks)*.
Disadvantages: e.g. it is technically difficult / it is more expensive than burning/landfill / the recycled nylon may not be suitable for its original purpose / the nylon can easily be contaminated during recycling *(1 mark for each, maximum 2 marks)*.

If you get an "advantages/disadvantages" question, make sure you discuss both. If you only give advantages or only give disadvantages you'll only get half marks, no matter how many correct points you've made.

Section 8 — Amino Acids, Proteins and DNA

1. Amino Acids

Page 234 — Application Question

Q1 a) A — 2-aminopropanoic acid
       B — 2-amino-3-hydroxypropanoic acid

    b) (i)

      (ii)

      (iii)

Page 234 — Fact Recall Questions

Q1   Amino acids are said to be amphoteric because they have a basic amino group and an acidic carboxyl group and so have both acidic and basic properties.

Q2   A zwitterion is a dipolar ion, i.e. an ion that has both a positive and a negative charge in different parts of the molecule.

Q3 $R_f = \dfrac{\text{distance travelled by spot}}{\text{distance travelled by solvent front}}$.

Q4   Ninhydrin or a fluorescent dye and UV light would be used to make the colourless amino acids visible to the naked eye.

2. Proteins
Page 238 — Application Question
Q1

Q2

Q3 a) Primary and secondary.
b) hydrogen bonds
c) i) disulfide bonding
   ii) tertiary structure

Page 238 — Fact Recall Questions
Q1 A polymer/sequence of amino acids joined together by peptide links.
Q2 E.g. α-helix and β-pleated sheet.
Q3 The amino acid cysteine, when it's part of a protein.
Q4 They bond different parts of the same protein molecule to help hold the 3D shape of the protein.

3. Enzymes
Page 240 — Fact Recall Questions
Q1 The lock and key model represents how an enzyme works with a substrate. The substrate fits neatly into the active site of an enzyme, forming an enzyme-substrate complex. The enzyme then catalyses the reaction of a substrate to form its products. The enzyme is left unchanged by the reaction.
Q2 An active site that only works on one enantiomer of a chiral substrate.
Q3 a) An inhibitor is roughly the same shape as a substrate of an enzyme. It fits into the active site of an enzyme, which blocks the substrate from getting to the active site.
b) E.g. Inhibitors can be used as drugs.

4. DNA
Page 244 — Fact Recall Questions
Q1 a) A phosphate ion, a 2-deoxyribose sugar molecule and a base.
b)

Q2 a) A covalent bond / phosphodiester bond
b) The phosphate group of one nucleotide and the 2-deoxyribose of another nucleotide.
Q3 a) adenine, cytosine, guanine, thymine
b) Adenine and thymine pair up and form two hydrogen bonds. Cytosine and guanine pair up and form three hydrogen bonds.

5. Cisplatin
Page 246 — Fact Recall Questions
Q1

Q2 a) A nitrogen atom on guanine forms a coordinate bond with the platinum ion of cisplatin, replacing one of the chloride ion ligands. Another nearby guanine molecule undergoes the same reaction by replacing the other chloride ion ligand of cisplatin. This stops the DNA double helix from unwinding and being copied properly, which means it can't replicate.
b) Cisplatin can bind to healthy cells and stop them replicating. This is a problem for cells that replicate frequently such as hair and blood cells and can lead to hair loss and a suppressed immune system.

Exam-style Questions — Pages 248-249
1 B *(1 mark)*
2 B *(1 mark)*
3.1 Tyrosine and cystine *(1 mark)*.
To find the R_f values, divide the distance of the spot from the origin by the distance of the solvent front from the origin. So for Spot A, 3.6 ÷ 6.5 ≈ 0.55, so Spot A could be tyrosine. For Spot B, 1.0 ÷ 6.5 = ≈ 0.15, so Spot B could be cytosine.
3.2

(1 mark)
3.3 The isoelectric point is the pH where the overall charge of an amino acid is zero *(1 mark)*.
3.4

(1 mark)
4.1 hydrolysis *(1 mark)*.

4.2

(2 marks available — 1 mark for each correct amino acid)

4.3 E.g. The primary structure of a protein is the chain of amino acids joined together by peptide links *(1 mark)*. The secondary structure is a result of hydrogen bonds forming between peptide links *(1 mark)*. This is often either an α-helix or a β-pleated sheet *(1 mark)*. The tertiary structure is due to bonds forming between different parts of the polypeptide chain, folding the chain in a characteristic 3D shape *(1 mark)*. These bonds may be hydrogen bonds or disulfide bonds *(1 mark)*. Hydrogen bonds form between polar groups on different amino acid residues *(1 mark)*. Disulfide bonds form between the sulfide groups on different cysteine residues *(1 mark)*.

Section 9 — Further Synthesis and Analysis

1. Organic Synthesis

Page 253 — Application Questions

Q1 a) e.g. H_3PO_4 catalyst, water (steam), 300 °C, 60 atm
b) Cl_2, UV light
c) CH_3COCl, $AlCl_3$ catalyst, reflux, non-aqueous environment
d) NH_3, heat

Q2 a) step 1: conc. H_2SO_4, conc. HNO_3, below 55 °C
product: nitrobenzene
step 2: Sn, conc. HCl, reflux, $NaOH_{(aq)}$
b) step 1: e.g. warm $NaOH_{(aq)}$ or $KOH_{(aq)}$, reflux
product: propanol
step 2: $K_2Cr_2O_7$, H_2SO_4, heat in distillation apparatus
You have to do this reaction in distillation apparatus so that you don't form the carboxylic acid.
c) step 1: e.g. Cl_2, UV light
product: e.g. chloroethane
step 2: $KCN_{(aq)}$, ethanol, reflux
d) step 1: $K_2Cr_2O_7$, H_2SO_4, reflux
product: butanoic acid
step 2: methanol, conc. H_2SO_4 catalyst, heat

Q3 step 1: conc. H_2SO_4, conc. HNO_3, below 55 °C
product: nitrobenzene
step 2: Sn, concentrated HCl, reflux, $NaOH_{(aq)}$
product: phenylamine
step 3: CH_3COCl, 25 °C
product: N-phenylethanamide

Q4 step 1: e.g. warm $NaOH_{(aq)}$ or $KOH_{(aq)}$, reflux
product: ethanol
step 2: $K_2Cr_2O_7$, H_2SO_4, heat, reflux
product: ethanoic acid
step 3: propanol, conc. H_2SO_4 catalyst, reflux
product: propyl ethanoate

Page 253 — Fact Recall Questions

Q1 E.g. limit the potential for accidents / environmental damage.

Q2 E.g. use processes with high atom economies and high percentage yields.
Use synthesis routes that have as few steps as possible.

Q3 E.g. solvents are often flammable and toxic so can pose safety risks. If the solvent has to be separated from the product or disposed of after the reaction is complete that can create a lot of waste too.

Q4 a) NaOH or KOH, warm ethanol, reflux
b) $HCN_{(g)}$ or acidified $KCN_{(aq)}$ and H_2SO_4, 25 °C
c) dilute H_2SO_4 catalyst, H_2O, reflux / dilute $NaOH_{(aq)}$, reflux
d) $LiAlH_4$, dry ether then dilute H_2SO_4 or H_2, Ni or Pt catalyst, high temperature and pressure

Q5 a) amine, 25 °C
b) alcohol, 25 °C
c) NH_3, 25 °C

2. NMR Spectroscopy

Page 255 — Fact Recall Questions

Q1 parts per million/ppm

Q2 E.g. TMS produces a single absorption peak. / Its absorption peak is well away from most other absorption peaks. / TMS is inert (so it doesn't react with the sample). / TMS is volatile (so it's easy to remove from the sample).

3. ^{13}C NMR Spectroscopy

Page 259 — Application Questions

Q1 a) 4
The number of peaks on the ^{13}C NMR spectrum is the same as the number of carbon environments in the molecule...
b) 3
c) 2
This one's a bit tricky. If you draw the molecule, you should see that three of the carbons are CH_3 groups joined to the central carbon atom. These carbons are all in the same environment.
d) 4

Q2 There are four peaks on the spectrum, so the molecule must have four carbon environments. All the peaks lie between $\delta = 10$ ppm and $\delta = 40$ ppm. Since the molecule only contains carbon and hydrogen, these must all represent carbon atoms in C–C bonds. The formula of the molecule is C_5H_{12}, so it must be an isomer of pentane with four carbon environments. The only molecule that fits this description is 2-methylbutane:

Carbon 1 and the methyl group carbon are in the same environment. Carbons 2, 3 and 4 are all in different environments.

Q3 There are three peaks on the spectrum, so the molecule must have three carbon environments. The peaks at δ = 8 ppm must represent carbons in C–C bonds. The peak at δ = 25 ppm could represent a carbon in an R–C–Cl, R–C–Br, C–C group, or a carbon adjacent to a C=O group. From the molecular formula, you can see that it can't be ab R–C–Cl or R–C–Br group, and as there is no peak equivalent to a carbon in a C=O group, it must be due to a carbon in a C–C bond. The peak at δ = 65 ppm must represent a carbon in a C–O bond. The formula of the molecule is $C_4H_{10}O$ and it must have three carbon environments. The only molecule that fits this description is 2-methylpropan-1-ol:

4. ¹H NMR Spectroscopy
Page 264 — Application Questions
Q1 These hydrogen atoms correspond to peak **B**.

This hydrogen atom corresponds to peak **A**.

These hydrogen atoms correspond to peak **C**.

Q2 There are three peaks, so there must be three hydrogen environments in compound **X**.
The peak at δ = 2.5 ppm is likely to be formed by hydrogens in a –COCH– environment.
It can't be an R –NH environment because that wouldn't fit with the molecular formula. And it can't be an R–OH group because the peak isn't a singlet.
The peak at δ = 2.1 ppm is also likely to be formed by hydrogens in a –COCH– environment.
This isn't likely to be an R–OH group because the area ratio tells you that the environment contains more than one hydrogen.
The peak at $\delta \approx 1$ ppm is likely to be formed by hydrogens in an R–CH₃ environment.
It can't be an R –NH group because that wouldn't fit with the formula, and it isn't an R–OH group because it isn't a singlet.
From the area ratios, there are two protons in the environment at δ = 2.5 ppm for every three protons in the environment at δ = 2.1 ppm and for every three protons in the environment at $\delta \approx 1$ ppm. To fit this data, the groups contained in compound **X** must be –COCH₂–, –COCH₃ and –CH₃.
We know that the molecular formula is C_4H_8O and that the –CH₃ group must be next to the –COCH₂– (because their peaks are split into a triplet and a quartet).
So, the molecule must be **butan-2-one**:

Page 264 — Fact Recall Questions
Q1 The number of hydrogen (proton) environments in a compound.
Q2 The relative number of hydrogen atoms in each environment.
Q3 Chemical shift data.
Q4 E.g. CCl_4 / D_2O / $CDCl_3$.

5. Chromatography
Page 268 — Application Questions
Q1 a) R_f value = $\dfrac{\text{distance travelled by spot}}{\text{distance travelled by solvent}}$
   Spot P: R_f value = 2.1 ÷ 8.0 = **0.26**
   Spot Q: R_f value = 3.7 ÷ 8.0 = **0.46**
   Spot R: R_f value = 5.9 ÷ 8.0 = **0.74**
   b) Spot P contains glycine, spot Q contains tyrosine and spot R contains leucine.
Q2 Components that are more strongly adsorbed to the stationary phase take longer to pass down the column so the pure product will leave the column after the impurities.

Page 268 — Fact Recall Questions
Q1 Chromatography is used to separate out the components of a mixture.
Q2 Draw a line in pencil near the bottom of the TLC plate and put a very small drop of each mixture to be separated on the line. Allow the spots on the plate to dry. Place the plate in a beaker with a small volume of solvent and place a watch glass on top of the beaker. Leave the beaker until the solvent has moved almost to the top of the plate. Then remove the plate from the beaker. Use a pencil to mark how far the solvent travelled up the plate. Place the plate in a fume cupboard and leave it to dry.
Q3 a) R_f values are used to identify different substances.
   b) R_f value = $\dfrac{\text{distance travelled by spot}}{\text{distance travelled by solvent}}$
Q4 A chromatography column has a liquid mobile phase, and a solid stationary phase. When a mixture of components is added to the column, some will be more soluble in the mobile phase and some will be more strongly adsorbed to the stationary phase. This means that the components will spend different amounts of time adsorbed onto the stationary phase and dissolved in the mobile phase. So the different components will take different amounts of time to pass through the column and will be separated out.

6. Gas Chromatography
Page 270-271 — Application Questions
Q1 a) The gas chromatograph (GC) separates out the chemicals in the water sample.
   b) E.g. the GC-MS machine will produce a mass spectrum for each individual chemical in the water sample. The scientist can compare these mass spectra to the mass spectrum of glyphosate looking for a match / use a computer to match up the mass spectra for each component of the mixture against a database.
Q2 a) peak A
   b) component B

Q3 a) 11 minutes
   b) Component A because it has the largest peak and the area under each peak tells you the relative amount of each component that's present in the mixture.
   c) butan-1-ol
   d) Run a sample of butan-1-ol under the same conditions as the sample of the mixture and see whether it has the same retention time as component A.

Page 271 — Fact Recall Questions
Q1 E.g. nitrogen gas.
Q2 The time taken from the injection of a sample to the detection of a substance.
Q3 The sample is separated out into its components using gas chromatography (GC). The separated components are fed into a mass spectrometer. This produces a mass spectrum for each component, which can be used to identify each one.
Q4 The components separated out by the GC can be positively identified by the MS. Identifying the components using GC alone can be impossible, because similar compounds often have similar retention times.

Pages 273-274 — Exam-style Questions
1.1 CH_3COCl *(1 mark)*, reflux in a non-aqueous environment *(1 mark)*, with an $AlCl_3$ catalyst *(1 mark)*.
1.2 E.g. aluminium oxide (coated with water) *(1 mark)*.
1.3 Some components of the mixture will be more soluble in the mobile phase and some will be more strongly adsorbed to the stationary phase *(1 mark)*. This means that the phenylethanone will take a different amount of time passing through the column to the impurities *(1 mark)*.
1.4 Spectrum C *(1 mark)*. Phenylethanone has six different carbon environments and so will have six peaks on its ^{13}C NMR spectrum *(1 mark)*.
2.1 E.g. $CDCl_3$ / D_2O / CCl_4 *(1 mark)*.
   Any solvent that contains no ^1H atoms would get the mark here.
2.2 The molecule is ethanol:

$$H-\overset{\overset{\displaystyle H}{|}}{\underset{\underset{\displaystyle H}{|}}{C}}-\overset{\overset{\displaystyle H}{|}}{\underset{\underset{\displaystyle H}{|}}{C}}-OH$$

   (1 mark for correctly identifying the molecule)
   Plus any five from: There are three peaks, so the molecule must have three hydrogen environments *(1 mark)*. The peak at $\delta = 1.2$ ppm must be due to hydrogens in an R–CH_3 environment *(1 mark)*. This peak is a triplet, so there must be two hydrogens on adjacent carbons *(1 mark)*. The singlet peak at $\delta = 2.2$ ppm must be due to a hydrogen in the alcohol group / an R–OH environment *(1 mark)*. The peak at $\delta = 3.8$ ppm must be due to a hydrogen in an R–O–CH environment *(1 mark)*. It is a quartet, so there must be three hydrogens on adjacent carbons *(1 mark)*.
3.1 The sample is separated using gas chromatography *(1 mark)*. The separated components are fed straight into a mass spectrometer, which is used to identify the individual components *(1 mark)*.
3.2 Gas chromatography uses retention times to identify the components of a mixture *(1 mark)*. Similar compounds have similar retention times, so can't be identified accurately *(1 mark)*.
3.3 5 *(1 mark)*
   If you had trouble with this, have a look back at the bit of the ^{13}C NMR topic about aromatic compounds and symmetry.

4.1 Some components of the mixture will be more strongly adsorbed to the stationary phase than others *(1 mark)*. So the components will spend different amounts of time adsorbed to the stationary phase and will travel different distances in the same time *(1 mark)*.
4.2 R_f value $= \dfrac{\text{distance travelled by spot}}{\text{distance travelled by solvent}}$
   $= 2.2$ cm $\div 9.2$ cm $= \mathbf{0.24}$ *(1 mark)*
4.3 The peaks will be: a singlet caused by the hydrogens attached to carbon d *(1 mark)*, a quartet caused by the hydrogens attached to carbon b *(1 mark)* and a triplet caused by the hydrogens attached to carbon a *(1 mark)*.

Glossary

A

Accurate result
A result that's really close to the true answer.

Achiral molecule
A molecule that can be superimposed on its mirror image.

Acid anhydride
A molecule formed from two identical carboxylic acid molecules, joined via an oxygen atom with the carbonyl groups on either side.

Acid dissociation constant, K_a
An equilibrium constant specific to weak acids that relates the acid concentration to the concentration of $[H^+]$ ions. $K_a = [H^+][A^-] \div [HA]$.

Acidic buffer
A buffer with a pH of less than 7 containing a mixture of a weak acid with one of its salts.

Acyl chloride
A molecule which contains the functional group $COCl$.

Acylation
When an acyl group ($-COR$) is added to a molecule.

Addition polymer
A type of polymer formed by joining small alkenes (monomers) together.

Adsorption
The attraction between a substance and the surface of the solid stationary phase in thin-layer chromatography, column chromatography and gas chromatography.

Aim
The question an experiment is trying to answer..

Alcohol
A substance with the general formula $C_nH_{2n+1}OH$.

Aldehyde
A substance with the general formula $C_nH_{2n}O$ which has a hydrogen and one alkyl group attached to a carbonyl carbon atom.

Amide
A carboxylic acid derivative which contains the functional group $CONH_2$.

Amide link
The -CONH- group which is found between monomers in a polyamide.

Amine
A molecule where one or more of the hydrogen atoms in ammonia have been replaced with an organic functional group, such as an alkyl or an aromatic group.

Amino acid
A molecule with an amino group (NH_2) and a carboxyl group ($COOH$).

Amphoteric
Having both acidic and basic properties.

Anomalous result
A result that doesn't fit in with the pattern of the other results in a set of data.

Aromatic compound
A compound that contains a benzene ring.

Arrhenius equation
An equation that links the rate constant, k, to temperature and activation energy.

Arrhenius plot
A graph where 1/temperature is plotted against $\ln k$, where k is the rate constant.

Autocatalysis
When a reaction is catalysed by one of its products.

B

Base (of DNA)
One of four molecules (adenine, thymine, cytosine, guanine) attached to the sugar-phosphate backbone in DNA.

Basic buffer
A buffer with a pH of more than 7 containing a mixture of a weak base with one of its salts.

Bidentate ligand
A ligand that can form two co-ordinate bonds in a complex ion.

Biodegradable
Will break down naturally.

Biodiesel
A mixture of methyl esters of fatty acids which can be used as a carbon neutral fuel.

Bond dissociation enthalpy (ΔH_{diss})
The enthalpy change when all the bonds of the same type in 1 mole of gaseous molecules are broken.

Born-Haber cycle
An enthalpy cycle that allows you to calculate the lattice enthalpy change of formation for a system.

Brønsted-Lowry acid
A proton donor.

Brønsted-Lowry base
A proton acceptor.

Buffer
A solution that resists changes in pH when small amounts of acid or alkali are added.

C

Calibration curve/graph
A graph which shows the relationship between a measurement taken in an experiment and a property of a substance. It can be used to determine an unknown value.

Carbocation
An ion containing a positively charged carbon atom.

Carbonyl compound
An organic compound which contains a carbonyl group ($C=O$) as its only functional group.

Carboxylic acid
A molecule which contains a carboxyl group ($COOH$).

Catalyst
A substance that increases the rate of a reaction by providing an alternative reaction pathway with a lower activation energy. The catalyst is chemically unchanged at the end of the reaction.

Catalyst poisoning
When impurities in a reaction mixture bind to a catalyst's surface, blocking reactants from being adsorbed and reducing the effectiveness of the catalyst.

Catalytic hydrogenation
A chemical reaction in which hydrogen is added to an unsaturated molecule by reacting the molecule with molecular hydrogen (H_2) in the presence of a catalyst.

Categoric data
Data that can be sorted into categories.

Cationic surfactant
A surfactant which is positively charged.

Causal link
The relationship between two variables where a change in one variable causes a change in the other.

Cell potential, E_{cell}
The voltage between two half-cells in an electrochemical cell.

Chelate effect
When monodentate ligands are substituted with multidentate ligands, the number of particles and the entropy of the system increases without enthalpy changing significantly. Reactions that result in an increase in entropy and little change in enthalpy are more likely to occur, so multidentate ligands form much more stable complexes than monodentate ligands.

Chemical shift
Nuclei in different environments absorb energy of different frequencies. NMR spectroscopy measures these differences relative to a standard substance — the difference is called the chemical shift (δ).

Chiral carbon
A carbon atom that has four different groups attached to it.

Chromatogram
A visual record (such as a pattern of spots or a graph) of the results of a chromatography experiment.

Chromatography
An analytical technique which uses a mobile phase and a stationary phase to separate out mixtures into their constituent components.

Cisplatin
A platinum-containing complex ion with a square planar shape that can be used as an anti-cancer drug.

Cis-trans isomerism
A special type of *E/Z* isomerism where two of the groups attached to the carbon atoms around the C=C double bond are the same.

Clock reaction
A reaction where, after a period of time, there's a sudden increase in the concentration of a product.

Colorimeter
An instrument for measuring how much light is absorbed by a sample.

Column chromatography
A type of chromatography where the stationary phase is a column packed with a solid, and the mobile phase is a liquid solvent.

Complex ion
A metal ion surrounded by co-ordinately bonded ligands.

Condensation polymer
A type of polymer formed through a series of condensation reactions.

Condensation reaction
A chemical reaction in which two molecules are joined together and a small molecule is eliminated.

Contact Process
An industrially used method of producing sulfuric acid.

Continuous data
Data that can have any value on a scale.

Continuous monitoring
A method of following a reaction by monitoring the formation of a product or the loss of a reactant, over the course of a reaction.

Control variable
A variable that is kept constant in an experiment.

Co-ordinate bond
A covalent bond in which both electrons in the shared pair come from the same atom (also called a dative covalent bond).

Co-ordination number
The number of co-ordinate bonds that are formed with the central metal ion in a complex ion.

Correlation
The relationship between two variables.

Corrosive substance
A substance that may cause chemical burns.

D

d-block
The block of elements in the middle of the periodic table.

d sub-level
A type of sub-level. Each can hold ten electrons.

Data logger
A device that can record data readings automatically at set intervals and store them to be looked at later.

Dative covalent bond
A covalent bond in which both electrons in the shared pair come from the same atom (also called a co-ordinate bond).

Dependent variable
The variable that you measure in an experiment.

Deuterated solvent
A solvent which has had all of its hydrogen atoms exchanged for deuterium atoms.

Deuterium
An isotope of hydrogen. It contains one neutron, one proton and one electron.

Diprotic acid
An acid that releases two H^+ ions per molecule.

Discrete data
Data that can only take certain values.

Distillation
A method of separating liquids with different boiling points by gently heating them.

Disulfide bond
A covalent bond between sulfur atoms in two different thiol groups.

DNA
Deoxyribonucleic acid — two complementary polynucleotide chains joined together in a double helix structure.

Double helix
A shape formed by two helices twisted around each other.

Drying agent
An anhydrous salt, such as magnesium sulfate or calcium chloride, that can be used to remove water from an organic product.

E

E/Z isomerism
A type of stereoisomerism that is caused by the restricted rotation about a carbon-carbon double bond. Each of the carbon atoms must have two different groups attached.

Electric heater
A piece of equipment used to heat a reaction mixture, consisting of a plate of metal that is heated to a set temperature.

Electrochemical cell
An electrical circuit made from two metal electrodes dipped in salt solutions and connected by a wire.

Electrochemical series
A list of electrode potentials written in order from most negative to most positive.

Electrode potential
The voltage measured when a half-cell is connected to a standard hydrogen electrode.

Electromotive force (EMF)
Another name for the cell potential.

Electrophile
An electron deficient (and usually positively charged) species which is attracted to regions of high electron density.

Electrophilic substitution
A reaction mechanism where an electrophile substitutes for an atom (or group of atoms) in a molecule.

Enantiomer
A molecule that has the same structural formula as another molecule but with four groups arranged around a chiral carbon atom so that it is a non-superimposable mirror image of the other molecule.

End point
The point in a titration at which all the acid is just neutralised and the pH curve becomes vertical.

Endothermic reaction
A reaction that absorbs energy (ΔH is positive).

Energy gap (ΔE)
The amount of energy needed for an electron to transfer to a higher orbital.

Enthalpy change of atomisation of a compound (ΔH_{at})
The enthalpy change when 1 mole of a compound in its standard state is converted to gaseous atoms.

Enthalpy change of atomisation of an element (ΔH_{at})
The enthalpy change when 1 mole of gaseous atoms is formed from an element in its standard state.

Enthalpy change of formation ($\Delta H^{\ominus}_{f}$)
The enthalpy change when 1 mole of a compound is formed from its elements in their standard states under standard conditions.

Enthalpy change of hydration (ΔH_{hyd})
The enthalpy change when 1 mole of aqueous ions is formed from gaseous ions.

Enthalpy change of solution ($\Delta H_{solution}$)
The enthalpy change when 1 mole of an ionic substance dissolves in enough solvent to form an infinitely dilute solution.

Entropy (S)
A measure of the amount of disorder in a system (e.g. the number of ways that particles can be arranged and the number of ways that the energy can be shared out between the particles).

Enzyme
A protein that acts as a biological catalyst.

Equilibrium constant, K_p
A ratio worked out from the partial pressures of the gaseous products and reactants once a reversible reaction has reached equilibrium.

Ester
A molecule that contains the functional group RCOOR.

Ester link
The -COO- group which is found between monomers in a polyester.

Esterification
Forming an ester by heating a carboxylic acid and an alcohol in the presence of a strong acid catalyst.

Exothermic reaction
A reaction that gives out energy (ΔH is negative).

F

Fatty acid
A long chain carboxylic acid which can combine with glycerol to form a fat or an oil.

Feasible reaction
A reaction that, once started, will carry on to completion, without any energy being supplied to it.

Fehling's solution
A blue solution of complexed copper(II) ions dissolved in sodium hydroxide which can be used to distinguish between aldehydes and ketones.

Filtration
A technique used to separate solids from liquids.

First electron affinity (ΔH_{ea1})
The enthalpy change when 1 mole of gaseous 1– ions is made from 1 mole of gaseous atoms.

First ionisation energy (ΔH_{ie1})
The enthalpy change when 1 mole of gaseous 1+ ions is formed from 1 mole of gaseous atoms.

Flammable substance
A substance that catches fire easily.

Free-energy change (ΔG)
A measure which links enthalpy and entropy changes to predict whether a reaction is feasible.
$\Delta G = \Delta H - T\Delta S$

Fuel cell
A device that converts the energy of a fuel into electricity through an oxidation reaction.

G

Gas chromatography (GC)
A type of chromatography where the stationary phase is a tube packed with a solid, and the mobile phase is an unreactive gas.

H

Haber Process
An industrially used method of producing ammonia.

Haem
A part of the haemoglobin molecule, consisting of a central Fe(II) ion bonded to four nitrogen atoms from a porphyrin ring.

Haemoglobin
A protein found in blood that helps to transport oxygen around the body.

Half-cell
One half of an electrochemical cell.

Half-equation
An ionic equation that shows oxidation or reduction — one half of a full redox equation.

Halogen carrier
A molecule which can accept a halogen atom (e.g. $AlCl_3$). Used as a catalyst in Friedel-Crafts acylation reactions.

Hess's law
The total enthalpy change of a reaction is always the same, no matter which route is taken.

Heterogeneous catalyst
A catalyst which is in a different physical state to the reactants.

Homogeneous catalyst
A catalyst which is in the same physical state as the reactants.

Hydrogen bonding
A type of weak bonding which occurs between hydrogen atoms and electronegative atoms in polar groups (e.g. $-NH_2$ and $-OH$).

Hydrolysis
A reaction where molecules are split apart by water molecules.

Hydroxynitrile
A molecule which contains a hydroxyl group (OH) and a nitrile group (CN).

Hypothesis
A suggested explanation for a fact or observation.

I

Independent variable
The variable that you change in an experiment.

Indicator
A substance that changes colour over a particular pH range.

Inhibitor
A molecule that is a similar shape to a substrate of an enzyme, that blocks the active site of the enzyme and stops it interacting with the substrate.

Initial rates method
An experimental technique that can be used to work out the orders of a reaction.

Integration trace
A line on a ^1H NMR spectrum that has a change in height that is proportional to the area of the peak it's next to.

Ionic product of water, K_w
A constant generated by multiplying the K_c for the dissociation of water by $[H_2O]$. $K_w = [H^+][OH^-]$.

Irritant substance
A substance that may cause inflammation or discomfort.

Isoelectric point
The pH at which the average overall charge on a molecule is zero.

K

Ketone
A substance with the general formula $C_nH_{2n}O$ which has two alkyl groups attached to a carbonyl carbon atom.

L

Lattice dissociation enthalpy
The enthalpy change when 1 mole of a solid ionic compound is completely dissociated into its gaseous ions.

Lattice formation enthalpy
The enthalpy change when 1 mole of a solid ionic compound is formed from its gaseous ions.

Le Chatelier's Principle
If there's a change in concentration, pressure or temperature, an equilibrium will move to help counteract the change.

Ligand
An atom, ion or molecule that donates a pair of electrons to a central metal ion in a complex ion.

Ligand substitution/exchange reaction
A reaction where one or more ligands are changed for one or more other ligands in a metal complex ion.

M

Melting point apparatus
Equipment that can be used to test the purity of an organic product by measuring its melting point.

Metal-aqua complex ion
A species formed when metal ions dissolve in water. The water molecules form co-ordinate bonds with the metal ions.

Method
A set of instructions detailing how to carry out an experiment safely.

Methyl orange
A pH indicator that changes colour between pH 3.1 and 4.4.

Mobile phase
A liquid or a gas used in chromatography which contains molecules that can move.

Mole fraction
A measure of the proportion of a mixture that is made up of a particular substance.

Monodentate ligand
A ligand that can only form one co-ordinate bond in a complex ion.

Monomer
A small molecule which can join together with other monomers to form a polymer.

Monoprotic acid
An acid that releases one H^+ ion per molecule.

Multidentate ligand
A ligand that can form two or more co-ordinate bonds in a complex ion.

Multiplet
A split peak on a ^1H NMR spectrum. (General term for a doublet, triplet, quartet, etc.)

n+1 rule
Peaks on a ^1H NMR spectrum always split into the number of hydrogens on the neighbouring carbon(s), plus one.

N-substituted amide
An amide where one of the hydrogens attached to the nitrogen has been substituted with an alkyl group.

Nitration
A reaction in which a nitro group (NO_2) is added to a molecule.

Nuclear magnetic resonance (NMR) spectroscopy
An analytical technique used to determine the relative environment of the nuclei in a compound.

Nucleophile
A species that forms a bond with an electrophile by donating a pair of electrons.

Nucleophilic addition-elimination
A reaction mechanism where a nucleophile adds on to the δ^+ carbon atom of a carbonyl group and another molecule is eliminated.

Nucleophilic substitution
A reaction mechanism where a nucleophile substitutes for an atom (or group of atoms) in a molecule.

Nucleotide
A molecule that is made up of a phosphate ion, a pentose sugar, and a (genetic) base.

O

Optical isomer
A molecule that has the same structural formula as another molecule but with four groups arranged around a chiral carbon atom so that it is a non-superimposable mirror image of the other molecule.

Orbital
A region of a sub-level that contains a maximum of 2 electrons.

Order of reaction (reaction order)
A number that tells you how the concentration of a particular reactant affects the reaction rate.

Ordered (ordinal) data
Categoric data where the categories can be put in order.

Oxidation
The loss of electrons.

Oxidation state
The total number of electrons an element has donated or accepted. Also called an oxidation number.

Oxidising agent
Something that accepts electrons and gets reduced.

Oxidising substance
A substance that reacts to form oxygen, meaning that other substances burn more easily in its presence.

P

Partial pressure
The pressure that an individual gas, in a mixture of gases, exerts on a system.

Pentose sugar
A sugar with five carbon atoms.

Peptide
A polymer formed from reactions between amino acids.

Peptide link (bond)
The bonds which hold amino acids together in a protein.

pH
A measure of the hydrogen ion concentration in a solution.
$pH = -\log_{10}[H^+]$

pH chart
A chart that shows the colour of an indicator at different pHs.

pH curve
A graph of pH against volume of acid/alkali added.

pH meter
An electronic device used to measure pH, made up of a probe connected to a digital display.

Phenolphthalein
A pH indicator that changes colour between pH 8.3 and 10.

Plane polarised light
Light in which all the waves are vibrating in the same plane.

Polyamide
A polymer containing amide links between the monomers. Can be formed from reactions between dicarboxylic acids and diamines.

Polyester
A polymer containing ester links between the monomers. Can be formed from reactions between dicarboxylic acids and diols.

Polymer
A long molecule formed from lots of repeating units (called monomers).

Polynucleotide
A polymer formed of nucleotides.

Polypeptide
A polymer formed from reactions between amino acids.

Porphyrin
A multidentate ligand found in a number of biological molecules including haemoglobin.

Precise result
Results where the data have a very small spread around the mean.

Prediction
A specific testable statement about what will happen in an experiment, based on observation, experience or a hypothesis.

Primary structure (of proteins)
The first 'level' that describes the structure of protein — i.e. the sequence of amino acids in the polypeptide chain.

Protein
One or more polypeptides folded into a structure which has a biological function.

Purely ionic model of a lattice
A model which assumes that all the ions in a lattice are spherical and have their charge evenly distributed around them. This model is also known as the perfect ionic model.

R

Racemate (or racemic mixture)
A mixture that contains equal quantities of each enantiomer of an optically active compound.

Random error
An error introduced by a factor that you cannot control.

Rate constant, k
A constant in the rate equation for a reaction at a certain temperature. The larger it is the faster the rate of reaction.

Rate-determining step
The slowest step in a reaction mechanism which determines the overall rate of a reaction.

Rate equation
An equation of the form rate = $k[A]^m[B]^n$ which tells you how the rate of a reaction is affected by the concentration of reactants.

Reaction rate
The change in the amount of reactants or products over time.

Recrystallisation
A process of purifying a solid organic compound.

Redistillation
A process of purification, by repeatedly distilling.

Redox potential
A measure of how easily an atom, molecule or ion is reduced.

Redox reaction
A reaction where reduction and oxidation happen simultaneously.

Redox titration
A titration which can be performed to determine how much reducing agent is needed to exactly react with a quantity of oxidising agent, or vice versa.

Reducing agent
Something that donates electrons and gets oxidised.

Reduction
The gain of electrons.

Refluxing
A method of heating a reaction so that you can increase the temperature of an organic reaction to boiling without losing volatile solvents, reactants or products. Any vaporised compounds are cooled, condense and drip back into the reaction mixture.

Repeatable result
A result is repeatable if you can repeat an experiment multiple times and get the same result.

Repeating unit
A part of a polymer that repeats over and over again.

Reproducible result
A result is reproducible if someone else can recreate your experiment and get the same result you do.

Retention
The process of being adsorbed onto the stationary phase in chromatography.

Retention time
The time taken for a component of a mixture to pass through a chromatography column to the detector at the other end.

R_f value
The ratio of the distance travelled by a spot to the distance travelled by the solvent in thin-layer chromatography.

Risk assessment
A procedure carried out to identify any hazards associated with an experiment and how to reduce the risks these hazards present.

S

Salt bridge
A connection between two half-cells that ions can flow through, used to complete the circuit. Usually a piece of filter paper soaked in a salt solution or a glass tube filled with a salt solution.

Sand bath
A piece of equipment used to heat a reaction mixture, consisting of a container filled with sand that can be heated to a set temperature.

Saturated fatty acid
A fatty acid that contains no double bonds — found in fats.

Second electron affinity (ΔH_{ea2})
The enthalpy change when 1 mole of gaseous 2− ions is made from 1 mole of gaseous 1− ions.

Second ionisation energy (ΔH_{ie2})
The enthalpy change when 1 mole of gaseous 2+ ions is formed from 1 mole of gaseous 1+ ions.

Secondary structure (of proteins)
The second 'level' that describes the structure of protein — e.g. how the primary structure folds and twists to form an α-helix or β-pleated sheet, held together by hydrogen bonds.

Separation
A technique to separate the water-soluble impurities out of an organic mixture. The aqueous and organic solutions can be separated as they are immiscible, and separate out into two distinct layers due to their different densities.

Solvent extraction
A form of separation, where the product is shaken vigorously with an immiscible solvent.

Solvent front
The distance travelled by the solvent in thin-layer chromatography.

Spectroscopy
The study of what happens when radiation interacts with matter.

Splitting pattern
Peaks in ^{1}H NMR spectra may be split into further peaks. The resultant group of peaks is called a splitting pattern.

Standard conditions
A temperature of 298 K (25 °C), a pressure of 100 kPa and all ion solutions having a concentration of 1.00 mol dm^{-3}.

Standard electrode potential
The voltage measured under standard conditions when a half-cell is connected to a standard hydrogen electrode.

Standard hydrogen electrode
An electrode where hydrogen gas is bubbled through a solution of aqueous H$^+$ ions under standard conditions.

Stationary phase
A solid, or a liquid held in a solid, used in chromatography which contains molecules that can't move.

Stereoisomer
A molecule that has the same structural formula as another molecule but with the atoms arranged differently in space.

Stereospecific active site
An active site that only reacts with one enantiomer of a chiral compound.

Strong acid/base
An acid or base that fully dissociates in water.

Sub-level
A subdivision of an energy level. A sub-level may be an s, p, d or f sub-level.

Substrate
A molecule that is acted on by an enzyme.

Surfactant
A compound which is partly soluble and partly insoluble in water.

Synthetic route (synthesis)
A method detailing how to create a chemical.

Systematic error
An error introduced by the apparatus or method you use in an experiment.

Tertiary structure (of proteins)
The third 'level' that describes the structure of protein — i.e. how the secondary structure folds and twists to form a 3D molecule, held together by hydrogen and disulfide bonds.

Thin-layer chromatography (TLC)
A type of chromatography where the stationary phase is a plate coated with a solid and the mobile phase is a liquid solvent.

Titration
An experimental technique that lets you work out exactly how much alkali is needed to neutralise a quantity of acid.

Tollens' reagent
A colourless solution of silver nitrate dissolved in aqueous ammonia which can be used to distinguish between aldehydes and ketones.

Toxic substance
A substance that can cause illness or even death.

Transition metal
A metal that can form one or more stable ions with a partially filled d sub-level.

Unsaturated fatty acid
A fatty acid that contains double bonds — found in oils.

Valid result
A result which answers the question it was intended to answer.

Variable
A factor in an experiment or investigation that can change or be changed.

Washing
A method of purifying a product by washing it with chemicals, such as washing with sodium hydrogen carbonate solution to remove acids.

Water bath
A piece of equipment used to heat a reaction mixture, consisting of a container filled with water that can be heated to a set temperature.

Weak acid/base
An acid or base that only partially dissociates in water.

Zwitterion
A dipolar ion which has both a negative and a positive charge in different parts of the molecule.

Acknowledgements

Photograph Acknowledgments

Cover Photo Science Photo Library, p 2 **Martyn F. Chillmaid**/Science Photo Library, p 4 © **Ecelop**/iStockphoto.com, p 5 **Andrew Lambert Photography**/Science Photo Library, p 7 (top) **Martin Shields**/Science Photo Library, p 7 (bottom) **Andrew Lambert Photography**/Science Photo Library, p 8 **Andrew Lambert Photography**/Science Photo Library, p 10 **Martyn F. Chillmaid**/Science Photo Library, p 15 **Gustoimages**/Science Photo Library, p 21 **David Taylor**/Science Photo Library, p 23 Science Photo Library, p 24 **Andrew Lambert Photography**/Science Photo Library, p 28 **Andrew Lambert Photography**/Science Photo Library, p 30 **Adam Hart-Davis**/Science Photo Library, p 33 Science Photo Library, p 44 (top) © **photongpix**/iStockphoto.com, p 44 (bottom) **Andrew Lambert Photography**/Science Photo Library, p 51 **Andrew Lambert Photography**/Science Photo Library, p 58 (top) **Andrew Lambert Photography**/Science Photo Library, p 58 (bottom) **Andrew Lambert Photography**/Science Photo Library, p 65 **Emilio Segre Visual Archives/American Institute of Physics**/Science Photo Library, p 68 **Martin Bond**/Science Photo Library, p 69 Science Photo Library, p 72 © **MichaelJay**/iStockphoto.com, p 74 **Charles D. Winters**/Science Photo Library, p 79 **Charles D. Winters**/Science Photo Library, p 80 **Martyn F. Chillmaid**/Science Photo Library, p 84 **E. R. Degginger**/Science Photo Library, p 87 **Andrew Lambert Photography**/Science Photo Library, p 91 (top) **Cordelia Molloy**/Science Photo Library, p 91 (bottom) **Martin Bond**/Science Photo Library, p 92 **Charles D. Winters**/Science Photo Library, p 99 **Charles D. Winters**/Science Photo Library, p 100 **Martyn F. Chillmaid**/Science Photo Library, p 101 **Martyn F. Chillmaid**/Science Photo Library, p 102 **Martyn F. Chillmaid**/Science Photo Library, p 103 **Andrew Lambert Photography**/Science Photo Library, p 107 Science Photo Library, p 108 (top) **Andrew Lambert Photography**/Science Photo Library, p 108 (bottom) **Andrew Lambert Photography**/Science Photo Library, p 110 **Andrew Lambert Photography**/Science Photo Library, p 114 **Charles D. Winters**/Science Photo Library, p 115 (top) **Charles D. Winters**/Science Photo Library, p 115 (bottom) **Andrew Brookes, National Physical Laboratory**/Science Photo Library, p 116 **Paul Whitehill**/Science Photo Library, p 124 **Charles D. Winters**/Science Photo Library, p 125 (top) **Andrew Lambert Photography**/Science Photo Library, p 125 (bottom) **Jerry Mason**/Science Photo Library, p 127 **Martyn F. Chillmaid**/Science Photo Library, p 130 **Klaus Guldbrandsen**/Science Photo Library, p 131 **Astrid & Hanns-Frieder Michler**/Science Photo Library, p 132 **Andrew Lambert Photography**/Science Photo Library, p 135 **Dr Mark J. Winter**/Science Photo Library, p 136 **Andrew Lambert Photography**/Science Photo Library, p 141 (left) **Andrew Lambert Photography**/Science Photo Library, p 141 (right) **Andrew Lambert Photography**/Science Photo Library, p 142 **Andrew Lambert Photography**/Science Photo Library, p 145 **Ower And Syred**/Science Photo Library, p 146 **Dr Tim Evans**/Science Photo Library, p 148 **Andrew Lambert Photography**/Science Photo Library, p 149 **Andrew Lambert Photography**/Science Photo Library, p 150 Science Photo Library, p 152 **Martyn F. Chillmaid**/Science Photo Library, p 153 **Andrew Lambert Photography**/Science Photo Library, p 156 **Sheila Terry**/Science Photo Library, p 157 **Andrew Lambert Photography**/Science Photo Library, p 160 **Andrew Lambert Photography**/Science Photo Library, p 161 (top) **Charles D. Winters**/Science Photo Library, p 161 (bottom) **Chris Hellier**/Science Photo Library, p 162 **Andrew Lambert Photography**/Science Photo Library, p 170 **Klaus Guldbrandsen**/Science Photo Library, p 175 (top) **Andrew Lambert Photography**/Science Photo Library, p 175 (bottom) **Andrew Lambert Photography**/Science Photo Library, p 176 **Andrew Lambert Photography**/Science Photo Library, p 180 **Tek Image**/Science Photo Library, p 182 **Cristina Pedrazzini**/Science Photo Library, p 185 **Maximilian Stock Ltd**/Science Photo Library, p 186 **Andrew Lambert Photography**/Science Photo Library, p 187 **Ria Novosti**/Science Photo Library, p 188 **Andrew Lambert Photography**/Science Photo Library, p 192 **Cordelia Molloy**/Science Photo Library, p 193 Science Photo Library, p 203 **Clive Freeman, The Royal Institution**/Science Photo Library, p 207 (top) © **rclassenlayouts**/iStockphoto.com, p 207 (bottom) Science Photo Library, p 210 © **rezkrr**/iStockphoto.com, p 215 **Martyn F. Chillmaid**/Science Photo Library, p 216 **Andrew Lambert Photography**/Science Photo Library, p 221 © **fotokostic**/iStockphoto.com, p 222 © **monkeybusinessimages**/iStockphoto.com, p 229 **Andrew Lambert Photography**/Science Photo Library, p 234 **Mauro Fermariello**/Science Photo Library, p 236 (top) **Laguna Design**/Science Photo Library, p 236 (bottom) **Laguna Design**/Science Photo Library, p 239 **Kenneth Eward**/Science Photo Library, p 240 **Jan Van De Vel/Reporters**/Science Photo Library, p 244 **A. Barrington Brown**/Science Photo Library, p 245 **Dr P. Marazzi**/Science Photo Library, p 252 **Martyn F. Chillmaid**/Science Photo Library, p 255 **Hank Morgan**/Science Photo Library, p 262 **Hank Morgan**/Science Photo Library, p 263 **Friedrich Saurer**/Science Photo Library, p 266 **Sinclair Stammers**/Science Photo Library, p 267 **Sinclair Stammers**/Science Photo Library, p 270 **Patrick Landmann**/Science Photo Library, p 280 (top) © **Achim Prill**/iStockphoto.com, p 280 (bottom) **Martyn F. Chillmaid**/Science Photo Library, p 286 © **AtomStudios**/iStockphoto.com

Index

A

accuracy 15
acid anhydrides 191, 192
acid dissociation constant, K_a
    102-104
acid hydrolysis 184
acidic buffers 114, 116, 118
acyl chlorides 188-190
adenine 241-244
alcohols 176, 182, 188
aldehydes 174-177
amide links 220
amides 189, 211, 212
amines 188, 209-211, 213-216
amino acids 232-236
ammonia 163, 188, 211, 213
amphoteric 161, 232
anomalous results 13
aromatic amines 211, 216
aromatic compounds
    202-208, 216
Arrhenius equation 64-67
Arrhenius plots 66, 67
aspirin 192
autocatalysis 157
average (mean) 11

B

bar charts 11
base hydrolysis 185, 186
basic buffers 115, 116
batteries 90
benzene 202, 203
bidentate ligands 135, 138, 147
biodegradable polymers 228
biodiesel 186, 187
bond dissociation enthalpy 22
Born-Haber cycles 23-25
Brønsted-Lowry acids 97
Brønsted-Lowry bases 97
buffers 114-118

C

^{13}C NMR 254-259
calibration graphs 44, 142, 143
carbon monoxide poisoning 145
carbonyl group 174
carboxylic acids 175, 181, 182
catalyst poisoning 156
catalysts 74, 132, 155-158
catalytic hydrogenation 214, 215
categoric data 10
cationic surfactants 210
cell potentials 79, 82, 87
chelate effect 147
chemical shift 255, 257, 261
chirality 170-173, 179, 232
chromatograms 265, 266, 269
chromatography 265-270
cis-trans isomerism 138, 139
cisplatin 139, 245, 246
clock reactions 58, 59
colorimetry 44, 141, 142
column chromatography
    267, 268
command words 288
complementary base pairing 244
complex ions 132, 134-139,
    144-147, 159-163
   isomerism 138, 139
   metal-aqua ions 159-163
   shapes of 136
   stability 146, 147
concentration-time graphs
    47, 48, 60
conclusions 14
condensation polymers 220-228
condensation reaction 220, 235
Contact Process 155
continuous data 10
continuous monitoring 42-45
control variables 1
coordinate bonds 134, 136, 159
coordination number 136, 141
correlation 13, 14
corrosive substances 4
curly arrows 289
cytosine 241-244

D

d-block elements 130
data loggers 6
delocalised electrons 202
dependent variables 1
deuterated solvents 263
dipeptides 235
diprotic acids 100, 111, 112
discrete data 10
displayed formulas 289
dissociation
   of acids 97, 102, 103
   of bases 97
   of lattices 21
   of water 98
distillation 194, 195
disulfide bonding 237
DNA 241-246
double helix 243, 244
drying agents 193

E

E_{cell} 79, 82, 87
EDTA 134, 135
electric heaters 6
electrochemical cells
    79-82, 90-92
electrochemical series 86
electrode potentials 80, 84-86
electron configurations 130, 131
electrophiles 206
electrophilic substitution
    206, 207
EMF 79, 82, 87
enantiomers 138, 170, 172
endothermic reactions 20
energy gap, ΔE 140
enthalpy change
   of atomisation 22
   of formation 22
   of hydration 22, 28
   of hydrogenation 203
   of lattice dissociation 21, 28
   of lattice formation
    20, 21, 23-26
   of solution 22, 28
entropy 30, 31

The Periodic Table

			Group 0
			4.0 He helium 2

Relative Atomic Mass (A_r)

Atomic (proton) number

1.0 H hydrogen 1								

Periods	Group 1	Group 2		Group 3	Group 4	Group 5	Group 6	Group 7	Group 0
1									4.0 He helium 2
2	6.9 Li lithium 3	9.0 Be beryllium 4		10.8 B boron 5	12.0 C carbon 6	14.0 N nitrogen 7	16.0 O oxygen 8	19.0 F fluorine 9	20.2 Ne neon 10
3	23.0 Na sodium 11	24.3 Mg magnesium 12		27.0 Al aluminium 13	28.1 Si silicon 14	31.0 P phosphorus 15	32.1 S sulfur 16	35.5 Cl chlorine 17	39.9 Ar argon 18
4	39.1 K potassium 19	40.1 Ca calcium 20	*transition metals*	69.7 Ga gallium 31	72.6 Ge germanium 32	74.9 As arsenic 33	79.0 Se selenium 34	79.9 Br bromine 35	83.8 Kr krypton 36
5	85.5 Rb rubidium 37	87.6 Sr strontium 38		114.8 In indium 49	118.7 Sn tin 50	121.8 Sb antimony 51	127.6 Te tellurium 52	126.9 I iodine 53	131.3 Xe xenon 54
6	132.9 Cs caesium 55	137.3 Ba barium 56		204.4 Tl thallium 81	207.2 Pb lead 82	209.0 Bi bismuth 83	[209] Po polonium 84	[210] At astatine 85	[222] Rn radon 86
7	[223] Fr francium 87	[226] Ra radium 88							

Transition metals (Period 4–6):

45.0 Sc scandium 21	47.9 Ti titanium 22	50.9 V vanadium 23	52.0 Cr chromium 24	54.9 Mn manganese 25	55.8 Fe iron 26	58.9 Co cobalt 27	58.7 Ni nickel 28	63.5 Cu copper 29	65.4 Zn zinc 30
88.9 Y yttrium 39	91.2 Zr zirconium 40	92.9 Nb niobium 41	96.0 Mo molybdenum 42	[98] Tc technetium 43	101.1 Ru ruthenium 44	102.9 Rh rhodium 45	106.4 Pd palladium 46	107.9 Ag silver 47	112.4 Cd cadmium 48
138.9 La lanthanum 57	178.5 Hf hafnium 72	180.9 Ta tantalum 73	183.8 W tungsten 74	186.2 Re rhenium 75	190.2 Os osmium 76	192.2 Ir iridium 77	195.1 Pt platinum 78	197.0 Au gold 79	200.6 Hg mercury 80
[227] Ac actinium 89	[267] Rf rutherfordium 104	[268] Db dubnium 105	[271] Sg seaborgium 106	[272] Bh bohrium 107	[270] Hs hassium 108	[276] Mt meitnerium 109	[281] Ds darmstadtium 110	[280] Rg roentgenium 111	

Elements with atomic numbers 112–116 have been reported but not fully authenticated

58–71: Lanthanides

140.1 Ce cerium 58	140.9 Pr praseodymium 59	144.2 Nd neodymium 60	[145] Pm promethium 61	150.4 Sm samarium 62	152.0 Eu europium 63	157.3 Gd gadolinium 64	158.9 Tb terbium 65	162.5 Dy dysprosium 66	164.9 Ho holmium 67	167.3 Er erbium 68	168.9 Tm thulium 69	173.1 Yb ytterbium 70	175.0 Lu lutetium 71

90–103: Actinides

232.0 Th thorium 90	231.0 Pa protactinium 91	238.0 U uranium 92	[237] Np neptunium 93	[244] Pu plutonium 94	[243] Am americium 95	[247] Cm curium 96	[247] Bk berkelium 97	[251] Cf californium 98	[252] Es einsteinium 99	[257] Fm fermium 100	[258] Md mendelevium 101	[259] No nobelium 102	[262] Lr lawrencium 103

CATB62